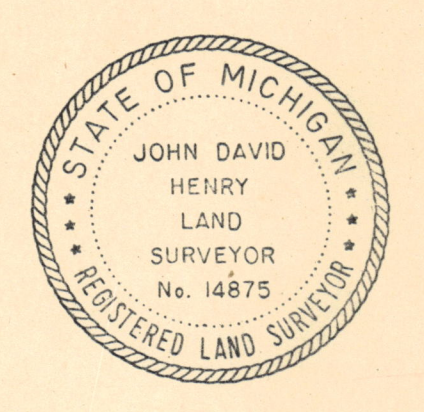

STATE OF MICHIGAN
JOHN DAVID HENRY
LAND SURVEYOR
No. 14875
REGISTERED LAND SURVEYOR

ORIGINAL INSTRUCTIONS GOVERNING
PUBLIC LAND SURVEYS
1815—1855

Original Instructions Governing Public Land Surveys 1815-1855

A Guide to Their Use in Resurveys of Public Lands

General Edition for Use in all Public Land States

J. S. Dodds, B.S. in C.E., C.E., *Editor*
Professor of Civil Engineering, Iowa State College

AMES, IOWA
J. S. DODDS
1944

Powers Press
AMES, IOWA
41726

PREFACE TO IOWA EDITION

The well-qualified land surveyor makes use of many sorts of reference works when preparing for a difficult land survey. He must be familiar with the technique of surveying operations and the theory and practice of surveying, whether of land lines or for construction.

He should have access to the field notes and plats of the original surveyors whose work he must retrace. He needs to know the law relating to land surveying and boundaries. This is available in such reference books as Patton on *Land Titles,* Clark on *Surveying and Boundaries,* and Skelton on *The Legal Elements of Boundaries and Adjacent Boundaries.* It is available in the annotated land laws to be found in good legal libraries.

In addition to the above he also needs to know as much as possible of the instructions under which the earlier work was done so that he can correctly retrace and interpret the meaning of the original notes and plats.

It has been the purpose of the voluntary committee which has prepared this volume to make available such early instructions for the original public land surveys of Iowa.

This material will be helpful in bordering states for surveys conducted at the same time. It makes the early original instructions available in printed form for the first time. Text book authors have tried to keep their books up to date by reproducing the most recent and current instructions. In this way they have made their books very misleading as a guide to the retracement of the early surveys.

To use this book properly on a resurvey in Iowa, refer to Chapter IV, for the actual special instructions under which the lines were originally run. Then read the general instructions in Chapter III covering the period in which the survey was made. The original survey notes should then be studied to learn what the surveyor did.

A glance at the map showing the location of resurveys in Chapter V will indicate whether some special situations may be expected. Equipped with the general and special instructions and the original notes the surveyor should apply the instructions given in Chapter VI. Special care must be taken to consider no corner or line lost until all efforts fail to produce evidence of the location of the lines or corners.

Many authorities upon land surveying have assisted the committee in the preparation of this book.

Special acknowledgment is made of the help and inspiration of Mr. W.

D. Jones, Chicago surveyor. Mr. Jones is the dean of land surveyors in Illinois and an able authority in land boundary matters. Mr. A. D. Kidder, of the General Land Office presented much of the helpful material of Chapter VI to the land surveyors of Iowa at one of the Iowa Surveying Conferences. Mr. Kidder has done much to increase the store of knowledge available to land surveyors and has been a guide and inspiring friend to the editor-in-chief and to many practicing land surveyors.

J. S. DODDS, C.E.
Editor-in-Chief

AMES, IOWA, *June, 1943*

PREFACE TO GENERAL EDITION

In this general edition of the *Original Instructions Governing Public Land Surveys of Iowa* all that material which relates to public land surveys in the public land states from 1815 to and including the instructions of 1855 is retained.

That material relating solely to Iowa and its boundaries is excluded. Although the matter left out is most interesting historically to many historians and expert surveyors in the other states, the original edition will be available in the principal libraries and this general or condensed edition will serve to provide the more frequently needed material long since out of print and otherwise unavailable.

It should be noted that the 1855 instructions were standard for the great body of U. S. Surveys for about fifty years. For surveys made at any time from 1855 to 1900 the 1855 instructions are a valuable handbook for any practicing surveyor on retracements of the original surveys.

The earlier instructions, from those of Tiffin in 1815 to the 1855 set, will be found helpful in Ohio, Indiana, Illinois, Missouri, Michigan, and in all states where U. S. land was subdivided earlier than 1855.

The material to be found in the Iowa edition, but not in this, includes the original letters of special instruction to deputies surveying the Iowa lands and the instructions for their use in resurveys. Also omitted are the chapters dealing with the Missouri, Minnesota, and other boundaries of Iowa. The chapters on Indian boundaries, resurveys, and that on early legislation are also left out of this book.

The associate editors of the Iowa edition, Professor L. O. Stewart, Professor J. P. McKean and Mr. G. F. Tigges were largely responsible for assembling the special Iowa material not included here.

J. S. DODDS

September, 1944.

TABLE OF CONTENTS

	PAGE
Chapter I	
Introduction	1
Chapter II	
General Instructions	
Tiffin's 1815 Instructions	5
General Instructions of 1831	11
Surveys and Contracts	13
Marking Corners	15
Field Books	16
Subdivisions of Sections and Fractional Sections	17
General Instructions of 1834	19
Method of Running Lines	20
Marking Corners	20
Meanders	22
Excess or Deficiency	23
River Crossings	24
Field Books	25
Field Notes	26
General Instructions of 1843	39
Form of Oath	39
Township Boundary Lines	40
Subdivisions	40
Measuring	42
Meandering	42
Limits of Closure	43
Marking Lines and Corners	43
Field Books	45
Form of Field Notes	46
General Instructions of 1846	53
System of Survey	53
Instruments	53
Marking Lines and Establishing Corners	54
Measurements and Meander Corners	56

	PAGE
Township Lines	56
Subdivisions	57
How and What to Meander	59
Field Notes	61
General Instructions of 1850	64
System of Survey	64
Contracts	66
Instruments	67
Running and Marking Lines	69
Measuring Lines	71
Establishing and Marking Corners	72
Subdividing Sections (Special Method)	74

NOTE: The method of subdividing Townships which is set out in this chapter is unlike the method described in all or nearly all of the original notes for Iowa Surveys of about 1850.

Meandering Rivers, etc.	77
Private Claims, Indian Reservations, etc.	79
Field Notes	80
General Instructions of 1851	86
System	86
Instruments	86
Marking Lines and Establishing Corners	87
Measurements and Where to Establish Meander Corners	89
Township Lines	90
Subdivisions	91
Corrections and Resurveys	93
How and What to Meander	95
Field Notes	96
General Instructions of 1855	101
System of Rectangular Surveying; Range, Township, and Section Lines; Mode of Numbering Townships and Sections. Standard Parallels	103
Of Measurements, Chaining, and Marking; Tally Pins; Process of Chaining; Levelling the Chain and Plumbing the Pins	105
Marking Lines; of Trial or Random Lines	106
Insuperable Objects on Line; Witness Points; Marking Irons	106
Establishing Corner Boundaries; at What Points for Township, Section, Quarter Section, and Meander Corners, Respectively	107
Manner of Establishing Corners by Means of Posts	107

	PAGE
Notching Corner Posts	108
Bearing Trees; How Many at the Different Corners, and How to Be Marked	109
Stones for Corner Boundaries; Minimum Size; Marking Same	109
Mounds Around Posts, of Earth or Stone; How to Be Constructed and Conditioned	110
Mound Memorials—Witness Mounds to Corners	111
Double Corners Only on Base and Standard Parallels	111
Meandering Navigable Streams, Lakes, and Deep Ponds	112
Field Books for Deputy Surveyors	113
Summary of Objects and Data to Be Noted in field Books	115
Swamp Lands Granted to the State by Act of 28th of September, 1850; Their Outlines to Be Specially Noted by the Deputy Surveyor	116
Noting of Settlers' Claims in OREGON, WASHINGTON and NEW MEXICO	117
Affidavits to Field Notes, and Provisions of Act of 8th August, 1846, Respecting the Same. Pains and Penalties which Attach to False Surveys	117
Forms of Official Oaths, Prior to Entering Upon Duty, for a Deputy and His Assistants	117
Exteriors or Township Lines; and Limitations Within Which They Must Close	118
Method of Subdividing	119
Limitations Within Which Section and Meander Lines Must Close	120
Of Diagram A, Showing a Body of Township Exteriors	120
Of Diagram B, Showing the Subdivisions of a Township into Sections (map facing p. 128)	121
Of Diagram C, Illustrating the Mode of Making Mound, Stake, and Stone Corners (diagram p. 180)	121
Subdivisions of Fractional Sections into Forty-Acre Lots Are to Be Made by the Surveyor General on the Township Plats, and to Be Designated by Special Numbers, Where They Cannot Be Described as Quarter-Quarters	121
Township Plats to Be Prepared by the Surveyor General in *Triplicate*	122
Township Plats to Be Furnished to the General Land Office and to the District Land Offices. Details to Be Shown Thereon, Respectively	122

	PAGE
"Descriptive Notes," showing the quality of Soil and Kind of Timber Found on the Surveyed Lines in Each Township, and Describing each Corner Boundary, Are to Accompany the Plat of the Same, to Be Furnished by the Surveyor General to the District Land Office	122
The Original Field Books of Surveys, Bearing the Written Approval of the Surveyor General, to Be Retained in His Office	122
Certified Transcripts of Field Books to Be Furnished to General Land Office	122
Meander Corners to Be Numbered on Township Plats	122
Variation of the Needle, and Mode of Ascertaining the Same	122
Specimen Field Notes A and B—the Former of the Exterior lines of a Township, and the Latter of the Subdivision of the Same—Constitute a Separate Series of Pages from 1 to 53, Inclusive; and They Are Preceded by an INDEX Referrring the Township, Section, Closing and Meander Lines, as Shown on Diagram B, to Their Corresponding Pages in the Notes A and B	129
The "General Description" of the Character of Public Land in the Township Follows the Subdivisional Notes, with a "List of Names" of Assistants, and the Mode of Authenticating the Survey, Under the Provisions of the Act of 8th August, 1846, and Form for Certifying Copies of Field Notes to be Transmitted to the General Land Office	168
Conclusion. "Table Showing the Difference of Latitude and Departure in Running 80 Chains, at Any Course from 1 to 60 Minutes"	170
W. D. Jones Comments on General Instructions	171
Measurements	171
Bearing Trees and Witness Trees	173
Monuments	174
Running of Line	175
1850 Method of Subdivision	179
Map Showing Meridians and Standard Parallels	180
Chapter III	
Restoration of Lost and Obliterated Corners	181
Problems of Retracement—References for Study	181
Erroneous Instructions for Establishment of the Center of a Section	182
Reasons for and Use of the Original Instructions	183

	PAGE
Aids to Retracement of Land Lines	186
The Judicial Functions of Surveyors	187
Hodgman on Retracement	192
Extracts from G.L.O. Circular No. 1452	196

Chapter I

INTRODUCTION

Historical background, which is both interesting and helpful to an understanding of the development of the public land surveys in the United States, is discussed in *Public Land Surveys—History, Instructions, Methods* by L. O. Stewart. The present volume will deal, almost exclusively, with the general instructions governing surveys from 1815 to 1900.

We should be aware of the objectives of the early public land legislation and understand the point of view of the early legislators lest we become unfairly critical of the surveys and surveyors of that period. Understanding these things, we are magnanimous in estimating whether the end justified the means.

Several factors influenced their decisions and actions. These were:
1. The urgent need of the treasury for money.
2. Settling of people on unsurveyed land, and the consequent unpleasant relationships between citizens and the government.
3. Because of this rapid settlement, surveys had to be pushed forward hastily.
4. Land prices were low ($1.25 per acre), which did not seem to warrant any delays incident to precision.
5. Settlements, frequently, occurred in isolated fragments which obviated any possibility of carrying on a continuous and progressive scheme of surveys.
6. Surveys were made only in territory belonging to the government. Additions to these lands were made from time to time by treaties with the Indians. Many of these acquisitions were irregular in shape and boundaries and, sometimes, left unceded land between old and new government holdings.
7. The contract system, which was in force during the completion of the major portion of the public land surveys, tended to encourage the deputies to use surveying methods that would produce results of the minimum acceptable precision.

The purpose of this book is to present all of the original instructions relating to public land surveys from 1815 to and including those of 1855, which remained almost unchanged for about fifty years. Some discussion has been included which will aid in understanding the original notes or which serves to explain their background.

Chapter III, which deals with retracement surveys, should be found very helpful. Many of the original surveys were begun more than one hundred years ago. In many instances all evidence of the original corner has disappeared. Later surveys and uses of the land have introduced numerous conflicting calls which the present surveyor must harmonize. A proper use of the information contained herein will prove very helpful in the solution of difficult land surveying problems.

This book is offered to all who are interested in land surveying either professionally or historically. As an illustration of the need for this book in the surveys it covers, the following correspondence is quoted:

OFFICE OF THE COUNTY ENGINEER OF WINNESHIEK COUNTY
Decorah, Iowa

DEAR SIR:

I ran into a snag on my survey between sec. 31 T. 99 N., R. 10 W. and sec. 6, T. 98 N., R. 10 W. This is the way our government field notes state, which is clearly in error. This is one mile north of the line wanted:

West between sec. 30 and 31, T. 99 N., R. 10, 49.73 intersect range line at post on var. 10° E. Therefore retraced on true line correct var. 10° E. 9.73 set ¼ corner in mound of earth; 49.73 section corner.

Now here is the 3rd correction line:

West on south side sec. 31 mag. var. 9° 20' E.: 40.00 chs. set post for ¼ corner and took two trees Burr Oak 12" N. 55° W. 44 lks. and Burr Oak 10" N. 52° E. 52 lks.; 83.00 chs. set post for corner to T. 99 N., R. 10 and 11. Burr Oak 12" N. 80° E. 11 lks. Burr Oak 6" N. 48° E. 92 lks., Burr Oak 16" N. 20° W. 23 lks. and Burr Oak 8" N. 35° W. 164 lks.

Here are the notes for the closing line from the south:

North on line between sec. 1, T. 98 N., R. 11 W. and Sec. 6, T. 98 N., R. 10 W.; 75.65 Int. 3rd correction line 33 chs. east of the SW. cor. T. 99 N., R. 10 W. and set corner to T. 98 N., R. 10 and 11, W. of the 5th P.M.

As can be seen from the first description above the section is 49.73 chs. long between 30 and 31, yet on the south side of the same section it is 83.00 chs. wide.

As the S¼ has to be relocated and the SE. cor. of sec. 31 by proportional government distances I must know what the correct distance to the range line is across south side sec. 31.

I understand you had the government survey notes in Des Moines from the Surveyor General's office. Could you give me this correct distance?

Thanking you for this information as soon as is possible, I am

Yours truly,

FRANK W. ARNESON, *County Engineer*

IOWA GEODETIC SURVEY
April 8, 1940

MR. FRANK W. ARNESON
  Winneshiek County Engineer, Decorah, Iowa
DEAR MR. ARNESON:

With reference to your inquiry on the apparent error which you feel exists in the original notes on the 3rd correction line on R. 10 W., in your County, I wish to give you the following information:

INTRODUCTION 3

Professor J. S. Dodds and I made a very thorough study of the old records in the state house to find some solution to your problem, and to determine if an error actually exists on the correction line as you pointed out in your letter. We found the answer to your letter given very conclusively in the manuscript for the book being prepared by the special committee of the Iowa Engineering Society.

I have prepared a copy of the original field notes of the lines in question, and

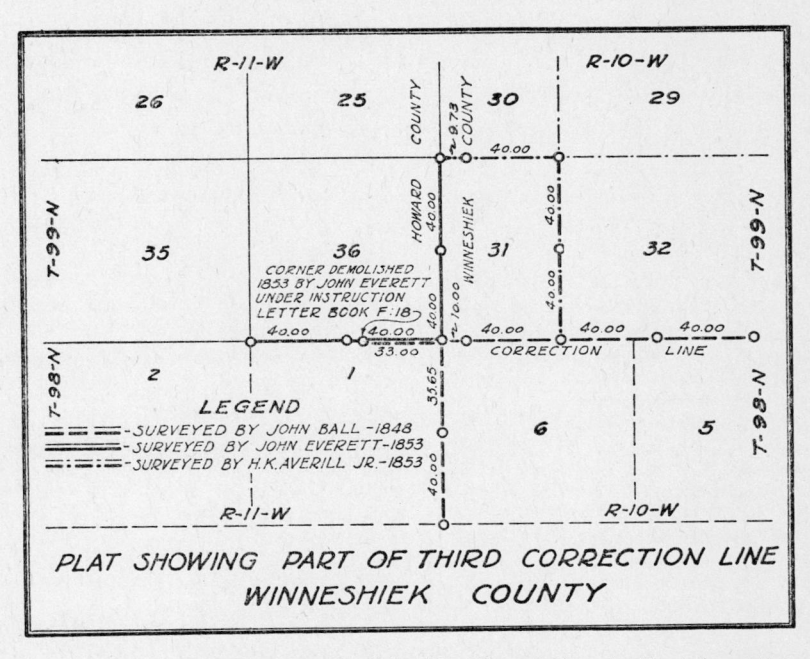

```
                    R-11-W                    |    R-10-W
           26              25        >-<      |  30              29
                                     2.73
                                   COUNTY    40.00
                                  40.00
                          HOWARD         40.00
   T-99-N   35              36   COUNTY  WINNESHIEK  31              32   T-99-N
                    CORNER DEMOLISHED
                    1853 BY JOHN EVERETT  40.00
                    UNDER INSTRUCTION     10.00
                    LETTER BOOK F:18
                    40.00  40.00         40.00   40.00   40.00
                                 33.00              CORRECTION   LINE
   T-98-N    2               1   35.65                                    T-98-N
                    LEGEND
              ===  - SURVEYED BY JOHN BALL - 1848        6              5
              ===  - SURVEYED BY JOHN EVERETT - 1853
              =.=  - SURVEYED BY H.K.AVERILL JR. - 1853
                                         40.00
                    R-11-W                    |    R-10-W

   PLAT SHOWING PART OF THIRD CORRECTION LINE
              WINNESHIEK    COUNTY
```

The above plat prepared by Mr. Tigges refers to the information contained in his reply to Mr. Arneson as quoted below. It will be clear to the land surveryor That The line between Ranges 10-W and 11-W was continued north from the closing corner of T. 98. Nothing in the records of the county engineer would give a clear picture of the situation created by the abandonment of Thirty three chains of the original connection line when the surveys were extended to the north and west of that point.

I have also enclosed those special instructions taken from the above manuscript that pertain to this problem. They are listed under Letter Book Number F:18, of which the second paragraph should be carefully studied.

After studying the special instructions issued to the Deputy, John T. Everett, by the surveyor general, under date of June 6, 1853, we know that specific instructions were given to destroy the 3rd correction line running through range 11 at corner to tps. 98 and 99. Checking the original field notes for this line in question, we find that the deputy, Mr. Everett, intersected the corner to Tps. 98 and 99 at 33.00 chains west of the closing corner and demolished said corner. The closing corner from which the above survey was started is noted on the original notes on the line on west side of sec. 6, T. 98 N., R. 10 W.

The distance on the south side of sec. 31, T. 99 N., R. 10 W., is without question 50.00 chains, with the quarter corner set at 40.00 chains, and the fractional distance to the township corner of 10.00 chains.

A study of the aerial photographs for this territory shows the subdivision in agreement with the above deductions.

Yours very truly,

GEROLD F. TIGGES

Chapter II

GENERAL INSTRUCTIONS

U. S. surveys were made under general instructions current at the time of the survey and special instructions issued to the deputy surveyor holding the contract. It is not always clear which general set of instructions was to control but the resurveyor may assume that any survey made at a certain date was made under the latest preceeding general set as shown herein. Any apparent discrepancies appearing in the original notes for the survey or on the plat of the survey will be found to comply with some requirement of the special instructions or with an earlier set of general instructions or will be an exception introduced by the deputy surveyor as his own idea. Surveyors should be familiar with the general instructions in this chapter for the period covering the surveys executed in the area where resurveys are located.

Thus upon a retracement of a survey which was made in 1847 anywhere in the public land states it would be expected that the general instructions of 1846 would apply and the notes and plats would be found to conform to these instructions.

To show what instructions were current before the time covered by the surveys of 1831-1855, the following "Tiffin" instructions are included here:

INSTRUCTIONS FOR DEPUTY SURVEYORS BY E. TIFFIN, SURVEYOR GENERAL UNITED STATES, 1815[1]

INSTRUCTIONS FOR SUBDIVIDING TOWNSHIPS

1. When the township lines are completed, you must begin the survey of sections at the southeast corner of the township, and move on in continued progression from east to west and from south to north in order that the excess or defect of the township as to complete sections may fall on the west and north sides of the township, according to the provisions of the act of the 10th of May, 1800.

2. Each side of a section must be made one mile in measure by the chain, and quarter section corners are to be established at every half mile, except, when in the closing of a section if the measure of the closing side should vary from 80 chains or one mile, you are in that case to place the quarter section corners equidistant, or at an average distance from the corners of the section, but in running out the sectional lines on the west or north side of the township you will establish your quarter section posts or corners at the distance of half a mile

---

[1] (From Sherman's *Ohio Land Subdivision,* p. 193, and Stewart's *Public Land Surveys,* p. 143).

from the last corner and leave the remaining excess or defect on the west or north tier of quarter sections, which balance or remainder you will carefully measure and put down in your field notes in order to calculate the remaining or fractional quarter section on the north and west side of the township; also in running to the western boundary, unless your sectional lines fall in with the posts established there for the corners of sections in the adjacent townships, you must set posts and mark bearing trees at the points of intersection of your line with the town boundaries, and take the distances of your corners from the corners of the sections of the adjacent townships, and note that and the side on which it varies in chains, or links or both.

3. The sections must be made to close by running a random line from one corner to another except on the north and west ranges of sections, and the true line between them is to be established by means of offsets.

4. In fractional townships on rivers it will be necessary to vary from the foregoing rules; and the lines must be continued from rectilinear boundaries of the township which may be parallel to the river, perpendicularly to those boundaries until they meet the river; the sections, however, must be made complete on the sides of the township bounded by straight lines, and all excess or defect of measure must be thrown into the fractional sections on the river; the measure of the lines from the last entire sectional corner should be made very exact in order to calculate the fractional section with exactness.

5. Great care must be taken that the north and south lines be run according to the true meridian as required by law, and the east and west lines be run at right angles to them as far as is practicable in closing, but if on running on a true east and west line you find the post you are running for lies very much to the north or south of the lines, you are then to mistrust the measure by the chain, and if possible, the line on which the posts are established must be remeasured; also in running a meridional line by the compass, if you find the measurement of the closing line of the sections, that is a uniform convergency or diagonally [sic] of these lines; you may then reasonably mistrust the accuracy of the direction of your lines by the needle. In this case it will be well to endeavor to run parallel to the meridian adjacent on which section closes, in order that it may contain a just or legal quantity, viz., 640 acres or one mile square.

6. As the measurement by the chain is the principal source of errors in surveying you will be careful to attend to your chainmen that they carry the chain horizontally, and to prevent their losing a tally rod, you must be provided with a set of them pointed with iron or steel, and to allow no other to be used but the precise number which you shall have selected for that purpose.

7. In meandering rivers you will take the bearings according to true meridian of the river and note the distance on any course when the river intersects the sectional lines, and the calculations of the contents of the fractions are to be made by the tables of difference of latitude and departure, and returned on your plats; but the quantity or contents of the whole section only are to be put down; in all the other sections, and each of them is to be accounted one mile square or 640 acres, unless your closing lines deviate very much from 80 chains, in which case you will be careful to put down their true length on your plats.

8. You must frequently while in the field attend to the correction of your chain; for this purpose you should be provided with some measure taken from the standard chain in the office of the Surveyor General.

9. All random lines, as well as the true, are to be noted in your field book at the time of running them, and are to be kept in the order in which the work is executed; also you must be careful to note the variation of the random lines from the corners or posts which they were intended to strike.

10. All courses of whatever lines must be taken with the sight or your compass set to the variation and estimated according to the true meridian for which purpose the variation of the needle at the place where survey must be taken or previously known and your compass regulated to it before you commence running the lines.

11. No lines of whatever description are to be run, or marks of any kind made by any person but yourself, or who may be under the immediate inspection of yourself or some deputy surveyor duly authorized from this office.

12. Any considerable departure from these instructions will be considered as a forfeiture of the conditions of the contract or any claim for payment; and loose, inaccurate, or precipitate work will not be admitted, either as it respects surveys in the field or their returns in paper.

13. You will take care that your posts be well driven into the ground and that there be one or two sight trees marked between every quarter section corner; also at the section corners that there be marks for every section corner where they corner.

General Instructions for Deputies

1. You will provide a good compass of Rittenhouse's construction, having a nonius[2] division and movable sights, and a two pole chain of 50 links; the chain must be adjusted by the standard chain in the office of the Surveyor General, and it will be of importance that both it and the compass be frequently examined in the field in order to determine any errors and irregularities which may arise from the use of them.

2. Whenever you may be obstructed by insuperable obstacles, such as ponds, swamps, creeks, rivers, etc., you will take the necessary offsets, or by work of traverse or trigonometry, in order to ascertain the distance on any line which is not actually run.

3. The courses of all navigable rivers, which may bound or pass through your district must be accurately surveyed and their width taken at those points where they may be intersected by township or sectional lines; also the distance of those points from the sectional corners and from the commencement of any course where you are meandering the river; you will likewise not fail to make special notice of all streams of water which fall in your way with their width and course from whence they appear to come or run.

4. All township or sectional lines which you may survey are to be marked in the manner hitherto practised in the surveys of the United States lands, viz.: all those trees which your line cuts must have two notches made on each side of the tree where the line cuts; but no spot or blaze is to be made on them, and all or most of the trees on each side of the line, and near it, must be marked with two spots or blazes diagonally or quartering towards the line.

---

[2] Nonius. Merr. dict. definition: probably Latinized names of Nunes, name of a Portuguese mathematician (1492-1577). A device formerly used in graduating instruments, etc., subsequently improved into the vernier. Rittenhouse was a famous English scientist and designer of surveying instruments.

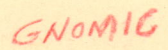

5. The posts must be erected at the distance of every mile, and half mile from where the town or sectional line commenced (except a tree may be so situated as to supply the place of a post) which post must be at least three inches diameter and rise not less than three feet. All mile posts must have as many notches cut on two sides of them as there are miles distance from where the town or sectional line commenced, but the town corner posts, or trees shall be notched with six notches on each side, and the half mile sectional posts are to be without any marks; the places of the posts are to be perpetuated in the following manner, viz.: at each post the courses shall be taken and the distances measured to two or more adjacent trees in opposite directions, as nearly as may be, which trees, called bearing trees, shall be blazed on the side next the post and one notch made with an axe on the blaze; and there shall be cut with a marking iron on a bearing tree, or some other tree within and near each corner of a section, the number of the section, and over it the letter T with the number of the township, and above this the letter R with the number of the range, but for quarter-section corners, you are to put no numbers on the trees; they are to be distinguished by this mark, ¼ S.

6. You will be careful to note in your field book all the courses and distances you shall have run, the names and estimated diameters of all corners or bearing trees, and those trees which fall in your line called station or line trees, notched as aforesaid, together with the courses and distances of the bearing trees from their respective corners, with the letters and numbers marked on them as aforesaid; also all rivers, creeks, springs and smaller streams of water, with their width, and the course they run in crossing the lines of survey, and whether navigable, rapid or mountainous; the kinds of timber and undergrowth with which the land may be covered, all swamps, ponds, stone quarries, coal beds, peat or turf grounds, uncommon natural or artificial productions, such as mounds, precipices, caves, etc., all rapids, cascades or falls of water; mineral, ores, fossils, etc.; the quality of the soil and the true situation of all mines, salt licks, salt springs and mill seats, which may come to your knowledge are particularly to be regarded and noticed in your note books.

7. In all measurements the level or horizontal length is to be taken, not that which arises from measuring over the surface of the ground when it happens to be uneven and hilly; for this purpose the chainmen ascending or descending hills must alternately let down one end of the chain to the ground and raise the other to a level as nearly as may be, from the end of which a plumb should be let fall to ascertain the spot where to set the tally rod or stick; and where the land is very steep, it will be necessary to shorten the chain by doubling the links together, so as to obtain the true horizontal measure.

8. Though the line be measured by a chain of two perches, you are notwithstanding to keep your reckoning in chains of four perches (or) of one hundred links each, and all entries in your field books, and all your plans and calculations must be made according to the decimal measure of a chain.

9. Your courses and distances must be placed in the margin of your field books on the left for which purpose it should be large, and your remarks made on the right in the manner following:

CHAINS LINKS
  north
  20   30   Between sections 35 and 36. Town 4. Range 6.
  37   40   A white oak 20 inch diameter.
                    A stream 30 links wide. S.E.

CHAINS	LINKS	
40	--	Set half mile post, from which a B oak 18 inch diameter bears S. 50 E. 40 links, and a sugar tree 15 inch diameter bears N. 10 W. 34 links.
east		Between No. 25 and 36 Town 4 Range 6 on a random.
16	40	A brook 30 links wide, course S. 20 W.
40	00	Set temporary quarter section post. This half mile over broken land. Timber oak, ash, etc.
64	30	A stream 25 links wide, course SE.
79	90	Intersected N. and S. line 20 links south of section corner. Over hilly land, soil rich and good for farming. Timber oak, hickory, poplar, ash, etc.
WEST		Between sections 25 and 36 Town 4, Range 6 on true line.
39	95	Moved temporary post to the average distance for ¼ section corner, from which a black jack 10 inch diameter bears S. 50 E. 100 links, and a white birch 19 inch in diam. bears N. 25 W. 20 links.
55	00	A white oak 11 inch in diameter.
79	90	Section corner.

In this manner you must enter all courses and distances in your field book; the date must follow the close of each day's work, which field book, written with a fair hand, of each township separately, or a true and fair copy, together with the original you will return to the office of the surveyor general.

10. The plat of each township and fractional part of a township must be neatly and accurately protracted on durable paper, by a scale of 2 inches to a mile, or 40 chains to an inch, and must be in such measure and proportions in every line and part as actually was determined by measurement in the field. A compass having the true and magnetic meridian, and the scale by which the lines are laid down, are to be placed on the SE corner of the plat.

11. The following certificate must be inscribed on your plat and signed by you:

Pursuant to a contract with, and instructions from_____Surveyor General of the United States, bearing date the_____day of_____I have admeasured, laid out and surveyed the above described township (or fractional part) and do hereby certify that it had such marks and bounds, both natural and artificial as are represented on said plat and described in the field notes made thereof, and returned with the plat into the Surveyor General's office.

Certified this_____day of_____.

SUBDIVISION INTO SECTIONS

Begin at N the southeast corner of the township, and run west 40 chains and establish the quarter section corner if it be not already established; continue 40 chains farther and establish the corner of sections 36 and 35; thence run a true north course 40 chains and mark the quarter section corner between 35 and 36; continue 40 chains farther on the north line and establish the corner 25-26-35 and 36. From this corner run a random line for the post or corner M without blazing; at the distance of every 20 chains on this line set up a stake or post or mark some other mark on the random line; if you strike the post or corner M exactly you have only to blaze the lines back and establish the quarter section corner at 1. and the corner between 25-26-35 and 36; but if running for the post M you fall north of it you must note the departure or deviation in your field book, and return on the true course, observing to correct it by means of offsets from your marks made on the random line.

From the corner of sections 25-26-35 and 36, run due north one mile setting the half mile post as before at 2 on the line from O and F; return south to O and establish at O and P your quarter section and section corners; then run north from P and establish quarter section and section corners as before, and run a random line from the section corner on the line $P\,E$ to the corresponding corner on the line $O\,F$; proceed in this manner till you arrive to the last corner towards the western boundary of the township from M to U, viz., between sections 29-30-31 and 32; from this corner run west and at the distance of 40 chains from it establish the quarter section corner at 6 in the line from M to U; continue west till you intersect the town boundary, suppose at U, note carefully the distance of the point of intersection from the last section or quarter-section corner, and also the distance of this point from its section corner of the adjacent township west of you, or the distance of U from M and on which side it lies, viz., either north or south; at the point of intersection U set the section post or corner and take bearing trees.

In this manner you will proceed until your township is completed, observing always to move either in a range of sections from that at the southeast corner of the township to the western boundary, or from that section to the northern boundary, but when you shall have completed the sections to the north boundary of the township you will proceed from the last section corners, establish quarter section corners at 40 chains from them, and continue north till you intersect the town boundary in the same manner as on the western side of the township, observing to note the distance at which you intersect the north boundary from the section or quarter section corner you left last. Also you will be careful to note the distance of the point of intersection from the corner of the section of the adjacent township and whether it be on the east or west side of it; then the distance from 6 to F or from 6 to E on the line OF and PE, must be carefully noted in your field notes and also the distance from F where you intersect O the post on the town above and on which side, whether east or west.

GENERAL INSTRUCTIONS OF 1831[3]

GENERAL LAND OFFICE
23rd September 1831

SIR:

I herewith communicate for your guidance and direction in the discharge of your official duties, the requirements of the Department in reference to the township surveys, and the mode of making the returns thereof, in order that you may model and adopt your contracts with your deputies, and instructions and forms of field books, precisely to suit those requirements.

In the preparation of the township plats it is requisite that they exhibit a perfect delineation of the country as represented in the field notes of the survey.

1st. The plats are to be so constructed as to indicate both by protraction and by figures, the courses and distances of all lines: viz. The exact distance between the posts planted at the corners of each section or fractional section, and the *courses of the lines when from any cause*, they *vary* from the *cardinal points*, also the precise delineation by courses and distances, of private claims, reservations, and other tracts of land not conforming to sectional lines.

2nd. Whenever the continuation of a surveyed line is interrupted by an *impassible swamp* or *from any other cause*, the distance of the line actually run between the starting and finishing posts, is to be truly represented by the platting and also by figures.

3rd. The distance on a *surveyed* line at the points where streams cross the same, is to be indicated by *figures*, and the general course of such streams where they are *not navigable*, between such different points of intersection, is to be delineated on the plat as nearly as the same can be conjectured. The courses and distances of the meanders of *navigable streams* are to be truly delineated and also represented by *figures on the plat* opposite the delineation, wherever it is practicable so to do, and where the same are too numerous to admit of their exhibition by *figures* on the plat, in that mode, the same are required to be exhibited in a detached tabular form, either on the face of the plat, or connected therewith as may be found most expedient. The width of all water courses, rivers, creeks, etc., is to be represented in *figures* on the plat.

4th. The plat is to exhibit the received names of all rivers, creeks, lakes, swamps, prairies, hills, mountains, and other natural objects, and the surveyor should be instructed never to give *original* names to such objects, where names have heretofore been given. All lakes and ponds of *sufficient magnitude* to justify such expense, are to be *meandered* and platted agreeably to courses and distances, which are also to be exhibited by figures. In passing such ponds or lakes as are not to be meandered, offsets are to be taken, which offsets are to be carefully noted on the plat to show that the distance across has been accurately ascertained. Such ponds or lakes are to be exhibited on the plat as accurately as practicable, from careful occular observation to be made by the Deputy and noted in his field book.

---

[3] Circular from General Land Office to Surveyor General, the original of which has been preserved at Des Moines in the old files of the Surveyor General.

5th. Swamps are to be represented in the ordinary method by slightly shaded *black* lines and dots, and the outlines of the same should be distinctly exhibited.

6th. *Prairies* are to be represented by slightly shaded *green lines* and dots, and the outlines of the same to be distinctly exhibited.

7th. The plats should also exhibit as accurately as practicable, *all mines, salt springs, salt licks, and mill seats,* also *towns, villages and settlements,* and the names of the same, also *forges, factories, cotton gins,* and all other such items of information, also the *general course of travelled roads and tracks,* denoting the place to which they may lead.

8th. The exterior lines of the township plat should be double the thickness of the sectional lines and both of them should be in *black* ink. The lines denoting the quarter section and the sub-divisions of fractional sections should be in *red*.

9th. The quantities of the subdivisions of fractional sections are to be indicated by *red figures* within the respective subdivisions. The numbers and quantities of sections and fractional sections are to be exhibited in black figures at the center of each as nearly as practicable, and in cases where the marks and figures on the plat are too numerous to admit of the convenient exhibition of the quantities in that way, the quantity of each section and fractional section is to be exhibited in a neat *tabular statement* on the *right side* of the plat, and where there are private claims in the township, the quantities of such claims are to be exhibited under a separate head in the tabular statement which is to exhibit *separate totals of public lands* and *private claims.* Where any private claim, Indian or other reservation, etc., is exhibited, the name of the *confirmee* or *reservee* must be given; also such other reference as will clearly identify the tract with the Report by which it was confirmed or the Treaty, etc., under which the individual claims the title.

In cases where the quantities are exhibited in the center of the section or fractional section, and it is not necessary to resort to a *tabular statement,* the sum total of the public lands in the township is to be exhibited as *one item* near the foot of the plat.

10th. At the foot of each plat the Surveyor General must give an official certificate of the following purport, viz., The above map of Township No.___, of Range No.___, is strictly conformable to the field notes of the survey thereof on file in this office, which has been examined and approved (or if any exceptions are taken to the field notes by reason of their not standing the test of correct platting, such exceptions are to be stated on the margin of the plat as before mentioned, and exhibited on the face of the plat by red dotted lines, and alluded to in the certificate thus "with the exception stated in the margin hereof.") The certificate is then to be closed by indicating the name of the deputy or deputies by whom the exterior boundary lines, and the subdivision lines were respectively surveyed, showing the sum total of miles run by each deputy surveyor, also the date of the contract, the quarter of the year in which the survey was made, and the quarter in which the same was paid for and charged in the accounts of the Surveyor General.

11th. All lines in a township survey which have not been actually run must be represented on your plat of survey by *red dotted lines,* and any portion of a survey *found* or *suspected* to be erroneous, must also be represented by red dotted lines, and payment for the same is to be suspended until the error is corrected, or the cause of suspicion done away to the full satisfaction of the Surveyor General; and in every case where the survey of a township is incomplete *from any cause*, such cause must be fully set forth by *marginal note* on the *face of the* plat, and certified in the mode designated in the 10th article of this letter.

12th. *Navigable streams* are declared by law to be *public highways*. Except in cases where navigable streams constitute the boundary line between two land districts, and where the ranges and townships in each district are numbered from different meridians and base lines, they are not to interrupt the regular survey of the township lines, which are to be continued across such stream for the exact distance. Each border of such stream is however to be meandered by course and distance, and a fractional portion of the same township will be constituted on each side thereof to be denominated, as the case may be, the fraction of township north or south, or east or west of such stream, having special regard, in such designation, to the *general course* thereof from its source to its mouth.

A deputy surveyor continuing surveys on the opposite banks of streams must invariably be made to show the connections of such survey with certain established posts or points in the opposite surveys, which connections, as well as the mode by which the same was ascertained, are to be shown in the field book and exhibited in the plat of survey, and in passing up or down rivers, frequent connections with the surveys across should be made and exhibited both in the field book and plat.

The *width* of *navigable streams* and *bayous* binding on the surveys, should frequently be ascertained by trigonometrical process. Where the width of the same does not sensibly vary in the township, the measurement there is to be made at the two extreme points of intersection of such objects with the township line; but where there is a sensible variation in the width, measurement thereof must be made as often as may be justly deemed necessary for the accuracy of the survey in connection with the adjoining lands, and the correct exhibition thereof in the township plats.

13th. Where it is necessary to make a return to this office of township *boundaries* merely prior to the subdivision of such townships into sections, and the rendition of the regular plats of survey, such boundaries are to be platted in connection on a scale of from two to three inches to six miles.

14th. The paper to be used in your plats of survey must be of the best quality and of uniform size.

The descriptive notes are to be written on paper of the folio post size, best quality. The records of the plats and field notes to be kept in your office, must be made out on paper of the best quality. Great care and neatness are to be observed in the execution of the work, and in the particular examination thereof after the same is completed.

SURVEYS AND CONTRACTS

15th. You are to require bond and approved security for the due execution of all surveying contracts in the penalty of *double* the *value* of the contract, and in case of failure to comply with the terms of a contract, unless such failure arise from causes satisfactorily proved to be beyond the control of the contractor, immediate measures are to be taken to recover the penalty of the bond, agreeably to law, and the deputy surveyor who has improperly failed to fulfil his engagements, is afterwards not to be employed by you, and of every such failure you are required to give immediate notice to the department.

The surveys are to be executed under the personal and immediate superintendence of the contractor. *Sub-contracts are illegal.* The contract and bond of the deputy are expressly to provide against sub-contracts.

16th. The act of 18 May 1796 (*Land Laws*, new edition, p. 420) provides, that the public lands "shall be divided by North and South lines run according to the true meridian, and by others crossing them at right angles, so as to form township lines of six miles square.

"The corners of the townships shall be marked with progressive numbers from the beginning; each distance of a mile between the said corners, shall be also distinctly marked with marks different from those of the corners."

The same law requires that "Townships shall be subdivided into sections, containing, as nearly as may be, six hundred and forty acres each, by running through the same, each way, parallel lines at the end of every two miles, and by marking a corner on each of the said lines at the end of every mile: The sections shall be numbered respectively, beginning with the number one in the northeast section, and proceeding west and east alternately, through the township, with progressive number, 'till the thirty-six be completed.

"And it shall be the duty of the deputy surveyors to cause to be marked on a tree near each corner made as aforesaid, and within the section, the number of each section, and over it the number of the township within which such section may be; and the said deputies shall carefully note in their respective field books, the names of the corner trees marked, and the number so made."

The act of 10 May 1800 (*Land Laws*, new edition, p. 456) prescribes the mode of subdividing sections into half sections of three hundred and twenty acres each, as nearly as may be. "By running parallel lines through the same from east to west, and from south to north, at the distance of one mile from each other, and marking corners at the distance of each half mile on the lines running from east to west, and at the distance of each half mile on those running from south to north." And making the marks, notes and descriptions prescribed to surveyors by the act of 18th May 1796. The same act also provides, that "In all cases where the exterior lines of the townships thus to be subdivided into sections or half sections, shall exceed, or shall not extend six miles, the excess or deficiency shall be specially noted, and added to or deducted from the western and northern ranges or sections or half sections in such townships, according as the error may be in running the lines from east to west, or from south to north; the sections and half sections bounded on the northern and western lines of such townships shall be sold as containing only the quantity expressed in the returns and plats respectively, and all others as containing the complete legal quantity." By a vigilant and faithful attention to duty on the part of the deputy surveyor, the excesses and deficiencies alluded to by the law, except to a trifling extent, will be of rare occurrence.

The act of 11 Feb. 1805 entitled, "An Act Concerning the Mode of Surveying the Public Lands of the U. S." (*Land Laws*, new edition, p. 515) prescribed general regulations for dividing townships into sections, and subdividing such sections into half sections and quarter sections. The following is a summary of those regulations:

The lands are to be laid off in townships of precisely six miles square, by lines running due north and south, and east and west. On each of those lines precisely at the distance of one mile apart, corners are to be established for sectional lines. Parallel lines are to be run through the township each way, from each sectional corner to the corresponding sectional corner on the opposite side of the township, on each of which lines sectional corners are to be established at the distance of one mile apart, which process will divide the township into thirty-six sections. In running the exterior township lines, and also the interior sectional lines, intermediate half mile posts or corners, (precisely equidistant between the corners of the sections) are to be established as the boundaries of quarter sections.

17th. Each deputy surveyor is to provide himself with two, two-pole chains containing each thirty-three feet and subdivided into fifty links which are to be regulated by the *Standard Chain* in the Surveyor's office. One of which chains is to be specially reserved by the deputy as a standard for his field work, and by which he will adjust the one in active use, at least every other day, if not oftener. Each deputy will also provide himself with a good compass with a nonius or theodolite (which latter in some respects, is preferable, by reason of its peculiar adaptation to the taking of long sights) which will be compared with the standard in the Surveyor's office.

18th. The surveys are required by law to be made agreeably to the true meridian, and at right angles therewith. The variation of the magnetic meridian is to be observed and ascertained from time to time, as often as the Surveyor General may deem expedient, and is always to be indicated on the township plat.

19th. The greatest care is to be taken in levelling the chains and plumbing the pins, so as to obtain the *true horizontal distance*, where the surface of the country is irregular and hilly.

The oath to be taken by the chainmen must specially provide for such levelling and plumbing. The deputy surveyor must ever be vigilant over the conduct of his subagents (chainmen, marker and flag bearers) whose oaths with that of the Deputies, are to be filed in your office.

You are to enjoin on your deputies a strict regard to the moral integrity of these subagents. None are to be employed in whom *implicit* confidence cannot be reposed, as the interest of the public service is at stake.

As to Marking

20th. The greatest possible caution is to be observed in marking the corners of townships, etc., in a plain, distinct and permanent manner.

When a tree is not found immediately at the corner, a corner is to be established by planting a post on which is to be marked the number of the township, over which is to be marked the number of the range, and underneath the number of the section.

The bearing and distance, also the names and the respective diameters of the nearest trees from such corner are to be carefully taken and noted in the field book. The nearest of such trees (where there are more than one) is to be *marked* to correspond with the *marked corner*. The mark should be in a *regular chop, squared off*, to be made into such tree, so as always to be distinguished from a mere *blaze*. The letters "B. T." to denote the fact of its being a "bearing tree" should be distinctly cut into the wood some distance below the other marks. All these particulars are to be used most intelligibly and minutely noted in the field book. The posts used in forming the corners of townships must always be larger (for the sake of distinction) than those which denote the sectional and quarter-sectional corners, and should be neatly squared-off at the top to correspond with the cardinal points.

The posts must always be made of the most durable wood that can be had, and should be set in the earth to depth of two feet and very securely rammed in with earth and stone.

The sectional posts are to indicate, by a number of *notches* on each of the four corners, directed to the cardinal points, the number of miles that it stands from the outlines of the township. The sides of the post will be numbered to correspond with the number of the section it faces. Each half mile post on a section line and quarter section post on a township line, should be marked to indicate that it is a quarter sectional "(¼ S)" post, and the nearest adjoining tree on *each side* of such post, must be similarly marked. The surveyor to note in his field book the kind of tree, its diameter, bearing and distance from the true corner.

Posts denoting the same kind or character of boundary, should be of uniform construction, and there should always be a striking difference between posts denoting different kinds of boundary.

In prairie countries where bearing trees cannot be had, mounds, to be covered with sod are, agreeably to contract, to be erected. Such mounds should be of uniform size and conform precisely to instructions to be given by you. As mounds are subject to be worn away by the action of the weather, and other causes, I would recommend that a stone be planted in the center of the mound and that a few handfulls of charcoal be enclosed therein. I would further recommend that at each corner of a square which will enclose the mound, and conform to the cardinal points, there be planted a chestnut, hickory nut, walnut, or acorn.

A stake to be set up in the center of the mound, to which is to be fastened a finger board on which is to be designated in black oil paint, the appropriate numbers.

All *the particulars* relative to the construction of a mound are to be minutely indicated in the field book.

The perpetuation of the corners of the Public Surveys is a subject of *primary importance*. Every possible care and precaution to secure correct and durable corners, must be observed by your agents, whose fidelity you should test by every means in your power.

As to Field Books

21st. You are to furnish your deputy surveyors with a printed specimen form of field books, which is to be so constructed as to exhibit every particular required, either by law or instruction, so as to permit of a perfect topographical exhibition of the country, and accompany such form with special instructions on every point in relation to which it can be presumed that instructions are necessary.

In the field books, the number of miles, chains, and links run on a line are to be exhibited in a column, which is to be added up at the foot of each page and carried forward from page to page, so as to form at the conclusion of the book, the aggregate of miles, chains and links run in the township or fractional township.

The act of Congress approved 18 May 1796 (*Land Laws*, new edition, p. 420) requires that "every surveyor shall note in his *field book* the true situation of all mines, salt licks, salt springs, and mill sites which shall come to his knowledge, all water courses over which the line he runs shall pass, also the quality of the lands. These field books shall be returned to the Surveyor General, who shall thereupon cause a description of the whole lands surveyed, to be made out and transmitted to the officers who may superintend the sales. He shall also cause a fair plat to be made of the townships and fractional parts of townships contained in the said lands, describing the subdivisions thereof and the marks of the corners. This plat shall be recorded in books to be kept for that purpose, a copy thereof shall be kept open at the Surveyor General's office for public information, and other copies sent to the places of sale, and to the Secretary of the Treasury."

As the protraction of the surveys at the office of the Surveyor General, from the field books furnished by his deputies, is the test of the accuracy or incorrectness of the survey, the greatest caution is to be observed in making such protractions.

The field books are to indicate the examination and approval thereof (or disapproval as the case may be) by the Surveyor General, with the date of such examination and approval under his own proper signature, also the date of the contract, the quarter of the year in which the land was surveyed, and payment made therefor.

The field books are to be signed by the deputy surveyor, and also by the chainmen, marker, and flagbearers employed in the survey.

SUBDIVISIONS OF SECTIONS AND FRACTIONAL SECTIONS

22nd. The act of 24th April 1820 entitled "An act making further provision for the sale of public lands." (*Land Laws*, new edition, p. 770) requires that the public lands be offered for sale in half quarter sections, and requires that the lines supposed to divide the quarter sections into half quarter sections are to be run *north* and *south*. This law also requires that the corners and contents of half quarter sections shall be ascertained in the manner and on the principles prescribed by the act of 11th Feb'y 1805 (*Land Laws*, new edition, p. 515).

The same act requires that "fractional sections containing one hundred and sixty acres and upwards, shall in like manner as nearly as practicable, be subdivided into half quarter sections under such rules and regulations as may be prescribed by the Secretary of the Treasury: but fractional sections containing less than one hundred and sixty acres, shall not be divided, but shall be sold entire.

The instruction of the Secretary of the Treasury under the aforesaid act is, that the lines of the subdivisions of fractional sections containing one hundred and sixty acres or upwards, may run either north and south or east and west, so as to preserve to the respective subdivisions the most compact and convenient forms.

The lines of the subdivisions of quarter sections and fractional sections are to be merely indicated on the maps. It is not contemplated by the existing laws that they should be actually surveyed at the expense of the United States.

In the subdivisions of fractional sections you are requested to observe as a general rule, points equidistant between the half mile posts, as the supposed

boundaries whether north and south or east and west, between the subdivisions.
I am, very respectfully, Your Obt. Servt.

(Signed)   ELIZAH HAYWOOD

P. S. It is invariably required that you furnish to this office, and to the registers of the proper land offices, copies of the same township plats and descriptive notes, at the same time. A failure to observe this rule, will necessarily embarrass the operations of the Government in the sale of public lands.

E. HAYWOOD'S INSTRUCTIONS CANCELLING ORDER REQUIRING FINGERBOARDS AND BRANDING IRONS

GENERAL LAND OFFICE
24 Oct. 1832

SIR:

I have received your letter of 21st ult. in reference to certain points in my letter of instruction of 23rd Septbr Last.

Inasmuch as you have suggested so many difficulties attending the use of branding irons in various situations in which the surveyors may be placed, I request that you will consider so much of the 20th article of my letter of instructions of 23rd Sept last as relates to that peculiar mode of marking, as being hereby suspended untill you receive further instructions. Meanwhile you will continue the mode of marking hitherto in use, enjoining on your surveyors the observance of every particularity necessary to effect the primary object of that instruction, which is the proper designation of boundaries, and the perpetuation of the same.

You propose to have *red* paint traced in the groove cut by the common marking irons to give a conspicious appearance to the letters or figures. I see no objection to this mode.

The objections to the charring and tarring of the posts appear to be principally the loss of time attending those operations for which the surveyors would require extra pay. Under these circumstances, as increased pay cannot be granted, those precautions against the decay of the posts, must by necessity be abandoned.

I am not satisfied with some of the reasons assigned by you against the use of *finger boards*,—but, although desirous of adopting them as a precaution against error of entry, and for increased facility in the discovery of boundary lines, it is not intended to introduce any innovation which would unnecessarily retard the execution of the public surveys. If surveyors cannot be found to undertake the placing of finger boards without increased pay, the plan cannot be put into operation.

I am, very respectfully, Your Obt. Servt.

E. HAYWOOD

GIDEON FITZ
Surveyor of Public Lands, Washington, Mississippi

GENERAL INSTRUCTIONS (1834) TO DEPUTY SURVEYORS IN ILLINOIS AND MISSOURI[4]

St. Louis,   183——

SURVEYOR'S OFFICE

To

Deputy Surveyor.

SIR:

In the execution of surveys under the authority of this office, the following General Instructions have been prepared for the government of the Deputy Surveyors, and must be strictly adhered to in all cases not otherwise provided for by special instructions, which may be rendered necessary on account of any peculiar circumstances.

You will provide yourself with a compass of excellent quality and approved construction, having a *nonious division*, and moveable sights; also, with two two-pole chains, of 50 links (of equal length) each. One of said chains must be adjusted to the standard in this office, and by it you will compare and adjust that which is used, at least once in every two days, and note their difference, if any, in your Field Book; and if there is no difference, state in your Field Book the fact of your having compared and found them to agree. You must likewise be provided with a full set of *tally rods*, of iron or steel, or pointed therewith, and allow none others to be used but the precise number you shall have selected for that purpose.

Your chain-men, axe-men and flag-men, must be men of strict moral integrity; none must be employed, in whom *implicit* confidence cannot be reposed;—and you will be ever vigilant over their conduct.

Each of your Field Books will commence with a list of your chain-men, axe-men and flag-men then in your service, and intended to be employed in performing the surveys you are about to execute. The first book under your contract will contain an attested record of their oaths, and a statement of their compensation; and whenever you may employ any others, you will insert their names, together with their oaths and compensation, in your Field Book, before they are permitted to commence work. You will also, when a chain-man, axe-man or flag-man is dismissed, or quits work from any cause *whatever*, note it in your Field Book, together with the cause of his dismissal, or the reason for which he quits work, and refer thereto by a note in the front part of your book.

(Form of Oath for Chain-men.)

I, A. B., do solemnly swear in the presence of Almighty God, that I will faithfully and impartially execute and fulfil the duties of a Chain Carrier; that I will level the chain, and plumb the pins, so as to obtain the true horizontal distance;

---

[4] Across face of these 1834 Instructions is written the following: Received January 9, 1834, with letter for U. S. Surveyor General.

and that I will make a true report of the length of all the lines that I may assist in measuring, to the best of my abilities, so help me God. A. B.

Sworn to and subscribed, before the undersigned,
    this   day of   183
    C. D. *Deputy Surveyor.*

(*Form of Oath for Flag-men and Axe-men.*)

I, E. F., do solemnly swear in the presence of Almighty God, that I will faithfully and truly perform the duties of a flag-man (or axe-man, as the case may require) to the best of my abilities, so help me God.   E. F.

Sworn to and subscribed, before the undersigned,
    this   day of   183
    C. D. *Deputy Surveyor.*

All lines must be run with the assistance of a flag or fore vane-man; and Township boundary lines, with the compass adjusted to the true meridian, unless otherwise instructed by this office.

If by reason of mineral attraction, or any other cause whatever, any line or lines cannot be accurately surveyed with the use of the needle, other means must be adopted, so as to ensure the correct execution of the work; and the manner of operating must be carefully noted in the Field Book.

All trees which your lines (except random lines) strike, must be noted in your Field Book, and have *two notches* cut on each side thereof in the direction of the line; but no other spot or blaze, whatever, is to be made thereon. All trees on each side of the lines, and near thereto, (except random lines) must be marked with two spots or blazes, diagonally or quartering towards the line.

Range lines (N. and S. township boundary lines) will be run north, and corners for sections and quarter sections will be established thereon at every half mile, and mile, for the sections and quarter sections to the west, and not for those to the east of the line, except at township corners. East and west standard lines will be run east or west, as the case may require, and corners established thereon for the quarter sections, sections, and townships, north of the line, and not for those to the south of it. East and west fractional township lines, which close to the boundary line of this Surveying District, or to an Indian or state boundary, will be run east or west, as may be required; and quarter section and section corners will be established thereon for the quarter sections and sections to the north of the line, and not for those south of it.

All other E. and W. Township lines will be run west on randoms, and corrected east from township corner to township corner; and the excess or deficiency must be added to, or deducted from, the south boundary of section 31, west of the quarter section corner.

Sub-division lines of a Township will be run with the compass adjusted to the east boundary thereof; but the true variation of the needle must be determined so as to show the difference (if any) between the said true variation and the variation at which the surveys are executed.

Section, fractional section, and township corners, will be perpetuated by planting a post at the place of the corner, of the most durable wood that can be had in the vicinity thereof. The posts must be set in the earth by digging a hole to admit them *two feet deep*, and be very securely rammed in with earth, and also with stone, if convenient—the township corner posts must be at least 5, and the section and fractional section corner posts *4 inches diameter*; they must be *neatly squared off* at top, and placed so, that the corners will correspond to the cardinal points. The posts at the corners of sections in the interior of a township must indicate, by a number of notches on each of the four corners directed to the cardinal points, the number of miles that it stands from the outlines of the township; the four sides of the post will be numbered to correspond to the number of the section they respectively face. If, however, a tree is at the place of any corner, it will be notched as aforesaid, and answer for the corner in lieu of a post.

Section corner posts on range and township lines, will indicate, by a number of notches on two corners directed to the proper cardinal points, the number of miles it stands from the nearest township corner; and two sides of said posts will be numbered to correspond to the number of the section they face.

Corner posts at township corners, will have 6 notches on each of the four corners, directed to the cardinal points, and each of the four sides thereof will be numbered to correspond to the number of the section they face.—Or in lieu of posts, you may insert endways into the ground, to the depth of 7 or 8 inches, a stone, which shall be not less than 12 inches wide, 14 inches long, and 3 inches thick.

You will ascertain and state in your field notes, the course and distance from the several section and township corner posts, trees and stones, to a tree in each section for which they stand as a corner; each of said trees you will mark with a *notch and blaze* facing the post; the notch to be at the lower end of the blaze; and on the blaze, which must be neatly made, you will mark, with a marking iron, in a plain, distinct and permanent manner, the letter S., with the number of the section, and over it the letter T., with the number of the township; and above this, the letter R., with the number of the range. And in all cases where there is no tree in any section within a reasonable distance of a corner, on which to mark the number of section, township and range, that fact must be stated in your field notes.

Township corners in a prairie, or other situation, where bearing or witness trees are not at hand, will be perpetuated by depositing in the ground, and at least three inches beneath the natural surface thereof, a portion of *charcoal* (the quantity to be specified in your field notes,) not less than two quarts, at the place of such corners, over which you will erect a *mound of earth*, three feet high, five feet square at the base, and two feet square at top; the sides whereof must be reveted or faced with sods laid horizontally and in successive layers on each other; each of said layers having an offset inwards, corresponding to the general slope of the face of the mounds; and in the mound you will insert a post of the dimensions and marked as before directed; or you may deposite at the place of the corner, three stones, not less than five inches square by three inches thick, all of which you will particularly describe in your field notes—the top of the uppermost stone to be three inches below the natural surface of the ground, and the other two successively and immediately beneath the first—and over said stones you will erect a mound similar to that directed to be made over the deposited charcoal—or, in lieu of charcoal or stone, to be deposited as before stated, you may perpetuate the corner by inserting endways into the ground, and to the depth of 7 or 8 inches, a stone, which shall not be less than 12 inches wide, 14 inches long, and 3 inches thick; over which no mound need be erected; but the kind of stone used, together with its shape and dimensions, and the manner in which it is set, must be particularly described in your field notes.

If a township corner, where bearing or witness trees are not to be found within a reasonable distance therefrom, shall fall within a ravine, or in any other situation where the nature of the ground or the circumstances of its locality shall be such as may prevent, or prove unfavorable to the erection of a mound, you will perpetuate such corner by selecting, in the immediate vicinity thereof, a suitable plot of ground as a site for a bearing or witness mound, and erect thereon a mound of earth in the same manner, conditioned in every respect, with charcoal or stone deposited beneath, as before described for a township corner; and measure, and state in your field notes, the distance and course from the position of the true corner of the bearing or witness mound so placed and erected.

Section corners in a prairie or other situation where bearing or witness trees cannot be had, will be perpetuated in the manner before directed for a township corner, except that, where *mounds* are made they will be only *two feet six inches high*, by four feet square at the base, and two feet square at the top.

Quarter-section corners will be perpetuated by a post (of durable wood) 3 inches diameter, placed in the ground and marked ¼ S., from which you will state in your field notes the course and distance to two of the most suitable trees in two different quarter-sections for which you are establishing the corner; which two trees you will mark with a blaze and notch facing the post; and on the blaze above the notch you will mark ¼ S., with a marking iron. And where bearing or witness trees are not at hand, you will perpetuate quarter-section corners by erecting a mound, beneath which no deposit need be made—the mound, to be of similar construction to those for section and township corners, except, that they will be only two feet high, three feet six inches square at the base, and 1 foot 6 inches square at the top.

Whenever your course may be obstructed by insuperable obstacles, such as ponds, swamps, marshes, lakes, rivers, creeks, etc., you will prolong the line across such obstacles by taking the necessary right angled off-sets; or, if this is inconvenient, by a traverse or trigonometrical operation, until you regain the line on the opposite side; and in case a north and south, or a true east and west line is regained in advance of any obstacle, you will prolong and mark the line back to the obstacle so passed, and state all the particulars in relation thereto in your field notes; and at the intersection of lines, with both margins of impassable obstacles, you will establish a *witness point* (for the purpose of perpetuating the intersections therewith,) by setting a post, and giving in your field notes the course and distance therefrom to two trees on opposite sides of the line, each of which trees you will mark with a blaze and notch facing the post, except on the margins of navigable water courses or navigable lakes; in these cases you will mark the trees with the proper number of the fractional section, township and range.

The townships are to be laid on as nearly six miles square as practicable, by lines running from south to north 6 miles, and the corresponding corners joined by lines running easterly and westerly; and they will be subdivided into 36 sections, containing, as nearly as may be, 640 acres each. The sections to be numbered by beginning with No. 1, in the northeast corner of the township, and going west and east, alternately through the township, with progressive number ending with 36, which will be in the southeast corner thereof.

The courses of all navigable rivers which may bound or pass through your district, must be *accurately surveyed*, and their width taken at those points where they may be intersected by section or township lines. Those navigable rivers which may pass through your district, must be surveyed on each side. You will also *meander* all lakes or ponds of sufficient magnitude to justify such expense. In meandering, you will state particularly in your field notes, at what corner you commence the meanders of each fractional section and also the corner to which you close. You will likewise state on which side of the river you are meandering, whether on the right or left bank, (going downwards,) and also whether on the *East, West, North, South, North-East, North-West, South-East* or *South-West* side of the river, or other water course, through or adjoining your district.

Any excess or deficiency in the length of any township boundary line, or excess or error in the falling off from the corner to which any closing township line shall be run, that may exceed five chains; or any excess or deficiency exceeding one chain in the length of any section line, or excess of error in the falling off from the corner to which any section line shall be run, that shall exceed one chain in closing the lines of a whole section; and at the same rate for the section lines, and at the rate of one chain and fifty links per mile of the meanders, in closing the meanders of a navigable river or other water course with the line or lines of a fractional section, must be corrected by you and reduced within those limits, before leaving the ground, by re-surveying the line or lines which may have occasioned the excess or deficiency in the length of such township or section line, or excess of error in closing the lines of a township, or of a whole or fractional section. All notes of corrections and re-surveys, must be entered as *such* in the proper place of the Field Book, according to the order in which they may be executed; and the former and erroneous survey must be referred to in the said entries. Also, in the margin of the pages containing erroneous surveys, that fact must be stated, and the page on which the notes of the re-survey or correction are entered, must also be referred to.

In subdividing townships you will commence at the corner to sections 35 and 36 on the south boundary of the township, (one mile west of the south-east corner thereof,) and move on in continued progression from east to west, and from south to north, in order that the excess or deficiency of the township, as to complete sections, may be added to, or deducted from, the northern and western ranges of quarter sections.

Each north and south section line must be made one mile in measure by the chain, except those which close to the north boundary of the township, so that the excess or deficiency will be thrown in the northern range of quarter sections, viz.:— In running north between sections 1 and 2, at 40.00 chains, establish the quarter section corner, and note the distance at which you intersect the north boundary of the township; and also, the distance you fall east or west of the corresponding section corner for the township to the north; and, at said intersection, establish a corner for the sections between which you are surveying.

The east and west Section lines, except those in the west range of sections and those which cross navigable water courses, will be run from the proper section corners, east on random lines, (without blazing) for the corresponding section corners. Temporary quarter section corner posts will be set at 40.00 chains, and the distance at which you intersect the range or section line, and your falling north or south of the corner run for, will be noted in your Field Book; from which corner you will correct the line west by means of off-sets from stakes, or some other marks set up or made on the random at convenient distances, and remove the temporary quarter section post, and place it and establish the corner on the true line, equidistant, or at the average distance between the proper Section corners. If, however, you strike the corner run for, you have only to blaze the line back, and establish the quarter section corner at the average distance.

The east and west lines, in the west range or sections, will be run west on true lines; the quarter section corner will be established at 40.00 chains; the corner for the proper sections will be established at the intersection with the range line, and the distance which it intersects north or south of the corresponding section corner west of the line, will be noted in the Field Book.

Whenever an east and west section line, other than those in the west range of sections, crosses a navigable river, or other water course, you will not run a random line and correct it as in ordinary cases where there is no obstruction of the land, but you will run east and west on a true line, (at right angles to the adjacent north and south lines,) from the proper section corner, to the said river or other navigable water, and make an accurate connection between the corners established on the opposite banks thereof; and if the error, neither in the length of the line, nor in the falling north and south of each other of the fractional corners on the opposite banks, exceed the limits before specified in these instructions for the closing of a whole section, you will proceed with your operations. If, however, the error exceeds those limits, you will state the amount thereof in your field notes, and proceed forthwith to ascertain which line or lines may have occasioned the excess of error, and reduce it within the proper bounds, by re-surveying or correcting the line or lines so ascertained to be erroneous; and note in your Field Book the whole of your operations in determining what line was erroneous, and the correction thereof.

If, by reason of bends in a river, or other navigable water course, the whole of any east and west section line would not be surveyed, if the parts which are run east and west respectively were to terminate at their first intersection with the said river or other navigable water course, that part of the line, which, by being prolonged, would give the survey the best form, must be continued to its last intersection with the said river or other navigable water; and from said last intersection of the line so continued, you will make the connection with the corresponding corner on the opposite bank, and if it is found that the error exceeds the limits before specified for the closing of a whole section, you will make the required correction in the manner before pointed out in these instructions.

All rivers, creeks, springs and smaller streams of water, with their width and the course they run in crossing the lines of surveys, and whether navigable, rapid or otherwise; also, all swamps, ponds, stone quarries, coal beds, peat or turf grounds, mounds, precipices, caves, rapids, cascades or falls of water, minerals, ores, salt springs, salt licks and fossils, prairies, hills and mountains, towns, villages and settlements, forges, factories and cotton gins; also, all uncommon, natural or artificial productions, which may come to your knowledge, are to be particularly regarded and noted in your Field Book. You will likewise note when the lines enter and when they leave creek or river bottom.

At the end of every half mile, in running section or township lines, and at the end of the meanders of each fractional section, you will give a particular description of the face of the country, whether level, hilly or mountainous; of the quality or rate of the soil, and whether it is fit or unfit for cultivation; and, particularly, whether the bottom land is liable to inundation or not; and, if it shall be liable to inundation, state, also, to what depth, so far as that circumstance may come to your knowledge, whether from observation of the water marks upon the trees, or any other source of information; and note the kinds and quality of timber and undergrowth, naming the different sorts in the order which they predominate.— The description of each half mile must be full, and not refer to any previous description. The names of all bearing or witness trees, and station or line trees, must be written out in full, and not abbreviated; nor must any word which relates to the course or length of a line, or any object noted thereon, or in the establishment of a corner, be abbreviated, except in stating the courses to the witness trees from the corners, the course of meanders, and the bearing or direction of small streams, mountains, etc., when they are not to the cardinal points; in these cases, the capital letters, N. S. E. and W., plainly and distinctly made, will be used.

The plots or sketches which you are to return, will exhibit, as accurately as practicable, from careful occular observation (in addition to the measurements on the line) to be made by you and noted in your Field Book, the true situation of all objects noted; including the courses and connections of all rivers and other water courses, and travelled roads or tracks, denoting the principal places to which they lead, and the enchainment and direction of remarkable hills or mountains.

Your Field Books for your original notes will be of such a size as you may deem most convenient; they will be of the best quality of foolscap paper; and the original field notes, which are to be returned to this office, together with a fair and correct copy thereof, must be kept in a plain and intelligable manner, according to the form hereafter prescribed in these instructions. Every entry must be so specific as not to admit of a doubt as to what is intended thereby, or a possibility of a misconstruction of your meaning. The said notes must be entered in the same order, from day to day, as the work is executed on the ground, including all re-surveys and corrections, and the date must follow each day's work.

Although your lines are to be measured with a chain of two poles, you are to keep your reckonings in chains of four poles, or one hundred links each; and all entries in your Field Book, and all plans and calculations are to be made according to the decimal measure of a chain.

The courses and distances on your lines must be placed in the margin of your Field Book, on the left hand, (for which purpose it should be large,) and your remarks on the right.

The Field Books in which you copy your notes, will be according to a form to be prescribed by this office.

In all measurements, the level or horizontal length is to be taken, and not that which arises from measuring over the surface of the ground, when it happens to be uneven or hilly.

Your Field Books, containing your original notes, will be signed by each of your chain-men, axe-men and flag-men, and they and the copies thereof, will be certified by yourself, according to a form to be prescribed by this office, in conformity with the requirements of your contract and instructions. The certificate to each book will state as many of the following facts as are applicable to the notes of the surveys contained therein, viz:—That all the witness trees to township and section corners, were marked with a blaze and notch facing the several corner posts; that the notch on each tree was at the lower end of the blaze; that the blaze was neatly made; and that there was marked, in a plain, distinct and permanent manner, with a marking iron, on the blaze of each witness tree, and above the notch, the letter S., with the number of the section; and over it the letter T., with the number of the township: and over this, the letter R., with the number of the range, in which the said trees respectively stand. That all the section and township corner posts were inserted two feet into a hole dug in the ground, and that they were securely rammed in with earth, and also with stone, when convenient; that the said posts were of the most durable wood that could be had in the vicinity; that the township corner posts were 5, and the section corner posts 4 inches diameter; that they were neatly squared at top and placed with the corners to the cardinal points, and that the several sides were marked with the number of the section which they faced; also, that the corners of township corner posts were marked with 6 notches each; that two of the corners of section corner posts on township boundary lines, were marked with as many notches facing the proper cardinal points as said posts are miles from the nearest township corners; and that the corners of the section posts, in the interior of a township, were marked with as many notches as the posts stand miles from the township boundaries; that the witness trees to quarter section corners were marked with a blaze and notch facing the post; and that ¼ S. was marked on the blaze above the notch; and also, that ¼ S. was marked on each corner post, and that the posts were at least 3 inches diameter and placed firmly in the ground. That the mounds were reveted or faced with sod, laid horizontally and in successive layers on each other, each layer having an offset inwards, corresponding to the general slope of the face of the mound; and that the mounds at township corners were 5 feet square at the base, 2 feet square at top, and 3 feet high; that the mounds at section corners were 4 feet square at the base, 2 feet square at the top, and 2 feet 6 inches high; and that the mounds at quarter section corners, were 3 feet 6 inches square at the base, 1 foot 6 inches square at the top, and 2 feet high.

(Form of keeping field notes of exterior boundary line of Townships, viz:)

Suppose the line to be surveyed, is the east boundary of Township 21 North, Range 6 east of the 4th principal meridian, and that the corner to Sections 1, 6, 31 & 36, of Townships 20 & 20, 21 & 21 North, Ranges 6 & 7 East, had been established by another surveyor, and that you were furnished with a description thereof from this office. You will commence your field notes as follows, viz:

If first book, oaths of chain-men, axe-men and flag-men, and a statement of their compensation.

   A. B., *hind chain-man,*
   C. D., *fore chain-man,*
   E. F., *flag-man,*
   G. H., *axe-man.*

each at a compensation of twenty dollars per month.

Measuring chain compared with the standard chain and found to be of the right length.

Took the variation of the needle last night, (27th of September, 1832) about 5 chains southwest of the corner to Townships 20 & 20, 21 & 21 North, Ranges 6 & 7 east of the 4th principal meridian, and found it to be 8° 20 min. east. I therefore adjust my compass to that variation, and commence at the corner to Sections 1, 6, 31 & 36, of Townships 20 & 20, 21 & 21 North, of Ranges 6 & 7 east of the 4th principal meridian, which agrees with the description furnished me by the Surveyor's Office, viz: A post, from which a white oak, 6 inches diameter, bears S. 67° east, 372 links; a hickory, 14 inches diameter, bears north 25° east, 13 links; and a white oak, 13 inches diameter, (stated to be 11 in the description furnished me) bears north 62° west, 135 links. The other witness tree (an ash, 16 inches diameter) has fallen down; I therefore mark, with the proper number of section, township and range, a black walnut, 24 inches diameter, which bears south 83° west, 127 links distant, and run from said township corner

NORTH
CHAINS

Along the east boundary of Section 36, Township 21, north of the base line, Range 6 east of the 4th principal meridian.

14.70   A brook, 25 links wide, with a rapid current, runs southwesterly about 10 chains, then turns to the N. W.

27.60   Left the creek bottom, and entered hills.

29.40   A white oak, 15 inches diameter.

33.70   A hickory, 24 inches diameter.

40.00   Set a quarter section corner post on the top of a ridge, bearing northeasterly and southwesterly; from which post, a white oak, 24 inches diameter, bears S. 28° W. 197 links, and a poplar, 18 inches diameter, bears N. 56° W., 14 links distant.

The S. 27.60 chains, level, creek bottom; subject to occasional inundation of about 4 feet, as appears from the water marks on the trees. The soil is good and fit for cultivation; timber, walnut, cherry and white oak; undergrowth, pawpaw and spice. The remainder of the line is too hilly and broken for cultivation, although the soil is good. Timber, hickory, white oak and walnut; undergrowth, redbud and dogwood.

49.07   A white oak, 8 inches diameter.

64.08   A walnut, 36 inches diameter.

80.00   Set a post, corner to Sections 25 and 36, Township 21 north, Range 6 east of the 4th principal meridian, from which a hickory, 17 inches diameter, bears south 57° west, 127 links; and a white oak, 13 inches diameter, bears north 23° west, 72 links distant. Land, too hilly and broken for cultivation, although the soil is rich; timber, hickory, white oak and walnut; undergrowth, pawpaw and spice.

Along the east boundary of Section 25, Township 21 north, Range 6 east of the 4th principal meridian.

13.80   Left the hills, and entered river bottom.

14.90   A burr oak, 36 inches diameter.

40.00   Set a quarter-section corner post, from which an elm, 13 inches diameter, bears north 85° west, 18 links, and a pin oak, 12 inches diameter, bears south 74° West, 39 links distant. The south 13.80 chains, rolling land; the remainder, river bottom. The soil on the half mile, is rich and fit for cultivation; timber white oak, poplar and hickory; undergrowth, sassafras and dogwood.

49.50   An impassable swamp. Set a post, from which a hickory, 12 inches diameter, bears south 76° west, 18 links; and a white oak, 13 inches diameter, bears south 85° east, 14 links. This swamp lies mostly west of the line; it extends in a southwesterly direction about 25.00 chains. Offset around said swamp, as follows, viz:

      East 4.50 chains,
      North 7.60 chains,
      East 6.70 chains,
      North 8.50 chains,
      West 7.50 chains,
      North 3.20 chains,

CHAINS	West 3.70 chains,—regained the line on the east boundary of Section 25, Township 21 north, Range 6 east, in advance of the swamp; I therefore run south 3.72 chains and intersected the northwest margin of the swamp, where set a post, from which an ash, 12 inches diameter, bears north 17° west, 18 links, and an elm, 13 inches diameter, bears north 12° east, 45 links distant. Thence continued the line north, along the east boundary of Section 25, Township 21 north, Range 6 east; counting the distances from the corner of Sections 25 & 36; the distance across the swamp, on the line, being 15.58 chains.
72.54	A white oak, 18 inches diameter.
80.00	Set a post, corner to Sections 24 & 25, Township 21 north, Range 6 east, from which a white oak, 18 inches diameter, bears south 18° west, 32 links; and a gum, 24 inches diameter, bears north 27° west, 34 links distant. Except the swamp, the land is low, wet bottom, unfit for cultivation; generally subject to overflow from 7 to 10 feet, as appears by the water marks on the trees; and, as I am informed by H———— J————, who lives in the vicinity thereof. Timber, gum, swamp maple and pin oak; no undergrowth. The swamp is covered with bushes of various sorts.

September 28, 1832

NORTH CHAINS	Proceed in a similar manner along the east boundary of Sections 24, 13 & 12; then along the east boundary of Section 1, as follows, viz: Along the east boundary of Section 1, Township 21 north, Range 6 east of the 4th principal meridian.
17.52	A road between Holmin's Ferry to the southwest, and Princeton to the northeast.
18.76	A white oak, 16 inches diameter.
19.75	A creek, generally called White Water, but by some Crooked Creek, 200 links wide, runs northeast—gentle current, not navigable. This creek is crossed by the road, noted above, at about 5 chains to the southwest.
32.50	A hickory, 15 inches diameter.
33.00	Left the timber and entered Prairie—bears southeast and northwest.
40.00	Raised a mound, in which set a post for quarter section corner. The timbered land is gently rolling; the soil is good, and fit for cultivation. Timber, white oak, hickory and walnut; undergrowth, dogwood and sumach. The prairie is level; soil rich and fit for cultivation.
59.32	Left the prairie and entered timber—bears northeast and southwest.
63.73	A white walnut, 16 inches diameter.
80.00	Set a post, corner to Sections 1, 6, 31 & 36, of Townships 21 & 21, 22 & 22 north, Ranges 6 & 7 east of the 4th principal meridian, from which a hickory, 17 inches diameter, bears south 56° east, 18 links; a white oak, 24 inches diameter, bears north 77° east, 36 links; a white oak, 14 inches diameter, bears north 27.1-2° west, 35 links; and a black walnut, 24 inches diameter, bears south 75° west, 137 links distant. Land, moderately rolling; soil, good and fit for cultivation; timber, white oak, black oak, hickory and walnut; undergrowth, sassafrass and hazel.

September 29, 1832

Suppose that the corner to Townships 21 & 21, 22 & 22 north, of Ranges

GENERAL INSTRUCTIONS OF 1834   29

              5 & 6 east, had been established, you would then proceed as follows:
              Chain compared with the standard chain and found to be correct.
WEST   On a random line along the south boundary of Section 36, Township 22
CHAINS   north, Range 6 east of the 4th principal meridian.
40.00   Set a temporary quarter-section corner post.
80.00   Set a post for temporary corner to Sections 35 & 36, Township 22 north,
              Range 6 east.
              On a random line, along the south boundary of Section 35, Township 22
              north, Range 6 east of the 4th principal meridian.
21.00   A remarkably fine spring, about 30 links to the north, runs northeasterly.
40.00   Set a temporary quarter-section corner post.
69.00   A quarry of excellent lime stone.
80.00   Set a post for temporary corner to Sections 34 & 35, Township 22 north,
              Range 6 east.

September 30, 1832

              Continue in this manner along the south boundary of Sections 34, 33 & 32;
              and then run
              On a random line, along the south boundary of Section 31, Township 22
              north, Range 6 east of the 4th principal meridian.
00.57   The southeast bank of a navigable lake, which lies mostly to the north
              of the line, it being about 2 miles in a northeastern direction to the north-
              ern end thereof; I therefore off-set around the south end, as follows, viz:
                       South 10.00 chains.
                       West 15.00 chains.
                       South 11.00 chains.
                       West 12.00 chains.
              North 21.00 chains, regained the random line along the south
              boundary of Section 31, in advance of the lake, and continue west, count-
              ing the distances from the temporary corner post to Sections 31 and 32.
40.00   Set a temporary quarter-section corner post.
64.00   A coal bed, in the west bank of Bear Grass Creek, which runs south.
82.75   Intersected the Range line 326 links south of the corner to Sections 1, 6,
              31 and 36, of Townships 21 and 21, 22 and 22 north, Ranges 5 and 6 east.
              Then, from said township corner, run
EAST   On a true line along the south boundary of Section 31, Township 22 north,
              Range 6 east of the 4th principal meridian.
00.32   A branch, 7 links wide, runs southeast.
17.50   A white oak, 18 inches diameter.
18.00   Bear Grass Creek runs south.
33.75   A hickory, 12 inches diameter.
42.75   Set a quarter-section corner post, on the true line, from which a persim-
              mon, 12 inches diameter, bears N. 26° W., 163 links, and a white oak, 24
              inches diameter, bears N. 42° E., 18 links distant.
              Land, rolling; soil, good and fit for cultivation; timber, white oak, black
              oak and hickory; undergrowth, pawpaw and spice.
57.60   Intersected the northwest bank of the navigable lake, (noted on the ran-
              dom line,) where set a post, corner to fractional Sections 6 & 31, of Town-
              ships 21 and 22, north, from which post a hackberry, 18 inches diameter,

CHAINS
EAST

bears N. 23° W., 18 links; and a white oak, 15 inches diameter, bears S. 65° W., 8 links. Thence offset around the lake as follows, viz:

West 4.00 chains with the marked line on the south boundary of Section 31.
South 16.00
East 28.00

North 15.82 chains, regained the true line on the south boundary of Section 31, 25 links east of the southeast margin of the lake; I therefore blazed the line back, west 25 links to the southeast bank of the lake, where set a post for corner to fractional Sections 6 and 31, Townships 21 and 22 north, Range 6 east, 81.35 chains east of the corner to Townships 21 and 21, 22 and 22 north, Ranges 5 and 6 east. From said post, a hickory, 12 inches diameter, bears north 23° E., 13 links, and an elm, 14 inches diameter, bears south 27° east, 54 links distant.

Then continue the line east along the south boundary of Section 31, counting the distances from the township corner.

81.90	A burr oak, 48 inches diameter.
82.75	Set a post on the true line for corner to Sections 31 and 32, Township 22 north, Range 6 east, from which a sycamore, 18 inches diameter, bears north 25° east, 32 links; and a white oak, 18 inches diameter, bears north 28° west, 13 links distant. Land, level and wet; soil, poor, not fit for cultivation; timber, white oak, burr oak and sycamore.

31st [sic] of September, 1832

Continue in this manner along the south boundaries of Sections 32, 33, 34 and 35, and then run

On a true line along the south boundary of Section 36, Township 22 north, Range 6 east of the 4th principal meridian.

14.50	Entered a field of about 40 acres, bearing northeast and southwest; it lies mostly south of the line.
20.17	A spring branch runs southeast, and empties into a creek in about 10 chains. The spring is about 5 chains in a northwestern direction, and is outside of the field.
30.00	Left the field, bearing northeast and southwest.
33.09	A white oak, 28 inches diameter.
40.00	Set a post for quarter section corner on the true line, from which a hickory, 17 inches diameter, bears north 18° west, 14 links; and a white oak, 15 inches diameter, bears north 27° east, 42 links distant. Land, rolling; soil, good and fit for cultivation; timber, white oak, hickory and black oak; undergrowth, hazel and vines.
42.10	A creek, 50 links wide, runs north 80° east; the current is rapid. About 5 chains up stream, in a southwesterly direction, is a mill seat, there being rock on both banks, and a fall of about 50 feet in 20.00 chains.
47.20	Diggins for lead, called New Design.
59.60	A smelting furnace, owned by J———— H————.
75.82	A wagon road, leading from Kingston and Holmes' Ferry to Galena, bears northwest and southeast.

80.00　　The corner to Townships 21 and 21, 22 and 22 north, Ranges 6 and 7 east. Land, rolling; soil, good, and fit for cultivation; timber, hickory, walnut & white oak; undergrowth, briers and hazel.

1st of October, 1832

Form of field notes in sub-dividing a township (say Township 21 north, Range 6 east of the 4th principal meridian,) after the outlines shall have been surveyed.
 A. B. Hind chain-man.
 C. D. Fore chain-man.
 E. F. Flag or fore-vane-man.
 G. H. Axe-man.

Measuring chain compared with the standard chain, and adjusted thereto, it having been found ¼ of an inch too long. Last night (14th of April, 1833) about 20.00 chains northwest of the corner to Townships 20 and 20, 21 and 21 north, Ranges 6 & 7 east, I ascertained the variation of the needle, by polar observations, to be 8° 35 min. east; I, therefore, adjust my compass at that variation; and, to determine the course of the east boundary of the township, commence at the corner, to Townships 20 and 20, 21 and 21 north, Ranges 6 and 7 east, and run—Thence, north on a blank line; at 40.00 chains, fell 15 links west of the quarter section corner; at 79.96 chains, fell 36 links west of the corner to Sections 25 and 36, Township 21 north, range 6 east; then from said corner to Sections 25 and 36, run north (on a blank line,) 39.97 chains, fell 18 links west of the quarter-section corner; 80.05 chains fell 37 links west of the corner to Sections 24 & 25. Therefore, to run parallel to said east boundary of Township 21 north, Range 6 east, my compass must be adjusted to an assumed variation of 8° 20 min. east; which is 15 minutes less than the true variation. I adjust it to that assumed variation, (viz: 8° 20 min. east) and commence at the corner to Sections 35 and 36, on the south boundary of the township, and run—Thence

NORTH CHAINS

   Between Sections 35 and 36, Township 21 north, Range 6 east of 4th principal meridian.
17.62　　A sugar maple, 18 inches diameter.
27.60　　A creek, called White Oak Creek, 40 links wide, gentle current, runs northwest.
40.00　　Set a post for quarter-section corner, from which a walnut, 20 inches diameter, bears south 16° east, 18 links; and a white oak, 18 inches diameter, bears north 23° west, 184 links.
40.32　　Entered river bottom; bears E. and W.
47.60　　The right bank of White River, a navigable stream, at an eastern bend thereof, runs northeasterly. Set a post, corner to fractional Sections 35 and 36, from which a white oak, 18 inches diameter, bears south 25° W., 18 links; and a hickory, 17 inches diameter, bears south 15° east, 39 links distant. The line will run down the river, and leave it again on the right side, without crossing over to the left; I, therefore, meander down stream on the right bank of said river, along fractional Section 36, from the be-

CHAINS EAST	fore described corner of fractional Sections 35 and 36, as follows, viz: North 27, east 16.00 chains. North 14, east 4.00 chains. North 3, west 2.00 chains. North 39, west 12.93 chains, regained the line between Sections 35 and 36, on the right bank of White River, where set a post, corner to fractional Sections 35 and 36, of Township 21 north, Range 6 east of the 4th principal meridian, from which a burr oak, 10 inches diameter, bears south 85° east, 27 links, and a hickory, 18 inches diameter, bears north 27° W., 134 links distant. This corner is 30.17 chains north of the corner established at 47.60 chains, on same bank of the river; and is 77.77 chains north of the corner to Sections 35 and 36, on the south boundary of the township. I continue the line north between Sections 35 and 36, counting the distances from the corner on the south boundary of the township.
80.00	Set a post, corner, to Sections 25, 26, 35 and 36, Township 21 north, range 6 east, from which a white oak, 14 inches diameter, bears north 17° E., 18 links; a white oak, 12 inches diameter, bears south 25° W., 13 links, and a walnut, 14 inches diameter, bears south 58° E., 32 links distant. There is no tree within a reasonable distance in Section 26. On a random line between Sections 25 and 36, Township 21 north, Range 6 east of the 4th principal meridian.
40.00	Set a temporary quarter-section corner post.
80.18	Intersected the east boundary of the township 37 links south of the corner to Sections 25 and 36; from which corner I run
WEST	On a true line, between Sections 25 and 36, Township 21 north, Range 6 east of the 4th principal meridian.
17.60	A white oak, 15 inches diameter.
29.40	A branch, 26 links wide, runs southwest.
40.09	Set a quarter-section corner post on the true line, at average distance; from which a pine, 17 inches diameter, bears south 32° east, 49 links; and a pine, 27 inches diameter, bears north 42° west, 132 links distant.
40.15	Left hills and entered bottom; bears northwest and southeast.
65.17	A walnut, 36 inches diameter.
80.18	The corner to Sections 25, 26, 35 and 36.

15th of April, 1833

NORTH	Between Sections 25 and 26, Township 21 north, Range 6 east of the 4th principal meridian.
27.62	A white oak, 12 inches diameter.
29.34	Intersected the right and southerly bank of White River, a navigable stream; runs easterly. Set a post, corner to fractional Sections 25 and 26, from which a burr oak, 17 inches diameter bears south 17° east; 39 links, and a black oak, 13 inches diameter, bears south 25° west, 142 links distant. Sent my flagman over the river, and caused the flag to be set on the left bank thereof, on the line between Sections 25 and 26; I then offset from the before described corner to fractional Sections 25 & 26, E. 5.00 chains, to a point from which the flag set as before said, on the left

General Instructions of 1834

NORTH CHAINS	bank of the river, and on the line between Sections 25 and 26, bears north 21° west, making the distance across the river 11.23 chains; therefore, at (29.34 more 11.23) equal to
40.57	Set a post on the left and north bank of White River, for corner to fractional Sections 25 and 26, Township 21 north, Range 6 east, from which a hickory, 13 inches diameter, bears south 65° east, 125 links; and a white oak, 17 inches diameter, bears S. 72° west, 19 links distant.—The place of the quarter-section corner is in the river; it cannot therefore be established.
56.42	A white oak, 13 inches diameter.
74.39	A black oak, 14 inches diameter.
79.16	A black oak, 14 inches diameter.
80.00	Set a post, corner of Sections 23, 24, 25 and 26, from which a white oak, 17 inches diameter, bears north 23° west, 27 links; a black oak, 14 inches diameter, bears north 62° east, 113 links; and a black oak, 14 inches diameter, bears south 36° east, 39 links. There is no tree within a reasonable distance in Section 26.
EAST	On a random line, between Sections 24 and 25, Township 21 north, Range 6 east of the 4th principal meridian.
21.32	Intersected the left bank of White River, a navigable water course, runs northeasterly; set a post, corner to fractional Sections 24 and 25, from which a hickory, 17 inches diameter, bears south 39° west, 18 links; and a white oak, 18 inches diameter, bears N. 85° W., 132 links distant. Not knowing that this line would intersect a navigable stream, when I commenced the survey thereof, I run it on a random line; I therefore, from this fractional section corner, run and blazed
WEST	On a true line between Sections 24 and 25, Township 21 north, Range 6 east.
4.06	A black oak, 13 inches diameter.
21.32	The corner of Sections 23, 24, 25 and 26.

16th of April, 1833

	Measuring chain compared with the standard chain and found to be 1 inch too long; made it of the proper length and commenced at the corner of Sections 24 and 25, on the east boundary of Township 21 north, range 6 east of the 4th principal meridian, and run—Thence
WEST	On a true line, between said Sections 24 and 25, Township 21 north, Range 6 east of the 4th principal meridian.
17.60	A white oak, 8 inches diameter.
32.40	A brook, 15 links wide, runs southwest.
40.00	Set a post for quarter section corner, from which a white oak, 13 inches diameter, bears north 32° west, 18 links; and a black oak, 15 inches diameter, bears S. 35° E., 14 links distant.
45.38	Intersected the right & southeasterly bank of White River, which runs northeasterly; set a post, corner to fractional Sections 24 and 25, Township 21 north, Range 6 east from which a white oak, 14 inches diameter, bears N. 80° E., 17 links; and an elm, 14 inches diameter, bears S. 17° E., 45 links distant. The post, corner to fractional Sections 24 and 25, es-

tablished on the left bank of White River, at 21.32 chains east of the corner to Sections 23, 24, 25 and 26, (see page 31 of this book,) bears S. 87¼° W., I then run south 65 links to a point from which the aforesaid post, corner to fractional Sections 24 and 25, on the left bank of White River, bears west. The Section, therefore, closes within the limits specified in my instructions.

NORTH
CHAINS Between Sections 23 and 24, Township 21 north, Range 6 east of the 4th principal meridian.
0.62 Left bottom and entered upland.
3.20 Entered prairie, bears N.E. and S.W.
40.00 Raised a mound, in which set a quarter section corner post.
62.00 A branch, 6 links wide, runs east.
80.00 Deposited 2 quarts of charcoal, 3 inches below the natural surface of the earth, and over said charcoal erected a mound, in which set a post, corner to Sections 13, 14, 23 and 24, of Township 21 north, Range 6 east.

EAST On a true line, between Sections 13 and 24, Township 21 north, Range 6 east of the 4th principal meridian.
7.00 Left the prairie and entered timbered land.
29.35 Intersected the left bank of White River, (runs northeasterly;) set a post, corner of fractional Sections 13 and 24, from which a white oak 18 inches diameter, bears S. 17° W., 183 links; and a hickory, 18 inches diameter, bears N. 74° W., 14 links distant. I then go to the corner of Sections 13 and 24, on the east boundary of the township, and run thence.

WEST On a true line between said Sections 13 and 24, Township 21 north, Range 6 east of the 4th principal meridian.
17.84 Intersected the left bank of White River; runs southeast. Set a post, corner to fractional Sections 13 and 24, from which an elm, 8 inches diameter, bears S. 42° E., 18 links, and a gum, 13 inches diameter, bears N. 46° 15 min. E., 73 links. Determined the distance across the river by causing my flag to be set on the opposite or right bank thereof, west from this corner, on the line between Sections 13 and 24, and run south 3.76 chains to a point under the bank of the river; from which the flag, set as aforesaid on the opposite bank bears N. 73½° W., which gives 12.76 chains the distance across the river west from the post, corner of fractional Sections 13 and 24, on the right bank, 17.84 chains west of the corner on the east boundary of the township; therefore, at 17.84 more 12.76 chains, equal to
30.60 West of the aforesaid corner to Sections 13 and 24, on the east boundary of the township, set a post, corner to fractional Sections 13 and 24, Township 21 north, Range 6 east on the right bank of White River, from which a white oak, 16 inches diameter, bears N. 57° W., 19 links; and a hickory, 15 inches diameter bears S. 69° W., 13 links.
37.54 Intersected the right bank of White River, runs northeast, where set a post, corner to fractional Sections 13 and 24, from which a red elm, 18 inches diameter, bears S. 16° E., 79 links, and a pin oak, 15 inches diameter, bears N. 87° E., 19 links.—From this corner, the corner to fractional Sections 13 and 24, on the right bank of White River, 29.35 chains east of the corner to Sections 13, 14, 23 and 24, bears S. 87¾° W.—I run thence south ?? links to a point from which the aforesaid corner of fractional

NORTH CHAINS	Sections 13 and 24, on the left bank of the river, bears west.—The section, therefore, closes within the prescribed limits. Between Sections 13 and 14, Township 21 north, Range 6 east of the 4th principal meridian.
00.16	Entered prairie.
40.00	Raised a mound, in which set a post for quarter section corner.
80.00	Placed three lime stones in the ground; the top of the uppermost one 4 inches below the natural surface thereof; and the other two, successively and immediately below it—The upper stone is 8 inches long, 6 inches wide at one end, 5 inches wide at the other end, and 3¼ inches thick; the stone, next below it, is 5 inches square and 4 thick; and the lowermost stone is 6 inches square and 3 inches thick; over said stones raised a mound, in which set a post corner to Section 11, 12, 13 and 14, Township 21 north, Range 6 east.

17th of April, 1833

A.B. Hind chain-man.
C.D. Fore chain-man.

Mr. A. B. quits work on account of sickness.—I have supplied his place with C. D., my former fore-chain-man, and employed J. K. as fore chain-man, at a compensation of Twenty Dollars per month.

(J.K.'s oath to be entered here.)

Proceed in this manner between Sections 12 and 13, 11 and 12, and 1 and 12;—Then run

Between Sections 1 and 2, Township 21 north, Range 6 east of the 4th principal meridian.

40.00	Raised mound, in which set a post for quarter section corner.
49.50	Left prairie and entered timber.
62.00	A creek 50 links wide, not navigable, runs northeast; rapid current.
80.76	Intersected the south boundary of Township 22 north, Range 6 east, 37 links west of the corner to Sections 35 and 36; and at said intersection set a post, corner to Sections 1 and 2, Township 21 north, Range 6 east, from which a white oak, 14 inches diameter, bears S. 26° E., 14 links, and a hickory, 13 inches diameter, bears S. 42° W., 18 links distant.

18th of April, 1833

Between Sections 34 and 35, Township 21 north, Range 6 east of the 4th principal meridian.

40.00	Raised a mound, in which set a post for quarter section corner.
80.00	Set a lime stone, which is 16 inches long, 14 inches wide at one end, 12 inches wide at the other end, and 4 inches thick, with the widest end 10 inches in the ground, the edges facing north and south, for corner to Sections 26, 27, 34 and 35.
EAST	On a true line between Sections 26 and 35, of Township 21 north, Range 6 east of the 4th principal meridian.
40.00	Raised a mound, in which set a post for quarter section corner.
46.17	Left the prairie and upland, and entered timbered bottom land.
60.32	Intersected the left bank of White River, where set a post, for corner to

fractional Sections 26 and 35, from which a hickory, 17 inches diameter, bears S. 65° W., 13 links, and a black walnut, 16 inches diameter, bears N. 72° W., 142 links distant.

Then commence at the corner to Sections 25 and 26, 35 and 36, and run

WEST
CHAINS

On a true line, between Sections 26 and 35, Township 21 north, Range 6 east of the 4th principal meridian.

5.61 Intersected the right and easterly bank of White River, runs northwesterly; at said intersection set a post, corner to fractional Sections 26 and 35, Township 21 north, Range 6 east, from which an elm, 18 inches diameter, bears S. 85° E., 13 links; and a white oak, 14 inches diameter, bears N. 27° E., 14 links distant.—Search for the corner of fractional Sections 26 and 35, on the opposite bank of the river, and find it to be at least 5 chains further south than the before described corner to the fractions of said Sections 26 and 35 on the right bank. The section does not, therefore, close within the limits specified in my instructions. I therefore proceed forthwith to ascertain in what line or lines the error was committed, and to make the required correction:—As the line between Sections 25 and 36 closed within the proper limits, the presumption is that the error is in the line between Sections 34 & 35; I go to the corner to said sections on the south boundary of the township and run—Thence

NORTH With the line already surveyed between Sections 34 and 35, Township 21 north, Range 6 east of the 4th principal meridian (see page 36 of this book).

40.13 The quarter section corner.—There is no error, therefore, in this half mile, the 13 links being not more than a reasonable difference in measurement; so I continue the line north, and count the distances from the corner on the south boundary of the township, adopting 40.00 chains as the length of that part of the line which lies south of the quarter section corner.

74.65 The corner established by me for Sections 26, 27, 34 and 35.—I therefore remove the stone, corner to said sections, and at

80.00 Set it for the corner to Section 26, 27, 34 and 35, said stone being as described on page 36, viz: 16 inches long, 14 inches wide at one end, 12 inches wide at the other end, and 4 inches thick, and is set with the widest end 10 inches in the ground, with the edges facing north and south.

Then run

EAST On a true line between Sections 26 and 35, Township 21 north, Range 6 east of the 4th principal meridian.

40.00 Raised a mound, in which set a post for quarter section corner; then go to the quarter section corner established by me on the line erroneously surveyed between Sections 26 and 35, & described on page 37 of this book, and destroy it by leveling the mound & removing the post, & return to the above described quarter section corner and continue the line east between Sections 26 and 35, counting the distances from the corner to Sections 26, 27, 34 and 35.

49.75 Entered timber.

61.17 Intersected the left and westerly bank of White River, (*establish the corner and make the connection with the opposite corner.*)—Then destroy the corner to fractional Sections 26 and 35, established by me on the left bank of White River, at the intersection therewith of the erroneous line between said Sections 26 and 35, described on page 37 of this book, by removing the post and defacing the marks on the witness trees.

NORTH
CHAINS
Between Sections 26 and 27, Township 21 north, Range 6 east of the 4th principal meridian.

40.00 Raised a mound in which set a post for quarter section corner.

86.00 The middle of a ravine, which runs southwest.—I therefore select the most suitable plot of ground in the vicinity, and deposit 3 quarts of charcoal, 4 inches below the natural surface of the ground, and over it erect a mound, in which set a post as a witness point to the corner of Sections 22, 23, 26 and 27; said witness point bears N. 26° W., 144 links from the true place of said corner to Sections 22, 23, 26 and 27, Township 21 north, Range 26 east.

19th of April, 1833

Continue in this manner until you get to the western range of sections, and after having established the corner to Sections 29, 30, 31, and 32, run

WEST On a true line between Sections 30 and 31, Township 21 north, Range 6 east of the 4th principal meridian.

40.00 Raised a mound, in which set a post for quarter section corner.
72.00 Entered timber—bears N.E. and S.W.
80.42 Intersected the east boundary of Township 21 north, Range 5 east, 62 links south of the corner to Sections 25 and 36, and at said intersection set a post, corner to Sections 30 and 31, Township 21 north, Range 6 east, from which a burr oak, 17 inches diameter, bears S. 25° E., 18 links, and a white oak, 17 inches diameter, bears N. 27° E., 184 links distant.

27th of April, 1833

(Form of keeping field notes of the meanders of a navigable water, or other water course:)

Commence at the corner to fractional Sections 25 and 26, Township 21 north of the base line, Range 6 east of the 4th principal meridian, on the right and southeasterly bank of White River, and run thence down stream, with meanders of the right bank of said river, along fractional Section 25, Township 21 north, range 6 east, as follows:

Chains.

N. 36° E., 14.00—Thence

N. 25° E., 17.20 to the mouth of a spring branch, 6 links wide, come from the southeast—Thence

N. 40° E., 30.00—Thence

N. 18° E., 00.40—to the corner of fractional Sections 24 and 25, Township 21 north, Range 6 east, on the right bank of White River.

Land, high, rich bottom, fit for cultivation; timber, walnut, cherry and white oak; undergrowth, spicewood and vines.

Thence from said corner to fractional Sections 24 and 25, down stream with the meanders of the right and southeasterly bank of White River, along fractional

Section 24, Township 21 north, Range 6 east of the 4th principal meridian, as follows:

Chains.

N. 13° E., 5.00; Thence

N. 3° E., 48.00; Thence

N. 9° E., 27.53—To the corner of fractional Sections 13 and 24, on the right bank of White River, and 37.54 chains west of the corner on the east boundary of the township.

Land high, rich bottom, fit for cultivation; timber, walnut, cherry and white oak; undergrowth, spicewood and vines.

In all cases where there are two or more fractional corners of like denomination on the same bank of a river, distinguish them in your meandering notes by stating their course and distance from the proper section corner.

(Form of certificate for your original field notes.)

I certify, that the foregoing notes on pages 1 to 65 inclusive, are the original field notes of the survey of *(here state the surveys described on said pages,)* as executed by me in the months of_____183___, under my contract with, and instructions from, Elias T. Langham, Surveyor of the Lands of the United States, in Illinois and Missouri, bearing date the_____day of_____183___. And I do further certify, that the marks, descriptions, courses and distances specified in said notes, are correct; and also, that the said notes were all set down at the time when, and in the order which, the work was performed on the ground.

Then state such of the facts designated on pages 15, 16 and 17, as are applicable to the case.—And, if there are any exceptions on account of re-surveys, or corrections, or any other cause whatever, they must be intelligibly and accurately specified in the proper place of the certificate.

The certificate to the copy will be similar to that to the original, with the necessary variations; such as, I certify that the foregoing notes on pages 1 to 73 inclusive, are correctly transcribed from the original field notes, etc.

C. KEEMLE, PRINTER

GENERAL INSTRUCTIONS [1843] TO DEPUTY SURVEYORS FROM THE SURVEYOR'S OFFICE AT LITTLE ROCK, ARK.

(As printed by Eli Colby of the *Arkansas Times* and *Advocate* in 1843)

To Deputy Surveyors:

In the execution of surveys under the authority of this office the following general instructions have been prepared for the guidance of the deputy surveyors, and must be strictly adhered to in all cases not otherwise provided for by special instructions.

You will provide yourself with a compass of excellent quality and approved construction, having a nonius division; also with two two-pole chains of fifty links (of equal length) each, both of which must be adjusted to a standard measure in this office, one to be kept for a standard and the other used in surveying. The chain you use in surveying must be compared and adjusted to your standard at least once in every two days, and their difference, if any, noted in your field book; and if there is no difference, state in your field book the fact of your having compared them and found them to agree.

You must likewise provide yourself with a full set of talley rods, of iron or steel, or pointed therewith, and allow none others to be used, but the precise number you shall have selected for that purpose.

It is enjoined on you not to employ any person whose principles are known or supposed to be corrupt, as chainman, marker, or any other important business connected with the execution of the surveys which you may have to perform; nor is any one to be employed in the capacity above stated who is not a free white person, and who has not attained years of discretion sufficient to understand the nature and solemnity of an oath.

Each of your field books will commence (on the third or fourth page from the beginning thereof) with a list of your chainmen, blazers, and flagmen then in your service and intended to be employed in performing the surveys you are about to execute. The first book under your contract will contain an attested record of their oaths; and whenever you may employ any others you will insert their names, together with their oaths, in your field book, before they are permitted to commence work. You will also when a chainman, blazer, or flagman is dismissed, or quits work from any cause whatever, note it in your field book.

Form of Oath for Assistants

State of Arkansas.
County of_____

I, A_____ B_____, do solemnly swear, (or affirm, as the case may be) in the presence of Almighty God, that, in measuring where the surface of the ground is hilly or irregular, I will level the chain and plumb the pins, so as to obtain the true horizontal distance, and faithfully and impartially execute and fulfill in all things the duty which may be assigned to me, as chainman, or blazer, or any other service which may be required in executing the surveys of the public lands, to the best of my abilities, so help me God.

                                                      A_____ B_____

Sworn to and subscribed before me in the county and state above mentioned, this_____day of_____, A. D. 18_____.

                                     E_____ F_____, *Deputy Surveyor.*

No lines of whatever description are to be run, or marks of any kind made, by any person but yourself, or persons under your immediate personal inspection. Subcontracts are illegal.

The townships are to be laid off as nearly six miles square as possible, by lines running north and south six miles (called range lines) and the corresponding corners joined by lines running east and west (called township lines); and they (the townships) are to be subdivided into 36 sections, each to be one mile square as nearly as may be. The sections to be numbered by beginning with No. 1 in the northeast of the township, and going west and east alternately through the township with progressive numbers, ending with 36 in the southeast corner thereof.

If by reason of local attraction, or other cause whatever, any lines cannot be accurately run with the use of the needle, the manner of operating must be fully and explicitly noted in your field book.

TOWNSHIP BOUNDARY LINES, HOW RUN

All township boundary lines must be run with the compass adjusted to the true meridian, unless otherwise instructed by this office. The variation of the needle should be taken by an astronomical observation at least once in every fourth range and township, and the results entered in your field book.

Range lines will be run north or south, as the case may require, and corners for quarter sections and sections will be established thereon, at every half mile and mile for the quarter sections and sections to the *west*, and *not* for those to the *east* of the line, except at township corners. [This provides for double corners on range lines. Ed.]

East and west *standard* lines will be run east or west, as the case may require, and corners established thereon, at every half mile and mile, for the quarter sections, sections and townships *north* of the line, and not for those *south* of it.

All east and west township boundary lines, other than standard lines, will be run west on randoms, and corrected east from township corner to township corner; and the excess or deficiency in the length of the boundary must be added to or deducted from the south boundary of section 31 west of the quarter section corner. The section and quarter section corners east of the quarter section corner on the south side of section 31 will be established on the corrected line at every half mile and mile therefrom.

At the intersections of all lines (randoms excepted) with navigable water courses, you will establish corners for fractional sections.

Whenever your course may be obstructed by impassable obstacles, you will state in your field book the precise way you may adopt to prolong the line across.

SUBDIVISIONAL LINES OF A TOWNSHIP, HOW RUN

Subdivisional lines of a township will be run with the compass adjusted to the east boundary thereof, and the operation of ascertaining it, and the result must be minutely stated in your field book.

In subdividing townships you will commence at the corner to sections 35 and 36, on the south boundary of the township, and move on in continued progression, in order that the excess or deficiency of the township, as to complete sections, may be thrown upon the lines between the northern and western tiers of sections, north and west of the quarter section corners on those lines.

All *north* and *south* subdivision lines, except those between the northern tier of sections, must be one mile in measure by the chain, at the end of which distance, section corners; and at 40 chains on each section line, quarter section corners must be established. In running north between the northern tier of sections establish the quarter section corners on the lines at 40 chains, so as to throw the excess or deficiency in the length of the lines north of the quarter section corners; at the intersection of those lines with the north boundary of the township establish corners (the bearing trees to be taken in the sections for which the corner stands), from each of which ascertain the distance to the nearest known corner on the boundary. [Provides for double corners. Ed.]

In fractional townships on navigable rivers it may be necessary to run the lines from the rectilinear boundary of the township, whether north, south, east or west, as the case may be, and throw the fractional sections on the river; it is preferable, however, where the exteriors of a township are one continued line, that the subdivision *north* and *south* lines should progress from south to north in their usual order, unless the barrier be insuperable.

If it should become necessary to run the lines between the northern tier of sections south from the corners on the north boundary of the township, you will take two bearing trees at each of those corners, which trees must be on the south side of the boundary, and in the sections for which the corner stands.

The *east* and *west* section lines, except those in the west tier of sections, and those which cross navigable water courses, will be run from the proper section corners, on random lines (without blazing) for the corresponding section corners; temporary quarter section corner posts will be set at 40 chains, and the distance at which you intersect the range or section line, and your falling north or south of the corner run for will be noted in your field book; from which corner you will correct back, by running in a direct line for the corner first run from, and remove the temporary quarter-section corner post, and place it, and establish the corner on the true line equidistant, or at the average distance between the section corners.

Where a township is not rectangular it may be convenient to deviate from the cardinal points in *running random lines*, in order to intersect near to the corner run for. There are no objections to this mode; but the exact course at which you run must in every instance be stated in your field notes.

The east and west lines in the west tier of the sections will be run west on true lines, and the quarter section corners established at 40 chains, in order to throw the excess or deficiency in the length of the lines west of the said quarter section corners; at the intersection of these lines with the west boundary of the township establish corners (the bearing trees to be taken in the section for which the corner stands), from each of which measure the distance to the nearest corner on the boundary. If it should become necessary to survey the lines between the western tier of sections east on true lines, or you should be required by special instructions to survey them west on random lines and correct them back from the corners on the range line, you will in either of these instances take two additional bearing trees on the east side of the range line at each section corner thereon for the sections in the township east of such range line, and make an entry of the same in your field book.

Whenever your east and west subdivision lines, other than those in the west tier of sections, cross a navigable river (or other water course) you will run from the proper section corners both east and west on true lines to the said river, and establish corners at each intersection on opposite banks, and make an accurate connection between corners thus established.

When from wide closes and the excess or deficiency in the length of the section lines of a township which you may be subdividing, you are led to believe that error exists, say to the amount of 1 chain and 50 links, in any particular mile of an exterior line, you will remeasure the suspected line and make an entry of the fact in your note book. But when the error is found to exceed 1 chain and 50 links or you find that each mile of an exterior line of a township is uniformly 100 or more chains [links] longer or shorter than a mile, you will in either of those cases make a resurvey of each boundary, and obliterate the old or former corners; provided, however, the subdivisional lines of the adjacent township have not been surveyed and closed upon said boundary; if the lines in the township adjacent have been surveyed and closed thereupon you are only required to remeasure the boundary from section corner to section corner as formerly established.

MEASUREMENT

As measurement by the chain is the principal source of errors in surveying, you cannot be too particular in your attentions to your chainmen. When the ground is uneven make them in every instance level the chain and plumb the pins so as to obtain the true horizontal distance.

Although your lines are to be measured with a chain of two poles, you are to keep your reckonings in chains of four poles, or 100 links each; and all entries in your field book, and all plats and calculations are to be made according to the decimal measure of a chain.

In the measurement of lines, whether exterior or subdivisional, the distances to objects on each mile must be counted from the particular section corner started from, and the count to cease as soon as the next section corner is reached.

All lines, both exterior and subdivisional, which have been run on randoms, must, when corrected back, be chained, so that the distance to all objects and offsets around impassable barriers shall appear in the notes of the corrected instead of the random lines. The length of the line as found on running the random will be used unless upon the measurement of the corrected line you find palpable error.

MEANDERING

All rivers that may bound or pass through your district, which are navigable, and all lakes of sufficient magnitude to justify the expense, must be accurately meandered; the courses and distances of the meanders to be entered in your field book, of the subdivision of the township, in the order the work is performed on the ground.

In meandering you will state particularly in your field notes at what corner you commence the meanders of each fractional section and also the corner to which you close. You will likewise state on which side of the river you are meandering, whether on the right or left bank, and whether up or down stream; and also, which side of the lakes, whether on the north, south, east, west, SE, SW, NW, or NE, sides. When closing meanders on a surveyed line, where no corner has been established, or if established has been destroyed, you will establish a corner on said line for the proper fractional sections, and measure therefrom and state in your field notes the distance to the nearest corner on said line.

If you should be compelled to base lines upon meanders, the latitudes and departure made in arriving at the line to be established must, in all such cases, be explicitly stated in your field book.

LIMITS WITHIN WHICH YOUR SURVEYS MUST CLOSE

After having made allowance for inaccuracy or obliquity in adjoining surveys, an excess or deficiency in the close or length of a township boundary line of more than 5 chains, of a section line of more than one chain, and of a mile of meanders, of more than 1 chain and 50 links, will be sufficient to cause a distrust in the accuracy of the survey, and will render a resurvey necessary, since no survey will be received that does not close within those limits; it will therefore be necessary for you, whilst on the ground, and immediately after surveying each township and section line and the line of meanders through each section, to test and satisfy yourself that they each close within the above prescribed limits; if they should not a resurvey must necessarily be made. By pursuing this course—which is hereby enjoined—you will save the time of the office, and the consequent trouble and expense to yourself of returning to correct errors, which would otherwise be overlooked.

LINES, HOW MARKED

All trees which your lines, both exterior and subdivisional (randoms excepted), strike, must have two notches cut on each side of each tree, exactly where the line strikes and leaves them, which places you can indicate to your blazer by striking the point of your jacob staff into the tree at the spot for the notches; no other mark or blaze whatever is to be made thereon: at least one or two of these line trees on every half mile, with its name and diameter, and the distance thereto must be accurately noted in your field book. All trees on each side of the line and near thereto (except randoms) must be marked with two spots or blazes, diagonally, or quartering towards the line. For the purpose of having the lines of survey well blazed, you are required to have two good blazers constantly employed, blazing the same line at the same time.

CORNERS, HOW MADE

Township, sectional, fractional section and quarter section corners will be perpetuated by setting a post of the most durable wood that can be procured in the vicinity thereof, firmly in the ground at the exact point for the corner.

In lieu of posts you may use stones, which are to be, each not less than equal to 6 inches square; the shape is not very material—an oblong, twelve or fourteen inches in length, set to the depth of seven or eight inches in the earth, would be the most preferable. Whether posts or stones are used, the fact must be stated in your field book. Posts used for township, section and fractional section corners, must be at least four inches, and those for the quarter section corners, three inches in diameter; they must be neatly squared off from about half way to the top, and placed in the ground so that the corners thereof will correspond to the cardinal points. If a tree should happen to be on the exact point for a corner, it must be well blazed on the sides toward the sections for which it stands as a corner, and the fact, with the kind and diameter of the tree, stated in your field book. From a township, section, and fractional section corner, you will ascertain and state in your field notes, the course and distance to a tree in each section for which said corner is made or stands; each of said trees you will mark with a blaze facing the corner; on this blaze which must be neatly made, you will mark with a marking iron, in a plain, distinct and permanent manner, the letter "R," with the number of the range, and under this the letter "T," with the number of the township, and under this the letter "S," with the number of the section; for instance, suppose a tree stood in section 1 as a bearing tree to the corner of sections 1, 2, 11 and 12, T. 1 N., R. 12 W., the marks on it would be as follows: "R12W, T1N, S1." In no instance should a bearing tree be taken in a section for which the corner is not established, unless compelled on account of the scarcity of trees, in which case the tree will only be marked with the letters "B.T.," and the fact stated in your field notes. When at any corner there is not a tree within a reasonable distance, in each of the sections for which the corner stands, which can be used as a bearing tree, the fact must be stated in your field notes. When there are but two trees within a reasonable distance of a corner, and those two should happen to be in the same section, you will take the bearing and distance to both, and mark one of them with the number of the section, township, and range, and the other with the letters "B.T.," and the fact of there being no other trees must also be stated in your field notes.

Two bearing trees must be taken at the quarter-section corners, which trees must be marked with a blaze facing the corner, and this "¼S" on the blaze.

You will select for bearing trees those which are the soundest and most thrifty in appearance, and of the size and kinds of trees which experience teaches will be the most permanent and lasting. In prairie or any other countries where bearing trees cannot be found within a reasonable distance, say 10 chains of a corner which you are to establish, you must in that case, and in all similar ones, erect mounds of earth covered with sod, to perpetuate such corners.

The mounds must be for quarter sections and section corners two feet six inches high and two feet in diameter at the base; for township corners, three feet high and three diameter at the base. At all corners where mounds are necessary you will deposit therein, at or near the bottom, a rock or rocks weighing not less than ten pounds, a cylinder of charcoal not less than six inches long and two inches diameter, or a quantity of glass or cinder from a blacksmith's shop, not less than half a pint.

Whenever a corner, whether a quarter section, section, or township corner, shall be inaccessible, a witness corner will be made on each margin of the obstacle, at the points where the surveyed lines intersect and leave it; for example, suppose the inaccessible corner is the corner for four townships or sections, four witness corners will, in that case, have to be established, one on each of the surveyed lines where they intersect the obstruction.

The Field Book

Entries to be made in the field book in addition to those already required to be made, to-wit: the distances from corner to corner; the name, diameter, course and distance to all bearing trees (the name of the bearing tree to be fully written out, and never abbreviated), the courses and distances of the meanders of navigable water courses; the closes of your lines at their intersections with exterior or other lines; the fallings of random lines; offsets around obstacles; the name, size and precise distance to the line trees; the distance to and where you leave all lakes, streams, swamps, fields, prairies, traveled roads and tracks (denoting the places to which, and from which they lead), creek and river bottoms, mountains, hills, bluffs, and other natural objects, with their courses as well as you can conjecture; the distance to all mines, salt and other mineral springs, salt licks, forges, factories, cotton gins and other houses; the distance to and where you leave towns and villages with their names. The location of other objects that are not on your lines which may come to your knowledge, such as salt springs, lead mines, houses, fields, etc., must also be noted in your field book. You will never give original names to such objects as have been already named.

At the end of every mile in running either exterior or subdivisional lines, and at the end of the meanders of each fractional section, you will give a particular description of the face of the country, whether level, hilly or mountainous; of the quality or rate of the soil, whether 1st, 2nd, or 3rd rate, or unfit for cultivation, and if liable to inundation state to what depth; of the kinds and quality of the timber and undergrowth. The description of each mile, must be for that particular mile, and not refer to any previous description.

All notes of corrections and resurvey and the cause thereof, must be entered in your field book as such, and reference must be made from the erroneous to the page which contains the resurvey, by writing the word "resurveyed," and the page upon which the resurvey is to be found, across the notes of the erroneous survey; the resurvey must be headed as such.

The entries must be made in the order from day to day as the work is executed on the ground, including all resurveys and corrections, and the date must follow each day's work.

If in the subdivision of a township, the notes of the random and true line (between the same sections) are taken on different pages, and are separated by intervening notes of other lines, reference must be made from the random to the page containing the notes of the true line.

You must, at the beginning of each of your field books, and at the commencement of each day's work, when starting a section line, write out in full, the name of the township, whether north or south of the baseline and east or west of the 5th principal meridian.

No memorandum or writing of any description should be made in the field book except such as relates exclusively to the surveys.

Your books into which your original notes are to be taken in the field will be of a size to be prescribed by this office; they must be of the best quality of paper, and the entries must be made in the plainest and fairest hand-writing, so plain and intelligible that a letter or figure cannot by possibility be taken for anything else than what is intended, or your meaning in any way whatever misconstrued.

The notes of the subdivision of each township must be kept in separate books. The meanders in a township are considered as subdivisional work. The notes of exterior lines must be kept to themselves in books of a convenient size.

The two outside pages of your field books must be left blank, and kept as clean as possible by a cover of leather or paper; which cover can be taken off when the books are returned to this office.

Your field books must be paged, and a neat index made in the front of each, immediately preceding the page containing the oaths of your chainmen.

If an instance should occur from inclemency of weather that you cannot write in your field book without obliterating and defacing your notes, you can, in that case, take notes on a detached piece of paper, which however, you must write off into your regular field book in the proper place as soon as the weather will permit; and the scraps must, in all such cases be returned with your regular original field book to this office, that they may be compared.

You will leave a margin of at least half an inch on each edge of every page of your field book, so as to admit of binding, and also to prevent the obliteration of the notes.

In taking your field notes you will abbreviate only those words which are abbreviated in the form for keeping the field notes hereto appended.

You must make, or have made out, and return with your original field books, a fair and correct copy thereof, to be on a form to be prescribed by this office. And you will also make out and return with your original field notes an accurate plat or sketch of your surveys, which must exhibit the true situation of all objects noted in your field book; and it would be well to make on the temporary outside cover of each field book, a plat, upon which you could portray, while on the ground, those objects.

FORM OF KEEPING FIELD NOTES OF EXTERIOR BOUNDARY LINES OF TOWNSHIPS

If first book, give oaths of assistants. Then say: Chain compared with the standard and found to be correct—

Adjusted my compass to the true variation of the needle, which is _____E.

Suppose the line to be surveyed is the east boundary of Township 1 north, range 12 west:

CHAINS	
	North along the east side of section 36, Township 1 north of the baseline, Range 12 west of the 5th principal meridian.
20.10	A brook 20 links wide runs NW.
35.00	A red oak 15 inches in diameter.
40.00	Set a ¼ sec. corner post, from which a red oak 10 in. dia. bears N. 30 W. 16 links, and a hickory 18 inches dia., bears S. 15 ½ E. 10 links.
55.25	An impassable lake bears NE. and SW., thence offset.
	East 10.00 chains.
	North 5.00 chains.
	East 2.50 chains.
	North 3.75 chains across the lake.

64.00	West 12.50 chains to the true line in advance of the lake; blaze the line south to the lake 3.25 chains; which is 5.50 chains wide on the line.
71.00	A black walnut 8 inches dia.
80.00	Set a post for corner to sections 25 and 36, from which a hickory 6 inches dia. bears S. 18 W. 11 links, and a white oak 20 inches dia. bears N. 72 W. 36 links. Land level, and first rate soil; timber, oak, hickory, hackberry, walnut, etc.; undergrowth, green briers, vines, etc.

Proceed in the foregoing manner along the east boundary of sections 25, 24, 13 and 12; then along the east side of section 1 as follows:

CHAINS	
	North along the east side of sec. 1, T. 1 N., R. 12 W.
8.00	A bayou 100 links wide runs NE.
9.50	A road leading from_____to_____bears NE. and SW.
12.16	Entered bottom of_____river, bears E. and W.
21.54	An ash 10 inches dia.
35.66	Intersected the right bank of_____River, runs E.; navigable; where set a post for corner to fractional sections 1, T. 1 N., R. 12 W., and 6, T. 1 N., R. 11 W., from which a cottonwood 30 inches dia. bears S. 41 W. 18 links, and a cottonwood 35 inches dia. bears S. 60 E. 28 links.
48.52	To the left bank of the_____River; distance across obtained by calculation; where set a post for corner to fractional sections 1, T. 1 N., R. 12 W., and 6, T. 1 N., R. 11 W., from which an elm 18 inches dia. bears N. 69 E. 18 links, and a sweet gum 15 inches dia. bears N. 19 W. 40 links.
63.11	A sweet gum 15 inches dia.
71.81	Left bottom which bears NE. and SW. and entered upland.
80.00	Set a post for corner to sections 1, 6, 31, and 36, and to Townships 1 and 2 N., Ranges 11 and 12 W., from which a red oak 10 ins. dia. bears S. 10 E. 11 links; a post oak 24 inches dia. bears S. 46 W. 23 links; a white oak 14 ins. dia. brs. N. 18 W. 38 links; and a white oak 10 ins. dia. brs. N. 35 E. 50 links. Land south of the bottom second rate soil; timber, oak and hickory; no undergrowth; the bottom first rate soil; timber, sweet gum, elm, cottonwood, etc., with heavy cane; north of the bottom, third rate soil and rocky; timber, mostly oak, some hickory; undergrowth, oak bushes. 1st_____18_____

Suppose the corner to Townships 1 and 2 north, Ranges 12 and 13 west had been established. Then proceed as follows:

Chain compared with the standard and found ½ inch too long, which I adjusted.

West on a random line along the south side of section 36, Township 2

48   ORIGINAL INSTRUCTIONS GOVERNING PUBLIC LAND SURVEYS 1815-1855

CHAINS   north of the baseline, Range 12 west of the 5th principal meridian.
40.00   Set a temporary ¼ corner post.
80.00   Set a post for temporary corner to sections 35 and 36.

Proceed in this manner along the south side of sections 35, 34, 33, and 32; then along section 31 as follows:

CHAINS   West on a random line along the south side of section 31, Township 2 north, Range 12 west.
16.00   A navigable lake bears north and south 10.66 chains wide; distance obtained by calculation.
40.00   Set a post for temporary ¼ section corner.
81.50   Intersected the range line 2.50 links south of the corner to Townships 1 and 2 north, Ranges 12 and 13 west.
                                                          2d_____18_____

Chain compared and found correct.

CHAINS   East corrected the line along the south side of section 31, Township 2 north of the baseline, Range 12 west of the 5th principal meridian.
13.10   Entered A. B.'s field; bears NW. and SE.
25.00   Left the field; bears NE. and SW.
25.88   An ash 10 inches dia.
41.50   Set a ¼ section corner post, from which an ash 15 inches dia. bears N. 18 E. 19 links, and an elm 18 inches dia. bears N. 35 W. 25 links.
55.23   Set a post on the west side of the lake, corner to fractional sections 6, T. 1 N., R. 12 W., and 31, T. 2 N., R. 12 W., from which a hackberry 6 inches dia. bears N. 60 W. 56 links, and sweet gum 12 in. dia. brs. S. 42 W. 47 links.
65.79   To the east side of the lake; distance across obtained by calculation; where set a post for corner to fractional sections 6, T. 1 N., R. 12 W., and 31, T. 2 N., R. 12 W., from which a box elder 10 in. dia. brs. N. 28 E. 14 lks.; and a willow oak 15 in. dia. brs. S, 64 E. 18 lks.
71.33   A white oak 15 in. dia. on the bank of a bayou, 50 lks. wide, runs SE. of the lake.
81.50   Set a post for corner to sections 31 and 32, from which a hickory 15 in. dia. brs. N. 18 W. 20 lks. Land level and 2d rate, soil inclined to be wet, subject to overflow from the lake, about two feet deep. Timber, oak, hickory, hackberry, sweet gum, etc. Undergrowth, small cane, green briers and vines.

Proceed in this manner along the south boundary of sections 32, 33, 34, and 35, thence along section 36, as follows:

CHAINS	
	East on a true line along the south side of section 36, T. 2 N., R. 12 W.
3.25	A spring branch runs SE., the spring 10 lks. to the north.
23.18	A white oak 20 in. dia.
25.30	Road leading from_____to_____brs. south.
40.00	Set a post for ¼ sec. corner, from which a white oak 16 in. dia. brs. N. 27 E. 15 lks., and a white oak 12 in. dia. brs. N. 44 W. 29 lks.
58.42	A white oak 12 in. dia.
60.10	A creek 10 lks. wide runs SE.
80.00	The corner to Townships 1 and 2 north, Range 11 and 12 west. Here describe the land, etc.

3d_____18_____

FORM OF KEEPING FIELD NOTES IN SUBDIVIDING A TOWNSHIP

(Suppose Township 1 north Range 12 west is the township to be subdivided.)
4th_____18_____commenced the subdivision of Township 1 north of the baseline, Range 12 west of the 5th principal meridian.

(If first book of survey, give oaths of assistants)

Chain compared and found to agree with the standard measure.

Adjusted my compass to the east boundary said township in the following manner:

With my compass set to a variation of 7° 30" east I run north along the east side of section 36. At 39.98 chains a point 52 links east of the ¼ section corner; at 80.03 chains a point 107 links east of the corner to sections 25 and 36. I therefore adjust my compass to a variation of 8° 15" east.

(If the east boundary of the township had been surveyed by yourself immediately previous, you will adjust your compass for subdividing as follows:)

By reference to the notes of the survey of the east boundary of the township as surveyed by me in_____, 18____, I find the said boundary to have been run at a variation of ____° east. I therefore adjust my compass to the same degree.

CHAINS	
	North between sections 35 and 36, Township 1 north of the baseline, Range 12 west of the 5th principal meridian.
11.53	A hickory 12 in. dia.
24.00	Entered cane, which brs. E. and W.
26.50	To the south side of_____Lake, which I consider navigable, bears west and NE.; where set a post for corner to fractional sections 35 and 36, from which a sweet gum 18 in. dia. brs. S. 38 E. 17 lks., and a hackberry 12 in. dia. brs. S. 45 W. 12 lks.
38.75	The north side of the lake; distance obtained by calculation; where set a post for corner to fractional sections 35 and 36, from which an elm 12 in. dia. brs. N. 14 E. 16 lks., and a cottonwood 30 in. dia. brs. N. 33 W. 9 lks.
40.00	Set a ¼ corner post from which a sassafras 8 in. dia. brs. N. 48 E. 21 lks., and an elm 18 in. dia. brs. S. 28 W. 39 lks.
56.00	Left the cane which bears NE. and SW.
63.50	A hackberry 12 in. dia.
79.00	Entered a hurricane which bears NE. and SW.
80.00	Set a post corner to sections 25, 26, 35, and 36, from which a hickory 12 in.

dia. brs. N. 63 E. 42 lks., and an elm 16 in. dia. brs. S. 41 E. 102 lks., and a white oak 20 in. dia. brs. S. 37 W. 168 lks.; there is no tree in sec. 26 within a reasonable distance.

(Here describe land)

CHAINS	
	East on a random line between sections 25 and 36, Township 1 north, Range 12 west.
40.00	Set a post for temporary ¼ section corner.
80.33	Intersected the range line 42 lks. S. of the corner to sections 25 and 36. West corrected the line between sections 25 and 36.
15.69	A white oak 20 in. dia.
17.00	Entered bottom land which brs. NE. and SW.
25.50	A creek 100 lks. wide runs NE.
30.00	Entered low, wet land.
40.16½	Set a post for ¼ section corner, from which a red oak 15 in. dia. bears S. 18 E. 25 lks., and a post oak 12 in. dia. brs. N. 61 W. 19 lks.
50.30	A bluff of rocks insurmountable.
	Offset south 10.00 chains.
	West 15.00 chains.
	North 10.00 chains regained.
65.30	The line at the west side of bluff.
66.14	A blackjack 8 in. dia.
68.00	Entered bottom land.
80.33	The corner to sections 25, 26, 35 and 36.
	Land except a few chains at the west end, broken and poor, not fit for cultivation. Timber, oak and hickory. Undergrowth oak and blackjack bushes.

                                          4th_____18_____

CHAINS	
	North between sections 25 and 26, Township 1 north of the baseline, Range 12 west of the 5th principal meridian.
25.00	Left the hurricane, bears NE. and SW.
26.89	An elm 15 in. dia.
27.00	A house about 100 lks. west of the line.
28.93	To the south end of a navigable lake, bears NE. and NW. where set a post for corner to fractional sections 25 and 26, from which a box elder 12 in. dia. brs. S. 32 E. 31 lks., and a black gum 16 in. dia. brs. S. 75 W. 15 lks.
	From the above corner to fr. secs. 25 and 26 I proceed to meander along the SW. bank of lake, through sec. 26.
	Thence N. 15 W. 11.00 chains.
	N. 21 W. 7.00 chains.
	North 10.00 chains.
	N. 9 E. 8.00 chains.
	N. 29 E. 5.00 chains.
	N. 40 E. 2.63 chains.
70.38	Here regained the line having made 41.45 chains northing where set a post for corner to fr. sections 25 and 26, from which a sweet gum, etc.
76.32	A sassafras 12 in. dia.

GENERAL INSTRUCTIONS OF 1843   51

80.00	Set a post for corner to secs. 23, 24, 25, and 26, from which a hickory, etc. (Here describe land, etc.)
	East on a true line between secs. 24 and 25, T. 1 N., R. 12 W.
5.06	A honey locust 10 in. dia.
14.67	To the NW. side of a lake; navigable; where set a post for corner to fr. sec. 24 and 25, from which a black walnut, etc.
	From this corner I measure east 50 links to the water's edge where set an object pole.
	(Here describe land, etc.)

	West on a true line between secs. 24 and 25, T. 1 N., R. 12 W. from the corner on range line.
40.00	Set a post for ¼ sec. corner from which a black gum, etc.
47.56	A black walnut 18 in. dia.
50.15	To the SE. bank of the lake, where set a post for corner to fr. secs. 24 and 25, from which a pecan, etc.
	The object pole on the opposite bank of the lake bears from this corner S. 88 ¼ W.; thence due south 46 links and it brs. due west.

Commenced at the corner to fr. secs. 24 and 25 on the east side of lake and meander along the east side of said lake through sec. 25, T. 1 N., R. 12 W.
   Thence S. 50 ½ W. 4.00 chains.
        S. 28 W. 7.00 chains.
        S. 55 W. 12.00 chains.
        S. 9 W. 10.00 chains.
        S. 9 E. 20.00 chains.
   At 19.00 chains on this course the outlet of the lake 50 lks wide runs NE.
        S. 23 W. 5.50 chains.
        S. 70 W. 5.50 chains.
        N. 87 W. 7.68 chains to the corner of fractional sections 25 and 26.
            (Here describe land, etc.)

Proceed in this manner until you arrive at the corner to secs. 1, 2, 11, and 12; thence between sections 1 and 2 as follows:

CHAINS	North between secs. 1 and 2, T. 1 N., R. 12 W.
40.00	Set ¼ sec. corner post, from which a hickory, etc.
51.10	A hackberry 8 in. dia.; and left bottom land and entered upland, which bears NE. and SW.
80.45	Intersected the south boundary of T. 2 N., R. 12 W. 25 links east of the corner to secs. 35 and 36; where set a post for corner to secs. 1 and 2, T. 1 N., R. 12 W., from which a burr oak, etc.
	(Here describe land, etc.)

(Resurveyed—see page__)

CHAINS	West on a true line between secs. 30 and 31, T. 1 N. of the baseline, R. 12 W. of the 5th principal meridian.
15.50	A path bears N. and S.
23.50	A white oak, 30 in. dia.
29.00	Entered a prairie, bears NE. and SW.
40.00	Raised a mound for ¼ sec. corner, in which deposited two rocks, weighing together about 20 lbs.
65.00	Left the prairie, bears NW. and SE.
85.50	Intersected the east boundary of T. 1 N., R. 13 W., 25 lks., south of the corner to secs. 25 and 36.

On examining my sketch I find that the line between sections 30 and 31 should be about 80.00 chains long. I therefore proceed to resurvey said line.

West on the line previously surveyed (See page __), between sections 30 and 31, T. 1 N., R. 12 W., on a resurvey.

15.48	A path bears N. and S.
23.49	A white oak 30 in. dia.
29.00	Entered prairie, bears NE. and SW.
35.96	The former ¼ section corner mound, which I destroy.
40.00	Raised a mound for ¼ section corner, in which deposited two rocks, weighing together about 20 lbs.
60.00	Left the prairie, bears NW. and SE.
80.50	Intersected the east boundary of T. 1 N., R. 13 W., 25 lks. south of the corner to sections 25 and 36; where set a post for corner to sections 30 and 31, T. 1 N., R. 12 W., from which a white oak, etc.

Each of your field books must be signed by yourself, and close with a certificate in the following form, to-wit:

I certify that the foregoing notes on pages 1 to __ inclusive are the original field notes of the surveys herein specified; that the surveys were executed, and the field notes taken by myself in person, (or by_____ _____, under my immediate and personal inspection) at the dates herein written.

A. B., *Deputy Surveyor.*

The foregoing instructions have been drafted with a view to insure the correct execution of surveys, and uniformity of returns, and with a special reference to the laws of the United States, and in relation to the surveys of the public land. They must be strictly adhered to in form and substance.

GENERAL INSTRUCTIONS OF 1846

OFFICE OF THE SURVEYOR GENERAL OF WISCONSIN AND IOWA
Dubuque, May 28, 1846

To_____
  Deputy Surveyor,

SIR:—You are to survey in person, or by the assistance of some duly authorized Deputy Surveyor acting under your immediate direction and supervision, the district assigned you under contract of_____, 18____, conformably to such parts of the following instructions as apply to the character of the work for which you have contracted, except so much thereof as is modified or countermanded by manuscript special instructions, hereinafter written.

SYSTEM OF SURVEY

1. The United States lands are surveyed into rectangular tracts, bounded by north and south, east and west lines. They are first surveyed into townships or tracts of six miles square, which are subdivided into thirty-six equal parts, called sections.
2. Townships and ranges number from base and meridian lines—the former bearing due east and west and the latter intersecting them at right angles, and bearing due north and south.
3. The base line of the surveys in Wisconsin is the south boundary of so much thereof as borders the State of Illinois; that of Iowa, is located near the geographical centre of the State of Arkansas.
4. The fourth principal meridian, to which the surveys in Wisconsin relate, starts from the mouth of the Illinois River. The fifth principal meridian, to which the surveys in Iowa relate, starts from the mouth of the Arkansas River.
5. The townships, both in Wisconsin and Iowa, number from their respective base lines, northward; the ranges, in each, number from their respective meridians, both east and west.
6. Sections are numbered from east to west and from west to east progressively, commencing with the northeast corner section.
7. Correction lines provide for the error that would otherwise arise from the convergency of meridians, and arrest that arising from the inaccuracies of measurement. They are run due east and west, at stated distances, forming a base to the townships north of them. This base, for each township, is extended sufficiently to meet the convergency for a given distance.

INSTRUMENTS

Base, meridian, correction and township lines are to be run with an instrument that operates independently of the magnetic needle, which is to be employed only to show the true magnetic variation. Section, meander and all other lines interior of a township, may be run either with the same instrument, or with the

Plain Compass, provided it is of approved construction and furnished with a vernier or nonius.

Assistants—Their Oaths

You are to employ no other assistants than men of reputable character, each of whom, must, before performing any duty as such, take and subscribe an oath (or affirmation) of the following form, which must be forwarded to or deposited in this office prior to or upon the return of your field notes:

For Chainmen

I, A. B., do solemnly swear (or affirm,) that I will impartially and faithfully execute the duties of Chain carrier, that I will level the chain upon uneven ground, and plumb the tally-pins whether sticking or dropping the same; that I will report the true distance to all notable objects, and the true length of all lines that I assist in measuring, to the best of my skill and ability.

Sworn and subscribed before
me at_____this
_____18_____.

_____ _____
Justice of the Peace
(or other officer authorized to administer oaths)
of_____, County
of_____, State or Territory of_____

For Flagmen or Axemen

I, C. D., do solemnly swear (or affirm) that I will well and truly perform the duties of axeman or flagman, according to instructions given me, and to the best of my skill and ability.

Marking Lines, Establishing and Marking Corners

1. All lines which you actually establish are to be marked as follows: Those trees which intercept your line are to have two notches upon the side where your line intersects and leaves them, without any other mark whatever.

2. A sufficient number of those trees which approach nearest your line, to render the same conspicuous, are to be blazed upon two sides, diagonally or quartering towards the line; the blazes to approach nearer each other the farther the line passes from the blazed trees, and to be as nearly opposite—coinciding with the line—as possible, in cases where they are barely passed.

3. Corner posts are to be made only of the most durable wood found in the vicinity of your lines. Township corner posts must not be less than five, section and meander corner posts four, and quarter section post three inches in diameter. These posts must be set or driven firmly into the ground, above which they are to appear, at township corners three feet, at section and meander corners two and a half feet, and at quarter section corners two feet.

4. All township and section corner posts are to be squared upon their upper ends and the angles of the square set with the cardinal points of the compass. Township corner posts must have six notches upon each of the said angles; section

corner posts, upon township lines, as many notches upon one of the said angles as they are miles distant from the township corner where the line commenced, and interior section corner posts as many notches both upon their south and east angles as they are miles distant from the south and east boundaries of the township respectively.

5. Quarter section and meander corner posts are to be blazed upon two opposite sides, and set with those blazes facing the sections between which they occur.

6. A tree supplying the place of a corner post is to be squared and marked as directed for posts.

7. All posts established at corner of sections are to be marked upon each side of their squared part with the number of the four sections which those sides respectively face; at meander corners with the number of the sections between which such posts are set and at quarter section corners with ¼ S. upon the two blazed sides.

8. Bearing trees are those of which you take the course and distance from a corner. They are distinguished by a large smooth blaze or chop, fronting the corner, upon which is marked, with an iron made for that purpose, the number of the range, township and section, except at quarter section corners where ¼ S. will supplant the number of the section, thus:

R_____E. or W.
T_____N.
S_____or ¼ S.

The letters B.T. are also to be marked upon a smaller chop, directly under the large one and as near the ground as is practicable.

9. Witness trees are signalized and marked as above, but the course and distance to them, as well as the small chop, are omitted.

10. Trees, employed either for the purpose of bearing or witness trees, are to be alive and healthy and not less than five inches diameter.

11. From all posts established for township corners, or for section corners upon township lines, four bearing trees, if within a reasonable distance, must be taken; one to stand within each of the four sections.

12. At interior section corners four trees, one to stand within each of the four sections, are to be marked; two of them as bearing and two as witness trees.

13. From quarter section and meander corners two bearing trees are marked, one within each of the adjoining sections.

14. Wherever bearing trees cannot be had, quadrangular mounds of earth or stone are to be raised around the corner posts, the four angles of which must coincide with the cardinal points of the compass.

15. Mounds, at township corners are to have a base of five feet, a top of two feet, and a height of three feet; at section, meander and quarter section corners, they are to have a base of four feet, a top of one and a half feet, a height of two and a half feet.

16. Where mounds are made of earth the place from which it is taken is styled the *Pit*, which is to be a uniform and stated distance from the mound in all instances where the same is practicable, viz.: at township corners there are to be two pits, one ten links due north, and the other ten links due south; at section corners one pit, eight links due south; at quarter sections corners one pit eight links due east, and at meander corners one pit eight links either due north, south, east or west. The distance of the mound and pit to be obtained by measur-

ing from centre to centre. The mounds are to be neatly covered with sod in all cases where the same can be had.

17. Posts established in mounds for township corners are to be marked upon each side of the square, with the appropriate number of the range and township; at section corners upon township lines with the appropriate number of the range and township upon two sides thereof, and at interior section corners with the range and township within which such post stands.

18. Whenever the true place of establishing a corner is inaccessible, except it occurs in a body of water that is to be meandered, you are to establish a witness corner as near thereto as is practicable and either due north, south, east or west of it. Such corner is to be constructed in all respects like the one for which it stands as a witness, with the addition of the letters W.C., immediately over the numbering, both upon the post and trees.

19. When a section or quarter section corner happens at the point for establishing a meander corner, the posts and trees are to be marked with the appropriate numbers for such sections or quarter section corners.

MEASUREMENTS AND WHERE TO ESTABLISH MEANDER CORNERS

1. Your distances are all to be noted and returned in chains and links and to be taken with a half or two-pole chain of fifty parts, each measuring seven inches and ninety-two hundredths. The length of your chain should be adjusted by means of a screw attached to the handle of the hind end; every tenth link should compose a swivel, and all the rings and loops should be welded or brazed. The accuracy of your chain is to be preserved by comparing it with a standard adjusted at this office.

2. Your tally pins, eleven in number, must not exceed fourteen inches in length, must be of sufficient weight to drop plumb, and are to be made of iron or seasoned wood pointed with steel.

3. The length of every line you run is to be ascertained by horizontal measurement.

4. Whenever your line is obstructed by an object over which you cannot measure with the chain, you are to pass the same by offsets, traverse or trigonometry; observing that the distance thus obtained, extends no farther than is necessary to actually pass the interposing object.

5. Whenever your course is so obstructed by navigable streams, or other bodies of water which are to be meandered, you are to establish a meander corner at the intersection of your lines with both margins thereof, and of all islands therein.

TOWNSHIP LINES

1. North and south lines are termed range lines; east and west, township lines. The former are styled, in the field notes, the line between certain ranges; the latter, the line between certain townships. Each mile both of a range and township line, is particularized by the number of the sections between which it is run, thus: north between sections 31 and 36, west between sections 1 and 36.

2. Upon the base or township line forming the southern boundary of your district, township corners are established at intervals of six miles. From each of these corners you are to run range lines due north, six miles; establishing a quarter section corner at the end of the first forty, and a section corner at the end of

the first eighty chains, and observing the same order and intervals of establishing quarter section and section corners to the end of the sixth mile, where you will temporarily set a township corner post.

3. You will then commence at a township corner upon the first range line east of your district, and immediately east of the township corner posts temporarily set by you, and from thence run due west across your whole district, intersecting your range lines at or within three chains and fifty links, due north or south, of your said six mile posts. At the point of intersection, if within the above limits, you will establish a township corner. Upon this township or last mentioned line, quarter section and section corners are to be established at the same distances and intervals as directed for range lines; observing that the length of each and every township line which you are to establish, is in no case to exceed or fall short of the length of the corresponding township boundary upon the south, more than three chains and fifty links. If, however, in closing your first tier of township, and all others closing to or upon old work, you find it impossible to preserve the true course of your lines and close within the above limits, you are to resurvey and examine until you detect the real cause of discrepancy, which if not in your own work, you will report to this office, and for which you will provide in the field, in all instances where the same is practicable, by adding to, or deducting from the length of your first range line or lines. And where, in order to close a township to or upon old work, you are compelled to employ a variation greater or less than the true magnetic variation, both must be stated.

4. After closing your first tier of townships, you are to run up and close successive tiers, to the completion of your district, by the same method of survey as directed for the first tier.

5. You are to observe and note the true magnetic variation, at least once upon every mile or section line, and as much oftener as there is a change therein.

6. The bearing trees, standing upon the west side of range, and upon the north side of township lines, are to be entered first in your field notes.

7. After a township corner is established as before directed, you are to complete the notes of the corresponding range line, by inserting the said corner, with the true distance thereto, and adding or erasing the notes of any topography or other minutes, that may be included or excluded by thus adding to or deducting from the length of the range line as temporarily established.

8. With your field notes you must return a diagram, drawn upon a scale of one and a half inches to six miles, on which you are to represent each boundary you have run with the length and variation thereof, and with all the topography thereupon that can be properly expressed upon that scale.

Subdivision

Length of North and South and East and West Lines, and Where to Establish Quarter Section Posts

1. Every north and south section line, except those terminating in the north boundary, are to be one mile in length. The east and west section lines, except those terminating in the west boundary, are to be within one hundred links of eighty chains in length; and the north and south boundaries of any section, except in the extreme western tier, are to be within one hundred links of equal length.

2. The length of the section lines closing to the north and west boundaries,

are to be governed by the length of the sixth or closing miles, both of the range and township lines, and must be as nearly of the same length, or of an average thereof, as is practicable.

3. Quarter section corners both upon north and south and upon east and west lines, are to be set equidistantly from the corresponding section corners; except upon those closing to the north and west boundaries, where the quarter section corners will be established precisely forty chains north or west of the respective section corners from which those lines start.

Method of Subdividing; Random, Corrected and True Line, and Diagram

1. The first mile, both of the south and east boundaries of each township you are to subdivide, is to be carefully traced and measured, before you enter upon the subdivision thereof. This will enable you to observe any change that may have taken place in the magnetic variation, as it existed at the running of the township lines, and will also enable you to compare your chaining with that upon the township lines.

2. Any discrepancy, arising either from a change in the magnetic variation or a difference in measurement, is to be stated as directed under the head of field notes.

3. After adjusting your compass to a variation which you have thus found will retrace the eastern boundary of the township, you will commence at the corner to sections 35 and 36, on the south boundary, and run a line due north, forty chains, to the quarter section corner which you are to establish between sections 35 and 36; continuing due north forty chains farther, you will establish the corner to sections 25, 26, 35 and 36.

4. From the section corner last named, run a random line, without blazing, due east for corner of sections 25 and 36, in east boundary. If you intersect exactly at the corner, you will blaze your random line back and establish it as the true line. But if your random line intersects the said range line, either north or south of the said corner, you will measure the distance of such intersection, from which you will calculate a course that will run a true line back to the corner from which your random started.

5. From the corner of sections 25, 26, 35, 36, run due north between sections 25 and 26, setting the quarter section post, as before at forty chains, and at eighty chains establishing the corner of sections, 23, 24, 25, 36. Then run a random line due east for the corner of sections 24 and 25 in east boundary; correcting back in the manner directed for running the line between sections 25 and 36.

6. In this manner proceed with the survey of each successive section in the first tier, until you arrive at the north boundary of the township, which you will reach in running up a random line between sections 1 and 2. If this line should not intersect at the post established for corner to sections 1, 2, 35 and 36 upon the township line, you will note the distance that you fall east or west of the same, from which distance you will calculate a course that will run a true line south to the corner from which your random started.

7. The first tier of sections being thus laid out and surveyed, you will return to the south boundary of the township, and from the corner of sections 34 and 35, commence and survey the second tier of sections, in the same manner that you pursued in the survey of the first; closing at the section corners on the first tier.

8. In like manner proceed with the survey of each successive tier of sections, until you arrive at the fifth or last tier. From each section corner which you establish upon this tier, you are to run random lines for the corresponding corners established upon the range line forming the western boundary of your township, and in returning, establish the true line as before directed.

9. All section lines are to be right lines, regardless of the number or nature of intervening obstacles; except in the event of their intersecting a lake or pond of such diameter, at the points of intersection, as forbids their continuance by means of a trigonometrical calculation, in which case, and in cases also where a river, lake, correction line, or reservation, form a portion of the boundary of a township, when the closing lines thereupon, will be *true lines*, the courses of which will have a strict reference to the variation and closing of the adjacent lines; the quarter section posts upon which are to be set forty chains from the section corner at which such true lines commenced.

10. In closing upon a correction line, you are to establish a section corner at the point of your intersection therewith, stating the true distance of such intersection from the nearest corner thereon.

11. Field notes of random lines are to embrace nothing but the variation, length and closing thereof.

12. Topography of every description, line trees and corners, are to be taken upon the corrected lines and included in the notes thereof, following which, is to be written the description of the land and timber.

13. With these instructions you are furnished a diagram, drawn upon a scale of one mile to an inch, upon which is represented the magnetic variation or variations and length of each township boundary of the district you are to subdivide, also the topography and corners upon the same, as returned by the township line surveyor. On this diagram you are to represent, as you progress with your survey, the crossing and courses of all streams of water and of the bottom land through which they meander; the intersection, situation and boundaries of all lakes, ponds, prairies, marshes, swamps, windfalls and all other objects, *mentioned in your field notes,* that can be shown upon said diagram. All the topography thus noted upon your diagrams must be joined or connected, so as to form a complete map of the townships of your district. These diagrams form an essential part of, and must be returned with your field notes.

14. Should you find a manifest error in the measurement of any of the township lines of your district, you are to correct the same, by resurveying and re-establishing such line or lines, from the point where the error was detected, to the north or west end thereof; noting your intersection with each one of the erroneous corners as you progress, which you are to demolish and deface with all evidences thereof. Of such remeasurement and corrections you are to take full and complete field notes, in a separate book, to be returned to the Surveyor General's Office, with the field notes of your subdivision. For such corrections, however, the Surveyor General is not authorized to make any compensation.

How and What to Meander

1. In subdividing any one township, you are to meander as hereinafter directed, any lake or lakes, pond or ponds, lying entirely within the boundaries thereof, of the area of forty acres and upwards, and which cannot be drained and are not likely to fill up, or from any cause to become dry.

2. Whenever required by special instructions, to meander any stream or body of water, passing through or lying within your district, you are also to meander all islands situated therein, which are valuable for their soil or timber.

3. Standing with your face towards the mouth of a stream, the bank on your left hand, is termed the *left bank*, and that upon your right hand, the *right bank*. These terms are to be universally used to distinguish the two banks of a river, both in running lines and in meandering.

4. In meandering rivers, you are to commence at a meander corner in the township boundary, and take the course and distance of the bank upon which you commence, to a meander corner upon the same or another boundary of the same township, carefully noting your intersection with all intermediate meander corners. By the same method you are to meander the opposite bank of the same river.

5. In meandering lakes, ponds or bayous, you are to commence at a meander corner upon the township line and proceed as above directed for the banks of a navigable stream; except where a lake, pond or bayou lies entirely within the township boundaries, when you will commence at a meander corner established in subdividing, and from thence take the course and distance of the entire margin thereof.

6. To meander a pond, lying entirely within the boundaries of a section, you will run a random line thereto from the nearest section or quarter section corner. At the point where this random line intersects the margin of such pond, you will establish a witness point, by fixing a post in the ground and raising a mound or taking bearings, as at a meander corner; except that the post and the large face upon the bearing trees, will be marked with the letter W., only.

7. In meandering islands, you are to proceed as directed in sections, 5 and 6 of this chapter, except that where there are no meander corners established upon an island, you are to take the course and distance of your starting point from the nearest meander corner, instead of section or quarter section corner.

8. The meanders of each fractional section, or between any two meander posts, or of a pond or island interior of a section, must close within one chain and fifty links.

9. Your field notes of meanders in any one township, are to follow immediately after the notes of the subdivision thereof. They are to state and describe, particularly, the meander corner from which they commenced, each one with which they close, and are to exhibit the meanders of each fractional section separately; following and composing a part of which, will be given a description of the land, timber, depth of inundation to which the bottom is subject, and the banks, current and bottom of the stream or body of water you are meandering

10. To furnish data that will enable this office to fix the exact location of all islands, whether to be meandered or not, you will take the bearing of the upper and lower points thereof, from both ends of one or more of your meander courses which form a base line of sufficient length for that purpose. You will repeat the same process in meandering the opposite bank or margin of the same stream, lake, pond or bayou. You will also note, in the proper place in the meanders of each fractional section, the exact position and extent of all falls and rapids; fords, portages and mill sites existing in, or connected with the river or other body of water which you are meandering.

11. No blazes or marks of any description are to be made upon your meander lines, though the utmost care must be taken to pass no object of topog-

raphy, or *change therein*, without giving a particular description thereof in its proper place in your meander notes.

FIELD NOTES

1. Your field notes are to form a full and perfect history of your operations in the field.

2. The field notes of the subdivision of every township, whether fractional or not, are to be written in a separate book.

3. No one page, either of the notes of township lines or subdivision, is to embrace the field notes of more than one section line.

4. Description of the timber, undergrowth, surface, soil and minerals, upon each section line, is to follow the notes thereof, and not to be mixed with them.

5. The language of your field notes must be so concise and clear, the hand in which they are written so plain and legible, that no doubt can exist as to your figures, letters, words or meaning.

6. No abbreviations are to be made in your field notes, except such as relate to course, to express which, the proper combinations of the capital letters N., S., E. and W. are to be used; except when a course is exactly to a cardinal point, in which case it is to be written full.

7. The description of each mile must be independent, and *not refer to a preceeding description*.

8. The date of each day's work must follow immediately after the notes thereof.

9. The variation is invariably to occupy a separate line.

10. The first page of a field book of subdivision—a sample of which will be shown or furnished you by this office,—is to embrace only the township and range, state or territory, name of the deputy, with the dates at which the survey was commenced and finished. The head of each subsequent page will express the township, range and meridian.

11. The second page will contain the notes of your resurvey of the first mile, both of the south and east boundaries of your township; stating the corner at which you commence, the variation you assume, and each corner with which you close.

12. All rivers, creeks and other streams, lakes, ponds, prairies, swamps, marshes, groves, hills, bluffs, windfalls, roads and trails, are to be distinguished in your field notes by their original and received names, only; and where such names cannot be ascertained or do not exist, your imagination is not to supply them.

13. Immediately following your field notes, you will give a general description of the township.

Objects and Data to be Embraced by Your Field Notes

You are to enter in their proper places in the field notes of your survey, a particular description and the exact location of the following objects:

1. The length and variation or variations of every line you run.

2. The name and diameter of all bearing trees, with the course and distance of the same from their respective corners.

3. The name of the material of which you construct mounds, with the course and distance to the pits.

4. The name, diameter and exact distance to all those trees which your lines intersect.

5. At what distance you enter, and at what distance you leave every river, creek or other "bottom," prairie, swamp, marsh, grove or windfall, with the course of the same at both points of intersection.

6. The surface, whether level, rolling, broken or hilly.

7. The soil, whether first, second or third rate.

8. The several kinds of timber and undergrowth; naming the timber in the order of its prevalency.

9. All rivers, creeks and smaller streams of water, with their actual or right angled widths, course, banks, current and bed, at the points where your lines cross.

10. A description of all bottom lands—whether wet or dry; and if subject to inundation, state to what depth.

11. All springs of water, and whether fresh, saline or mineral, with the course and width of the stream flowing from them.

12. All lakes and ponds, describing their banks and the depth and quality of their water.

13. All coal banks, precipices, caves, sinkholes, quarries and ledges with the character and quality of the same.

14. All waterfalls and mill sites.

15. All towns and villages, houses, cabins, fields and sugar camps, factories, furnaces and other improvements.

16. All metalliferous minerals or ores, and all diggings therefor, with particular descriptions of both, that may come to your knowledge, whether intersected by your lines or not.

17. All roads and trails with the courses they bear.

18. All offsets or calculations by which you obtain the length of such parts of your lines as cannot be measured with the chain.

19. The precise course and distance of all witness corners from the true corners which they represent.

AFFIDAVIT

1. Following the field notes and general description, in each of your field books, an affidavit of the following form is to be written, and to be signed by yourself and each of your assistants in the field:

I, A. B., Deputy Surveyor, do solemnly swear (or affirm) that, in pursuance of a contract with C. D., Surveyor General of the United States for Wisconsin and Iowa, bearing date the_____day of_____, 18____, and in strict conformity to the laws of the United States, and the instructions of the said Surveyor General, I have regularly surveyed_____

principal meridian (State or Territory) of_____
_____and I do further solemnly swear (or affirm) that the foregoing are the true and original field notes of the said survey, executed as aforesaid.

                      A. B., *Deputy Surveyor*

 G. H.) *Chainmen*
 J. K.)
 L. M., *Marker*
 N. O., *Flagman*

 Subscribed by said A. B., Deputy Surveyor, and sworn before me at_____ _____this_____day of_____, 18____, P. Q., *Justice of the Peace* (or other officer authorized to administer oaths) of_____ _____in the county of_____ State (or Territory) of_____

 2. Your attention is directed to the following section of an act of Congress, approved, August 8th, 1846, entitled "an act to equalize the compensation of the Surveyors General of the public lands of the United States, and for other purposes:"

 3. "That the Surveyors General of the public lands of the United States, "in addition to the oath now authorized by law to be administered to deputies on "their appointment to office, shall require each of their deputies, on the return of "his surveys, to take and subscribe an oath or affirmation that those surveys have "been faithfully and correctly executed, according to law and the instructions of "the Surveyor General; and, on satisfactory evidence being presented to any court "of competent jurisdiction that such surveys, or any part thereof, had not been "thus executed, the deputy making such false oath or affirmation shall be deemed "guilty of perjury, and shall suffer all the pains and penalties attached to that "offence; and the district attorney of the United States for the time being, in whose "district any such false, erroneous, or fradulent surveys shall have been executed, "shall, upon the application of the proper Surveyor General, immediately insti-"tute suit upon the bond of such deputy; and the institution of such suit shall act "as a lien upon any property owned or held by such deputy, or his sureties, at the "time such suit was instituted."

 The above section of the said law, applies to the foregoing affidavit, and will be in all particulars and in every instance, rigidly enforced.

FIELD NOTES OF TOWNSHIP LINES, SUBDIVISION AND MEANDERS, WITH A DIAGRAM

 The following illustration of the manner of arranging and style of entering field notes; is to be regarded by you as a part of your instructions. A single page has been made to embrace the notes of more than one mile, in order to preserve a convenient size for this book; in this particular, therefore, you will be governed by section 3 under head of field notes. The diagram attached to forepart of this book was platted from the following field notes, and shows the importance of carefully noting all the topography your lines intersect; otherwise your diagram, upon which nothing is to appear that is not mentioned in your field notes, will be but a partial and disconnected representation of the topography of the township.

                            Surveyor General.

GENERAL INSTRUCTIONS
To His
D E P U T I E S ;
By The
SURVEYOR GENERAL OF THE UNITED STATES,
for the
STATES OF OHIO, INDIANA AND MICHIGAN.

DETROIT:
PRINTED BY W. W. HART, BOOK & JOB PRINTER.

1850.

OFFICE OF THE SURVEYOR GENERAL OF
OHIO, INDIANA AND MICHIGAN,
Detroit, 18

TO

Deputy Surveyor:

SIR,—You are to survey in person, or by the assistance of some duly authorized Deputy Surveyor, employed by you under the sanction of this Office, and acting under your immediate supervision and direction, while you are yourself with him, so as to inspect his work, the District described in your contract dated 18 conformably to the following printed instructions, so far as they are applicable to the character of the work which you have contracted to perform, excepting so much thereof as is modified or countermanded by manuscript special instructions, hereinafter written.

SYSTEM OF SURVEY

1. The public lands of the United States are surveyed in a uniform mode, established by law, by lines run by the cardinal points of the compass; the north and south lines coinciding with the true meridian, and the east and west lines intersecting them at right angles, giving to the tracts thus surveyed the rectangular form.

2. The public lands are laid off and surveyed, primarily, into tracts of six miles square, called *Townships*, containing, each 23,040 acres. The townships are subdivided into thirty-six tracts, called *Sections*, each of which is one mile square, and contains 640 acres. Any number, or series, of contiguous townships situated north or south of each other, constitute a *Range*.

3. To obtain and preserve a convenient and uniform mode of numbering the ranges and townships, it is usual, in commencing the survey of an insulated body of public lands, to run, or assume, two *Standard Lines*, as the basis of the surveys to be made therein. One of these standard lines is run due north and south, and is called the *Principal Meridian*, to which the ranges are parallel, and form which they are numbered eastward and westward. The other standard line is run due

east and west, and is called the *Base Line*, and from which the townships are numbered northward and southward.

4. To distinguish from each other, the systems or series of surveys thus formed, the several Principal Meridians are designated by progressive numbers. Thus, the Meridian running north from the mouth of the Great Miami river, is called the *First* Principal Meridian; the Meridian running north through the centre of the State of Indiana, is called the *Second* Principal Meridian; that running north from the mouth of the Ohio river through the State of Illinois, is called the *Third* Principal Meridian; that running north from the mouth of the Illinois river, through the States of Illinois and Wisconsin, is called the *Fourth* Principal Meridian; and that running North from the mouth of the Arkansas river, thro' the States of Missouri and Iowa, is called the *Fifth* Principal Meridian.

5. The surveys in Ohio and Indiana were begun before the present system of surveying the public lands was fully adopted. The only regular base line in Ohio is run due east from the point in the first principal meridian, about one hundred and thirty-three miles north of the beginning of that meridian at the mouth of the Great Miami river. The base line for the surveys in Indiana, crosses the second principal meridian about thirty miles north of the commencement of that meridian, on the Ohio river, and extends west to the Mississippi river forming, also, a base for the surveys in the State of Illinois. The base line for the surveys in Wisconsin, is the south boundary of that State, established in latitude 42 30 North.

6. The State of Michigan has a base line and principal meridian of its own, separate from those of the adjoining States. The base line begins at a point on Lake St. Clair, 173 links south of the northeast corner of private claim No. 222, and extends thence west to Lake Michigan. The principal meridian was run due north from the Maumee river, at Fort Defiance, opposite the mouth of the Auglaize river, in the State of Ohio, but is not adopted as a principal meridian for any other surveys than those of Michigan.

7. Correction lines correct the error that would otherwise arise from the convergency of meridians, and arrest that proeceeding from the inaccuracies of measurement. They are run due east and west at stated distances, generally at the end of every tenth township, and each forms a base for the townships north of it.

8. Each range of townships should be made as much over six miles in width, on each base and correction line, as it will fall short of the same width where it closes on to the next correction line north, the excess or deficiency of width being always thrown into the last half mile, on all the lines closing out to the west boundary of each township.

9. This mode of executing the public surveys, conduces more, perhaps than any other which could be devised, to the simplicity, regularity, and symmetry of the work; and to the ease and certainty with which any tract may be identified.

10. The public lands are surveyed under the direction of the Surveyor General, by Deputies appointed by himself. He selects for his deputies none other than skilful and experienced practical surveyors, men of good moral character, in whose integrity and fidelity the fullest confidence can be reposed. Their duties are prescribed in the following code of General Instructions, a copy of which is furnished to every deputy, for his government.

11. Each deputy surveyor is required, before he enters upon the duties of

his appointment, to take and subscribe an oath or affirmation for the faithful performance thereof; which oath or affirmation is to be filed in the office of the Surveyor General. The following form of this oath or affirmation, or the substance thereof) will be used:

"I, A_____ B_____ do solemnly swear (or affirm) that I will well and faithfully perform the duties of a deputy surveyor of the United States Lands, to the best of my skill and ability, and according to the Laws of the United States, and the Instructions of the Surveyor General, as I shall answer to God at the Great Day.

A_____ B_____
Justice of Peace

Sworn and subscribed before me, at_____county of_____state of _____this____day of_____18____.

J_____ K_____

12. Each deputy surveyor appoints his own chain carriers, markers, and flag bearers, who must severally take and subscribe an oath, or affirmation, for the faithful performance of the trust reposed in them; which oath, or affirmation, may be administered by the deputy surveyor himself, or by a Justice of the Peace, and must be written and subscribed to on some of the pages, immediately after the title page, of the first field book that may be used in describing the surveys which they may assist in making. The following is the oath to be taken by the chainmen:

"I, C_____ D_____ do solemnly swear (or affirm) that I will well and faithfully perform the duties of chain carrier, in all surveys of United States Lands in which I shall be employed as such; and that I will level the chain, in measuring over uneven ground, and plumb the tally-pins, whether sticking or dropping the same; and that I will report the true distance to all notable objects, and the true length of all lines that I may assist in measuring, and mark correctly the letters and numbers at all corners that I may be required to mark, to the best of my skill and ability   C_____ D_____
Sworn and subscribed before me, this_____day of_____18

A_____ B_____
Deputy Surveyor.

13. The oaths of the markers and flag-bearers may be varied to apply to their duties respectively.

OF CONTRACTS

1. Before entering upon the execution of any surveys which may be allotted to a deputy surveyor, he enters into a written contract with the Surveyor General, in which the surveys to be performed are described, and the period for their completion, and the compensation per mile, fixed; and wherein the deputy binds himself to a faithful performance of the work, according to the terms of the contract, and pursuant to the laws of the United States, and the instructions of the Surveyor General. To the contract is annexed a bond, executed by the deputy with approved security, conditioned for the faithful performance of the work, in the penalty of double the estimated amount or value of the contract. The place of residence of the deputy, and of each of his sureties, must be given in the body of the bond, which must be signed by them in presence of at least two subscribing witnesses,

whose places of residence must be given opposite their respective signatures. At the end of the contract, there is also the oath before mentioned, which must be taken and subscribed by the deputy, before some person authorized to administer oaths, previous to commencing his work. Three copies of each contract and bond are required to be executed; one for the Deputy, one for the Surveyor General's office, and the other to be sent, by the Survyor General, to the Commissioner of the General Land Office.

2. The surveys must be executed, in all cases, by the deputy contracting for the same, in his own person, or under his immediate personal superintendence and direction, excepting random lines, which may be run by an assistant surveyor, as hereinafter provided. All sub-contracts are illegal.

3. In case of failure to comply with the terms of a contract, unless such failure arise from causes satisfactorily proven to be beyond the control of the contractor, immediate measures are to be taken to recover the penalty of the bond, agreeably to law. And no deputy surveyor who shall improperly fail to fulfil his engagements, will afterwards be employed in the public surveys; and of every such failure the Surveyor General is required to give immediate notice to the Commissioner of the General Land Office.

4. And where any portion of a survey is found or suspected to be erroneous, payment therefor will be suspended until the error is corrected, or the cause of suspicion done away to the full satisfaction of the Surveyor General.

OF SURVEYING INSTRUMENTS

1. You will provide yourself with *Burt's Improved Solar Compass*, or some other equally good instrument, by which, when the sun shines, any survey may be accurately and expeditiously made without the use of the magnetic needle, which compass, unless it contains within itself the means of correctly adjusting all its parts, must be compared with, and adjusted by, the standard compass in this office.

2. You will likewise procure a *Surveying Chain*, two poles, of thirty-three feet, in length, and containing fifty links; which is to be compared with and adjusted by the *Standard Chain* in the Surveyor General's Office. It should be made of good iron wire, of such size as to prevent the chain from stretching by use, and yet light enough to be readily straightened in measuring. The handles should be made of iron or brass, at least a fourth of an inch in diameter.

3. You must be provided likewise with the *measure* of the standard chain, which may be made similar to your surveying chain, of smaller wire. And by this your surveying chain must be compared and adjusted, at least every other day, or oftener.

4. You will use eleven tally pins, made of steel, not more than fourteen inches in length, large enough near the point to make them drop perpendicularly, and having a ring at the top in which is fixed a piece of red cloth, or something else of conspicuous color, that they may be more readily seen when stuck in the ground. They should always be counted, by both of the chainmen, at the end of every tally, to see that none have been lost.

5. Good marking tools, made especially for that purpose, must be provided and used for marking, neatly and distinctly, all the letters and figures required to be made at corners.

6. You will likewise provide yourself with a good telescope, from 16 to 18

inches in length, with parallel lines correctly set in its principal focus, forming an angle in the field view of not less than 50 minutes, or 5-6 of a degree, to be attached, in a suitable manner, to the sights of your compass, when necessary. Also, two common targets, and a good tape measure, at least two poles long, correctly divided into links on one side, and into feet, inches and tenths on the other. The telescope will often be useful in identifying lines and corners across bays and lakes, and in connection with the tape line and targets, as hereinafter mentioned may, in some cases, be advantageously used in measuring inaccessible distances, and in meandering the shores of lakes and rivers which cannot be so easily or correctly meandered in any other way.

7. Your compass and chain must be frequently examined in the field, in order to discover and rectify any error or irregularity which may arise in the use of them.

8. The aberrations of the needle, are a fruitful source of error in surveying. These may arise from a variety of causes. "Local attraction," owing to the presence of iron mineral, is generally assigned by surveyors as the principal cause of the disturbance of the needle. But it is believed that in many instances, the true source of the errors complained of, is to be found in the carelessness or inattention of the surveyor, in the use and management of his compass, or the erroneous measurement of his lines. All these must be constantly and vigilantly guarded against, by every means in your power.

OF THE VARIATION OF THE COMPASS

There is a certain irregular curve line which passes around the earth towards the north and south poles, called the *"line of no variation."* On every part of this line the magnetic needle coincides with the true meridian. But on each side of it, the needle declines from the true meridian towards it. This declination is usually called the *"variation of the compass;"* and increases gradually, but irregularly, in receding either eastward or westward from the line of no variation, until it reaches its maximum, beyond which it gradually decreases again to the line of no variation. This line is not stationary; but moves to the eastward for a series of years, and then to the westward through another series of years, but without any regular period, or any known proportion between the *time* of this movement and the *amount* thereof. Hence the variation of the compass, at any place, is continually changing, to an extent corresponding to the change of place in the line of no variation.

The line of no variation at this time, passes through Lake Huron, and across the eastern end of the Northern Peninsula of Michigan, coinciding very nearly, in some places, with the true meridian; in other places, varying very much from it. East of this irregular line, the needle points to the west of the true meridian, and west of it, to the east of that meridian. Its variation increases in going westward, until, at the mouth of the Montreal River, on the northwesern boundary of the State, a distance of about three hundred miles, it amounts to more than seven degrees. It changes, however, almost continually during the day, and, on some days as much as half a degree in the course of seven or eight hours. This change is called the *diurnal variation of the needle*, and is much greater in the summer than in the winter months. The north end of the needle reaches its greatest daily eastern declination, between one and two hours after sunrise, and its greatest western declination between one and two hours after noon, and points out the magnetic meridian about sunset. Its daily movements may be better understood by an examination of the following table:

OBSERVATIONS MADE BY WM. A. BURT, D. S., IN LATITUDE 42 DEGREES 42 MINUTES NORTH, NEAR DETROIT, IN JULY, 1839.

1839 July	Thermometer 5½ A.M.	1 P.M.	6½ P.M.	Weather A.M.	Weather P.M.	Wind	Magnetic Variations 5½ A.M.	1 P.M.	6½ P.M.
13	60	79	62	clear	light showers	W. S. W.	1° 42'	1° 28'	1° 42'
14	59	72	67	clear	flying clouds	N. W.	1 42'	1 26	1 33
15	56	73	64	cloudy	light showers	N. W.	1 32	1 28	1 28
16	55	71	66	cloudy	some cloudy	West	1 38	1 28	1 30
17	52	80	69	clear	clear	W. N. W.	1 30	1 28	1 30
18	55	85½	88	clear	clear	West	1 41	1 28	1 35
19	56	89	82	clear	flying clouds	S. W.	1 40	1 28	1 35
20	63	80	74	clear	cloudy	S. S. W.	1 40	1 25	1 35
21	70	82	77	clear	cloudy	South	1 42	1 28	1 30
22	72	86	75	cloudy	some cloudy	West	1 40	1 28	1 35
23	65	88	77	clear	clear	East	1 41	1 23	1 36
24	72	86	77	rain	clear	W. S. W.	1 43	1 25	1 35
25	69	88	80	clear	clear	N. W.	1 41	1 15	1 32
26	66	88	79	clear	cloudy	West	1 40	1 23	1 35
27	69	80	76	clear	showers	West	1 41	1 30	1 37
28	64	86	80	clear	clear	West	1 42	1 24	1 30
29	66	87	78	cloudy	clear	West	1 41	1 21	1 30
30	69	90	79	clear	showers	West	1 41	1 25	1 33

OF RUNNING AND MARKING LINES.

1. All surveys of every description, where the magnetic variation is not uniform, must be made with Burt's improved solar compass, or some other equally good instrument, operating independently of the needle. All range, township, and section lines, must be run and marked on the true meridian, or at right angles to it, as nearly as practicable, and the courses of these, and of all other lines, must be entered in your field notes, with reference to that meridian. In all cases, where a line or part of a line is run by the needle, the fact that it is so run must be distinctly stated in your notes.

2. All lines which you actually establish, are to be marked as follows: Those trees which your line cuts must have two notches made on each side of them, where the line intersects and leaves them, without any other mark. These are called "sight trees," "line trees," or "station trees." A sufficient number of other trees, standing nearest on either side of your line, to render the same conspicuous, are to be blazed on two sides, diagonally or quartering towards the line; the blazes to approach nearer each other the farther the line passes from the blazed trees, and to be as nearly opposite each other as possible, coinciding with the line, where the trees stand very near it. Great care must be taken to have your lines well marked, so that they may be easily seen and followed. Random lines are not to be blazed, but may have the bushes lopped, and stakes set at every ten chains, and, occasionally, a tree blazed on one side, to enable the surveyor to follow and correct them.

3. Whenever, in running lines, your course may be obstructed by insuperable obstacles, as swamps, marshes, lakes, rivers, precipices, or other objects over which you cannot pass, you will take the necessary offsets, or work by traverse, or by trigonometry, in order to pass the obstacle, and to ascertain the exact distance on so much of the line as, by reason of such obstructions, may not be actually run. By

whatever method you pass such inaccessible parts of the lines, the utmost accuracy is necessary, to obtain the true measure thereof.

4. No lines, of whatever description, embraced in your contract, excepting the random lines that may be run by your assistant (should you employ one under the provisions for that purpose,) hereinafter contained, are permitted, in any case, to be run or surveyed by any person but yourself, or some regularly accredited Deputy Surveyor, duly authorized by the Surveyor General. Nor are letters, numbers, or marks of any kind, to be made by any other person than yourself, or such Deputy, except it be in your presence, and under your immediate and personal direction; in which case you are to inspect such letters, numbers, or marks, to see that they are neatly and correctly made.

OF EXTERIOR TOWNSHIP LINES

1. The Act of Congress of the 18th of May, 1796, requires that the public lands "shall be divided by north and south lines, run by the true meridian, and by others crossing them at right angles, so as to form townships of six miles square." In laying out and surveying the exterior boundaries of townships, in conformity to this provision of the Act, the greatest possible accuracy must be observed, both in the course and measurement of the lines.

2. Celestial observations to find the variation of the needle, must be made whenever there may be reason to suppose there is any material change therein, and at least as often as once in each mile, whether there be any change or not, which observations must be entered in your field notes.

3. The following is the order and method to be pursued in running exterior township lines: a base line, or a township line assumed as a base, is run due east and west, across the southern boundary of the tract of country to be surveyed. On this line the quarter-section, section, and township corners are established at the full measure. The western portion of the south boundary of section 31, in each township should, however, be made as much over 40 chains in length, as the western portion of section 6, will fall short of 40 chains in length on the next correction line north, so that each range shall average six miles in width" From each of the township corners on this line, range lines are run due north, the section and quarter-section corners established thereon, and at the end of the sixth mile on each of those lines, temporary township corner posts are set. But, at the end of the sixth mile on the most easterly line, a township corner is established. From this corner, a township line is run due west across the whole district, intersecting the range lines previously run; which, if the work be well done, will be at or near the temporary township corner posts placed at the end of them. Exactly at the points of intersection, whether at the temporary posts or north or south of them, the township corners are to be established. The distances from the points of intersection, to the temporary posts, must be accurately measured and noted, showing whether they are north or south of those posts. On this west line, the intermediate section and quartersection corners will be established, as the survey of the line advances. The same process will be repeated, in running up due north, from the township corners on this last west line, another series or tier of range lines to temporary six miles posts; establishing as before the most easterly one, and from thence extending another due west township line across the whole district, in the manner before directed The same method is pursued in each successive tier of townships, until the survey

of the township lines is completed. On account of the convergency of meridians, however, correction lines should be established at the end of every sixty miles north, on which lines, corners should be established on the same principle as on the base line.

5. Variations from this order and mode of running township lines, will sometimes be necessary, to accommodate them to the situation and boundaries of the tract of country to be surveyed, or to connect with prior surveys. Such cases, as they occur, will be provided for in Special Instructions.

6. Whatever excess or deficiency may occur in the measurement of the exterior township lines, is to be carried to the north and west end of those lines. But by a vigilant and faithful attention to duty on the part of the skilful and experienced surveyor, those excesses or deficiencies, except to a trifling extent, will be of rare occurrence. As the interior section lines must necessarily conform, both in their course and measure, to the township lines; any error committed in the latter will unavoidably be carried out into the former, and may mar the beauty and order of the entire sub-divisions of the township.

7. It will be seen, then, how very important it is, that the townships be, as nearly as possible, six miles square; that the exterior boundaries be run exactly by the true meridian; and that the measures thereof be truly and accurately made.

8. North and south lines are termed range lines, and east and west lines township lines. The bearing trees standing on the west side of range, and on the north side of township lines, are to be entered first in your field notes.

9. With the Field Notes of exterior township lines, the surveyor must return a map or diagram of the lines run, drawn on a scale of three miles to an inch; on which will be represented the length of each line, in miles, chains and links; the variation of the compass by which it is run; and also the water courses, lakes, prairies, swamps, roads, and such other objects as may be shown on a map.

OF MEASURING LINES

1. In all measurements, the level or horizontal length is to be taken, and not that which arises from measuring along the surface of the ground, where it happens to be uneven, rolling, or hilly. For this purpose, in ascending or descending hills, the chainmen must let down one end of the chain to the ground, and raise the other end to a level therewith, as nearly as may be; from the end of which a tally pin should be plumbed and let fall, to ascertain the spot for setting it. And where the surface of the ground is very steep, it may be found necessary to shorten the chain to one-half its length, or even less, so as to obtain the true horizontal measure.

2. Though your lines be measured by a chain of two poles or perches in length, you are notwithstanding, to keep your reckoning in chains of four perches of one hundred links; and all your entries in your Field Book, and all your calculations, plans, etc., must be made accordingly in four-pole chains, and decimal parts (or hundredths) thereof.

3. In measuring lines, every five chains are called a "tally," because at that distance the last of the ten tally pins with which the forward chainman set out, has been set. He then cries "tally," which cry is repeated by the other chainman, and each registers the distance, by slipping a thimble, on a belt worn for that purpose, or by some other convenient method. The back chainman then comes up,

and having counted, in the presence of his fellow, the tally pins which he has taken up, so that both may be assured that none of the pins have been lost, takes the forward end of the chain, and proceeds to set them. Thus the chainmen alternately change places, each setting the pins that he has taken up, so that one is forward in all the odd and the other in all the even tallies, which contributes to the accuracy of the measurement, facilitates the recollection of the distances to notable objects on the line, and renders a mis-tally almost impossible.

4. You are to pay the strictest attention to the frequent examination and correction of your surveying chain by the standard measure taken with you. The greatest attention must likewise be observed in obtaining, and entering in your Field Book, the exact measure on the lines, to every object which is noted therein. These measurements are very frequently found to be important, after many years, both in tracing the lines and in identifying the corners.

5. The principal source of error in surveying is in the measurement by the chain. And as the interest of the public service, the rights of public purchasers of the public lands, as well as your own standing as a surveyor, are at stake, it is enjoined on you, in selecting your chaincarriers, to have strict regard to their character and fitness for the trust: and to employ those only, in whose moral integrity, capacity, and faithfulness, you can repose the most implicit confidence. You are required to attend vigilantly to the manner in which your chainmen perform their duty, and to cause it be faithfully and correctly executed; to see, especially, that they carry the chain horizontally on hilly ground; and that all the lines which you may run, be not only correctly measured by them, but the length thereof truly reported to you, for *immediate entry in the Field Book.*

6. In measuring across streams of water, you are to give the width directly across the channels thereof. The distances to the posts which you shall establish on the banks of rivers, lakes, or bayous which are to be meandered, are to be taken with great accuracy.

OF ESTABLISHING AND MARKING CORNERS

1. The corners of townships, sections quarter sections, and fractions are to be established and marked in the following manner:

2. On the exterior township lines, corner posts must be erected at the distance of every mile and half mile from the township corner. The mile posts are for the corners of sections, and the half mile posts for the corners of quarter sections. These posts are always to be made of the most durable wood that can be had, and should be very securely set or driven into the ground and the sides of the posts are to be neatly squared off at the top—the angles of the square to be set in the direction of the cardinal points of the compass. All mileposts, on the township lines, must have as many notches cut on them, on one of the angles thereof, as they are miles distant from the township corner where the line commenced. But the township corner posts shall be notched with six notches on each of the four angles of the squared part. The mile posts on the section lines shall be notched, on the south and east angles of the square, respectively, with as many notches as those posts are miles distant from the south and east boundaries of the township. Whenever a tree may be so situated as to supply the place of a corner post, it is to be blazed on the four sides facing the sections to which it is the corner, and

will be notched as the corner posts are, and at least one bearing tree must be taken, in addition thereto, and marked in the usual manner.

3. At all posts thus established for meander section or township corners, there shall be cut with a marking iron, on a bearing tree or some other tree, within each section, and as near as may be to the corner thereof, the number of such section; and over it the letter T, with the number of the township, and annexed thereto, the letter N or S as the township may be north or south of the base line; and above this, the letter R, with the number of the range, and annexed thereto, the letter E or W, as the range may lay east or west of the principal meridian; thus:

R 15 W
T 53 N
36

4. The letters and numbers thus marked must be neatly and very distinctly cut into the wood of such tree with a good marking tool, the bark thereof having been first hewn or peeled off from a spot on the side facing the corner, large enough for that purpose, unless the tree be a beach, in which case its bark, if smooth, may remain on.

5. But at the quarter-section corners there are no numbers to be made; the post is to be flattened on two opposite sides, and thus marked: "1-4 S," to indicate that it is a quarter section post; and the nearest adjoining tree on each side of the sectional line, must be similarly marked.

6. The place of all corner posts, of whatever description, which may be established, are to be perpetuated in the following manner, viz.: from each post the courses shall be taken, and the distances measured, to two or more adjacent trees, in opposite directions as nearly as may be; which trees are called "Bearing trees," and shall be blazed near the ground, with a large blaze facing towards the post, and have one notch neatly and plainly made with an ax, square across, and a little below the middle of the blaze. On each bearing tree the letters BT to denote the fact of its being a bearing tree, or, in case of re-surveys, the letters N B T to denote the fact of its being a new bearing tree, must be distinctly cut into the wood, in the blaze, a little above the notch. At all township corners, and at all section corners on range, or township lines, four bearing trees are to be marked in this manner, one within each of the adjoining sections.

7. Wherever the section or township lines intersect lakes, streams of water, or islands, which are to be meandered, posts are likewise to be established on the margin or banks thereof, at the points where the lines intersect or leave them. These posts are to be flattened on the two sides, coinciding with the lines on which they are set; and on each of these sides is to be marked, the number of the section which it faces.

8. Wherever bearing trees cannot be had, quadrangular mounds of earth or stone are to be raised around the corner posts, the four angles of which must coincide with the cardinal points of the compass.

9. Mounds at township corners are to have a base of five feet, and a top of two feet in diameter, and a height of three feet. At section, quarter section, and meander corners, they are to have a base of four feet, a top of one and a half feet, and a height of two and a half feet.

10. When mounds are made of earth, the place from which it is taken is

called the *"Pit,"* the centre of which must in all cases, where practicable, be made at a uniform distance, and in a uniform direction from the centre of the mound, viz.: At township corners there are to be two pits, one ten links due north, and the other ten links due south; at section corners, one pit, eight links due south; at quarter section corners, one pit eight links due east; and at meander corners, one pit directly on the line, eight links further from the water than the mound. Whenever the pits are not made as here directed, the course and distance to each must be given in your field book. The mounds are to be neatly covered with sod, placed grass side up, so that the grass may be kept alive, in all cases where sod can be found.

11. The posts established in mounds must be squared, and show above the top of the mound about ten or twelve inches, and, on each side of the square, must be marked the number of the section towards which it faces, and above this, on two opposite sides, at all section corners on township and range lines, there must be marked the appropriate letters and numbers to indicate the township and range.

12. When a section or quarter section happens at a point for establishing a meander corner, the posts and trees are to be marked with the appropriate letters and numbers for such section or quarter section corner.

13. Whenever the proper place for establishing a corner is inaccessible, unless it be in a river or a body of water which is to be meandered, you are to establish a witness corner, as near thereto as practicable, and either due north, south, east, or west of it. Such corner is to be constructed in all respects like the one for which it stands as a witness, with the addition of the letters W C and the number of links from the true corner, immediately over the usual marks.

OF SUBDIVIDING TOWNSHIPS

1. Each Township is laid off and surveyed into thirty-six sections of one mile square, by lines running due north and south, crossed by others running due east and west. The sections are known and designated by progressive numbers, beginning at the north-east corner of the township, and numbering westward and eastward, alternately, as shown in the following diagram:

2. Each side of a section must be made one mile in measure by the chain. Quarter section corners are to be established at every half mile, except in closing a section, when the closing line varies from eighty chains or one mile; in which case you are to place the quarter section corner equidistant, or at the average distance from the corners of the section. But in running out the

6	5	4	3	2	1
7	8	9	10	11	12
18	17	16	15	14	13
19	20	21	22	23	24
30	29	28	27	26	25
31	32	33	34	35	36

last section lines, to the north and west boundaries of the township, the quarter section corners are to be established at the distance of forty chains from the last section corner, and the excess or deficiency of measure (if any) carried out into the last half mile, and cast upon the north and west sides of the township, as required by law.

3. You will begin on the east boundary of the township, at the corner of Sections 13 and 24, and run and measure a random line west, or parallel to the South boundary, to the West boundary of the township, and note your intersection, whether at, or north, or south of the corner of sections 18 and 19, and if not at that corner, how far from it. On this random line you will set temporary section and

quarter section posts; and also set stakes, or make some other marks, at all the even tallies, or outs, between those posts. From the corner of sections 18 and 19, on the west boundary, you will then return on the true line, straight towards the corner where you commenced the random, blazing and marking that line, and verifying its course by means of off-sets from the posts and stakes set, or other marks made, on the random line, and mark and establish the proper section and quarter section corners thereon.

4. From the corner of sections 13, 14, 23 and 24, run and measure a random line south, or parallel to the east boundary, to the south boundary of the township, and note the intersections thereof, whether at, east or west of the corner of sections 35 and 36, and if not at that corner, how far from it. On this random line, as it is run, you will set temporary section and quarter section posts, and make other marks for the even tallies, or outs, as directed on the random line through the middle of the township. From the corner of sections 35 and 36, on the south boundary, you will return on the true or direct line, blazing and marking that line, and establishing the quarter section and section corners thereon, <u>at their average distances, or proportionate parts</u> of the whole distance, to the corner of sections 13, 14, 23 and 24 on the middle line.

You will also run and measure a random line east from the corner of sections 25, 26, 35 and 36, to the east boundary of the township, and note its intersection, whether at, or north, or south of the section corner, and how far from it, and correct, mark and establish this line back to the corner from which you set out, in the manner before directed for the correction of random lines, establishing the quarter section corner thereon equidistant between the section corners. Proceed in like manner with each east and west section line, as you progress north, until you close at the corner of sections 13, 14, 23 and 24.

5. From this corner, run and measure a random line north, or parallel to the east boundary, to the north boundary of the township, and note its intersection, whether at, or east, or west of the corner of sections 35 and 36 in the township north, excepting where you close on a correction line, in which case you will note the distance east or west to the nearest section or quarter section corner, and establish a corner thereon, for sections 1 and 2, one mile west of the north-east corner of the township, according to the measure of the correction line. In running this random line, posts must be set for temporary section and quarter section corners, and stakes or some other marks must be left to indicate the places of all the even tallies, or outs, as before directed in similar cases. From the corner of sections 1 and 2, return on the true line, in the direction of the place of beginning the random, to the corner of sections 1, 2, 11 and 12, blazing and marking the same as before directed for true lines, and establishing the quarter section corner so as to leave the excess or deficiency of <u>the whole measure in the half mile next to the north boundary</u> of the township. From the corner of sections 1, 2, 11 and 12, run and measure a random line east for its corresponding corner on the east boundary. Note its intersection, and correct back, and establish the quarter section corner on the true line at equal distances between the section corners, blazing and marking the corrected line as before directed. In like manner proceed to run, measure, mark and establish all the subdivision lines on this part of the eastern tier of sections, until you close at the corner of sections 13, 14, 23 and 24.

6. Proceed in the same manner with each successive tier of sections, to the last, changing the order only so far as necessary, when interrupted by lakes or

other interferences. From the section corners on the east side of the last tier, run random lines west for their corresponding corners on the west boundary of the township, note your intersections, correct back from those corners, as directed in other cases, before mentioned, and establish the quarter section corners on the corrected lines at the distance of forty chains from the section corners east of them, so that the excess or deficiency of measure may be thrown into the half mile next to the west boundary, as required by law.

7. Bearing trees are to be taken, and the proper marks and numbers made, for and within the sections between which the lines are run out to the north and west boundaries of the township, in all cases where such bearing trees have not been taken, and such marks made, for the section corners on those boundaries at which those lines close.

8. The plan here laid down is intended to illustrate the principles on which the townships must be subdivided, so that section lines may all run parallel either to the east or south boundaries thereof, and that each section may contain 640 acres, as nearly as practicable. To effect these objects, it is indispensably necessary that for *every section line*, unless it be irregular or fractional, there should first be run a random or trial line, which must afterward be corrected, where necessary, and run, marked, and established, in its proper place, as the corrected or true line. This must always be done according to some regular order, which, when once begun, must, as far as practicable, be continued throughout the township.

As a general rule, the order above prescribed is believed to be the best and most convenient that can be adopted; but if you find any other more convenient, and by which the surveys can be made with equal or greater accuracy, you are at liberty to adopt it, provided you give a clear and distinct statement, at the end of your field notes in each book, showing what that order is. A departure from the *principles* above laid down, will not, however, *under any circumstances, be permitted*.

9. To enable you to have all your random lines correctly run by the sun, as far as practicable, independently of the use of the magnetic needle, you are allowed to employ, by the month, an assistant surveyor, who is well skilled in the use of the solar compass, to run and measure such lines, and take the field notes thereof, under your direction, in accordance with the above instructions. The field notes of such assistant must, in all cases, be taken in separate books, and be sworn to and subscribed by him, before some person authorized to administer oaths, and returned by you to this office.

10. The true lengths of all north and south, as well as of all east and west section lines, must be given *according to your measure*, whether they agree with the lengths of the same lines as ascertained by the compass and the measure of the township lines, or not.

11. You are referred, here, to the accompanying specimen of the Field Notes of a Township, in which the whole process of the subdivision is illustrated at large by example.

12. The foregoing mode of subdividing townships into sections, it will be perceived, is intended for, and can be fully applied only, to *entire* townships. In the subdivision of *fractional* townships, however, the order of the survey will be varied no farther than may be necessary to adapt it to the situation and boundaries of such fractional township. As a general rule, from which there will be few exceptions, it will be found best to make entire sections on the township lines bound-

ing a fractional township, and making the work to close on the *irregular* boundaries thereof.

13. An act of Congress of the 24th of May, 1824, authorizes a departure from the ordinary mode of surveying the public land on any river, lake, or bayou, whenever, in the opinion of the President of the United States, the public interest would be promoted thereby; so as to survey such lands in tracts of two acres in width, fronting on such river, lake, or bayou, and running back to the depth of forty acres. But as no general rules could be framed to govern all such surveys, this branch of the service is left to be provided for in *Special* Instructions, as cases thereof may occur.

14. Should you find a manifest error in the measurement of any township line within, or bounding your district, (which will be readily detected by the closing lines thereon,) you are to correct such error, by re-measuring such township line, from where the error is found, to the north or west end thereof. The section and quarter section corners thereon are to be removed to the proper distances, and there established; and the marks and numbers at the cancelled corners are to be cut out or effaced, and the distances at which you pass those corners must be noted by you. Of such re-measurement and corrections you are to take full and complete Field Notes, in a separate book, to be returned to the Surveyor General's Office, with the Field Notes of your subdivisions. For such corrections, however, the Surveyor General is not authorized to make any compensation, unless the amount thereof can be obtained from the Deputy by whom the erroneous survey was made, or shall be allowed by the Commissioner of the General Land Office.

ON MEANDERING RIVERS, &C.

1. You will accurately meander, by course and distance, all navigable Rivers which may bound or pass through your district; all navigable bayous flowing from or into such rivers; all lakes and deep ponds, of the area of forty acres and upwards; and all islands suitable for cultivation. At all those points where the township or sections lines intersect the banks of such rivers, bayous, lakes or islands, posts are to be established, as before directed. In meandering, you are to intersect all these posts, closing at each post the course and distance on which it is intersected. You will likewise notice all streams of water falling into the river, lake, or bayou, which you are surveying, with their width at their mouth; all springs, noting the size thereof, and whether pure or mineral water; the head and mouth of all bayous, all rapids, falls, or cascades; all islands and bars, with intersections to their upper and lower points, to establish their exact situation. This must be done with the greatest accuracy, in relation to all islands which you shall meander, so as to determine and show their precise location and bearing on the maps of the surveys, and particular care must be taken to pass no object in any degree worthy of note, nor any change in the topography along the waters that you meander, without giving a particular description thereof in its proper place in your meander notes.

2. Should any lake or pond which you shall meander, be situated within any one section, so as not to be intersected by any of the lines thereof, you will run and measure a line very exactly, but without marking, from one of the corners, or one of the half mile posts, or other given point on one of the lines of said section, to the point on the margin of the lake at which you shall commence the meanders

thereof. The true location of such lakes is necessary, in order to calculate the contents of the subdivisions of such sections.

3. The width of streams of water or bayous binding on, or forming a boundary of your surveys, must be ascertained at every intersection of your lines therewith, by trigonometrical process, or otherwise; which can generally be most conveniently done in taking the meanders. This is necessary for the correct exhibition, of such streams on the township plats.

4. Except in cases where navigable streams constitute the boundary line between two series or systems of surveys commencing from different standard lines, such streams are not to interrupt the regular survey of the townships through which they pass, the lines of which shall be continued across those streams to the complete measure. And where the surveys have been closed on a stream, as a boundary of a cession, or from other cause, and are afterward to be continued across such stream, the surveyor continuing the surveys on the opposite side, must extend the lines across the stream, so as to make the sections thereon complete.

5. To establish a uniform and simple mode of designating and distinguishing the two sides of navigable streams, the terms "Right bank," or "Left bank," will be used, in all cases, thus:—suppose yourself standing at the head of the river, looking down stream; then that bank of the stream on your right hand is to be called and referred to in your field notes as the "right bank," and that on your left hand as the "left bank" And these terms, thus applied to navigable rivers, are to be used in all cases, whether in running lines or taking meanders.

6. Great care must be taken to describe clearly the post at which any meanders of a river, bayou, lake or island commence; and also all the posts, on township or section lines, which may be intersected in the progress of the meanders.

7. The Field Notes of meanders are to be written at the end of the subdivisions. The courses are to be inserted in a column on the left of the page; the distances, in chains and links, in a column next to this, and the notes or remarks on the right, opposite the proper course and distance. The column of distances must be added up at the foot thereof, on each page.

8. Errors in meandering are of very frequent occurrence, arising principally, it is believed, from bad chaining. Your special attention is called to the manner in which this part of the work is executed; and all possible accuracy is enjoined, both in the courses and measurement, and the entry thereof in your field book.

9. Where the meanders of small lakes cannot be accurately run and measured by course and distance, in the usual manner, by reason of obstacles along their shores or banks, a well constructed series of triangles may be made across the lake, so connected that all the angles of the lake coast can be accurately platted. A map of these triangulations must be made on a scale of 8 inches to the mile, and their reduction into the meanders of the lake coast must be carefully entered in your field book.

10. Streams to be meandered, having shores of like character, may have their courses taken with a solar compass, and measured by the angles made between two parallel lines so placed in the principal focus of a suitable telescope, attached to the sights of the compass, as to form an angle in the field view of at least 50 minutes, or 5-6 of a degree. For this purpose, the telescope is made to bear upon a rod, divided into feet, inches and tenths, and furnished with two targets, the upper one stationary, and the other moveable on the rod, to suit the angle seen through the

telescope at various distances. The distance between the two targets on the rod being then the measure of the angle formed by the two lines in the focus of the telescope, represents the distance between the compass and the rod, which may be taken out, in chains and links, from a table previously prepared for that purpose.

11. By observing, accurately, the number of feet, inches, and tenths, which the targets are apart, when they measure the angle formed by the parallel lines in the telescope, at a given distance, of from three to five chains from the compass, you will have the data from which such a table may be readily constructed for all other distances at which the telescope will enable you to observe a difference in the distance between the targets of one-tenth of an inch.

12. Wherever meanders are made by this method, the fact that they are so made should be distinctly shown in the heading of your field notes, and the precise angle between the parallel lines in the focus of your telescope, must also be stated. The stations at which observations are made must be designated by progressive numbers, and all the observations made at each station must be set down with great care and accuracy. Where a distance is noted, as measured by the telescope, the number of tenths of an inch on the rod, which corresponds to that distance, must also be carefully given, in order to facilitate the detection of errors, wherever they may occur.

13. Having taken the width of the river so frequently, and made such observations, on both sides of it, as to enable you to protract, accurately, its shores, you will make a plat thereof on a scale of eight inches to a mile, and from it enter the meanders of each shore in your field book in the usual manner, immediately after the field notes of your telescopic observations for each township. All such plats, whether of rivers or lakes, must be returned with your field notes to this office.

OF PRIVATE CLAIMS, INDIAN RESERVATIONS, &C.

1. In surveying Private Claims, Indian Reservations, or other tracts not conforming to section lines, the location thereof must be particularly described, and the place of beginning clearly stated in your Field Notes; also the name of the claimant in whose right the survey is made, with the number by which it is known; and if a reservation, the quantity contained in it, and the name of the reservee. The Field Notes of all the lines of each tract must be complete, and are to be entered in the Field Book separately from the notes of other tracts. The Field Notes of Private Claims and Indian Reservations, must be entered in separate books.

2. Wherever a section or township line intersects a line of a private claim or Indian reservation, there a corner must be established. The particular line intersected, with its course, and the name of the claimant or reservee with the number or other designation by which it is known, must be noted. And from such intersection, the private claim or reserve line must be carefully measured, each way along said line, to the end thereof, unless it should be intersected by another section or township line before the end be reached.

3. The course of every line of the survey of a private claim or Indian reservation, with the length thereof, and the variation of the compass, and date of the survey, are to be inserted in the Field Notes, which are to be certified and signed by you.

OF FIELD NOTES

1. The field books are all to be made of one uniform size, viz: foolscap octavo; or a sheet of common sized cap paper, folded into sixteen pages. The paper must be of good quality, and the books covered with morocco or other leather, and neatly stitched and trimmed, and contain space enough for all the field notes of a township. The pages are to be ruled with red ink and feint lined.

2. The field notes of the subdivision of every township, whether fractional or not, are to be written in a separate book.

3. No one page, either of the notes of township lines, or of subdivisions, is to embrace the field notes of more than one section line.

4. The description of the surface, soil, minerals, timber and undergrowth on each section line, is to follow the notes of the survey of such line, and not to be mixed up with them.

5. The language of your field notes must be so concise and clear, and the hand in which they are written so plain and legible, that no doubt can exist as to your figures, letters, words or meaning. If otherwise, they must be accompanied with true and fair copies.

6. The only abbreviations allowable in your field notes, are—"in. diam." for "inches, diameter," and the capital letters N., S., E. and W., for North, South, East and West. These latter words, however, must always be written in full, except when combined to express some course varying from the cardinal points.

7. The description of each mile must be independent, and not refer to a preceding description.

8. The field notes must be taken, in all cases, precisely in the order in which the work is done on the ground, and must show truly the direction in which each line is run and measured.

9. The date of each day's work must follow immediately after the notes thereof.

10. All your writing, of every description, whether of field notes, memorandums, or arithmetical or trigonometrical calculations, relating to surveys that you may execute, must be taken, either in your regular field notes, or in memorandum or miscellaneous books, of the same size and shape, which, when called for, must be returned to this office. It is not, therefore, allowable to make any notes, memorandums, or calculations, on loose pieces of paper.

11. On the first page of your field book of each township, insert in a plain and neat manner, by way of title, the number of the township and range, with the date of the commencement, and the date of completing the subdivision of the same.

12. Between the second and third pages, insert, without fastening there, a diagram neatly folded, drawn on tough bank note paper, on a scale of half a mile to an inch. On this diagram you will accurately delineate, as near as may be practicable by occular observation on the spot, as you progress with the work, the crossing and courses of all streams of water, the intersection, situation, and boundaries of all prairies, marshes, swamps, lakes, hills, and all other things mentioned in your field notes, the situation of which can be conveniently shown on the diagram. You will also insert thereon, in small figures, the length of all the section lines of the township.

13. On the fourth page, make an index diagram, representing all the sections

in the township, on a scale of two miles to an inch, on each line of which, after the survey thereof is completed, you will write or print, in a neat and distinct manner, the number of the page of the book where the notes of that line may be found, and, where the notes of the random line and of the corrected line are on different pages, the former must be referred to in red, and the latter in black ink."

14. Leaving, after this, sufficient room for the oaths of your chainmen and markers, if necessary, at the head of each subsequent page, on which the field notes are written, you will insert a running title, designating the number of the township and range, which is to be separated from the field notes by a double red line.

15. The *Field Notes* of the surveys furnish primarily the materials from which the plats and calculations of the public lands are made; and are the source from whence the description and evidence of the location and boundaries of those surveys are drawn and perpetuated. It is evidently, then, of the utmost importance that the Field Notes should be, at once, an accurate, clear, and minute record of every thing that is done by the Surveyor and his assistants, (in accordance with these Instructions,) in relation to running, measuring and marking lines, establishing corners, etc., as well as full and complete topographical description of the country surveyed, as it regards every thing which may afford useful information, or gratify public curiosity.

16. For this purpose, you are to enter in your Field Book, in a neat and distinct manner, notes or minutes of the following objects, viz.:

17. The description, course and length of every line which you may run, beginning with the variation of the needle, if known to you, at the corner where you start.

18. The name, and estimated diameters of all corner and bearing trees, and the courses and distances of the bearing trees from their respective corners.

19. The name of the material of which you construct mounds, with the course and distance to the pits.

20. The names and estimated diameters of at least one or two of those trees which fall in your lines, called *station or line trees*, with their exact distances on the line, between every two corners. They should be so taken as to divide the line as nearly into equal parts as practicable.

21. The face of the country, whether level, rolling, broken, hilly, or mountainous.

22. The quality and character of the soil, and whether first, second or third rate.

23. The several kinds of timber and undergrowth with which the land may be covered, naming each kind of timber in the order in which it is most prevalent; and in prairie, the kind of grass or other herbage which it produces.

24. All rivers, creeks and smaller streams of water, with their right-angled width, and the course they run where the lines of your survey intersect or cross them, and whether the current be rapid, sluggish, or otherwise.

25. All rapids, cataracts, cascades, or falls of water, and the estimated amount of their fall, in feet.

26. All springs of water, and whether fresh and pure, or mineral; showing also on which side of the line situated, and the distance therefrom, and the course of the stream flowing from them.

27. All lakes and ponds, with the description of banks surrounding them, and whether the water be deep or shallow, pure or stagnant.

28. The meanders of all lakes, navigable rivers, bayous, islands, and streams forming boundaries.

29. All prairies, swamps, and marshes.

30. All coal banks or beds, and peat or turf grounds.

31. All precipices, caves, stone quarries, and ledges of rock, with the kind of stone found in them.

32. All towns and villages, Indian towns and wigwams, houses or cabins, fields or other improvements, sugar-tree groves, and sugar camps.

33. All minerals and ores, with particular descriptions of the same, as to their quality and extent.

34. All diggings for minerals, smelting or other furnaces, forges and factories.

35. The exact situation, and description of all mines, salt springs, salt licks and mill-seats, which you may discover, or that may come to your knowledge.

36. All fossils, petrifications, and other natural curiosities, with descriptions thereof.

37. All travelled roads, and "trails," with their courses, and denoting the places from, or to which they lead.

38. The tracks of tornadoes or hurricanes, commonly called "windfall," or "fallen timber,' showing the direction of the wind, as indicated by the fallen trees.

39. All ancient works of art, as mounds, fortifications, embankments, ditches, or other similar objects.

40. All offsets, or methods of whatever kind, by which you shall obtain the measurement or distance on any line which cannot be actually measured.

41. At what distance you enter and at what distance you leave every lake, bay, pond, creek, bottom, windfall, grove, prairie, ravine, marsh and swamp, with the course of the same at both points of intersection; also the distances at which you begin to ascend, arrive at the top, begin to descend, and reach the foot of all hills and ridges, with their course, and estimated heights in feet above the level land of the surrounding country, or above the bottom lands, ravines, or waters on which they are situated.

42. The variation of the needle must be noted at, and on each side of all places on the lines where there is any material change of variation, and the distances to the points where the observations are made must be given.

43. The precise course and distance of all witness corners from the true corners which they represent, must be stated in the descriptions of those corners.

44. In addition to the foregoing items, you will insert notes of any others as the occasions therefor may occur. The field notes are to be written out in your book, on the spot, as you proceed with the work. Nothing in your notes must be left to be supplied by memory.

45. Rivers, creeks, and smaller streams, lakes, swamps, prairies, hills, mountains, or other natural objects, are to be distinguished in your field notes by their received names only, where names have heretofore been given. In any case you are not to give original names.

46. Besides the ordinary Field Notes taken on the lines, you will add at the end of your field book, such further description or information as you may be able to give, concerning any thing in the township, worthy of particular notice, or which you may judge necessary or useful to be known. And you will add also, a general notice or description of the township in the aggregate, as it regards the face of the country, soil timber, etc.

47. In your field book, the courses and distances must be placed in a column on the left hand side of the page, and your notes and remarks on the right. The *original* field notes must in all cases, be returned into the office of the Surveyor General.

48. Following the general description of each township, at the end of the field notes in each book, you will give a list of the names and residences of all the persons who may have assisted either in running, measuring or marking, the lines and corners therein described, stating the capacity in which each acted; and below such list, a certificate must be written affirming its correctness, and that the township has been in every respect well and faithfully surveyed, according to the instructions of the Surveyor General, which certificate must be subscribed and sworn to by the persons named in the list, either before yourself, as a Deputy Surveyor, or before some other person duly authorized to administer oaths. The following forms, as far as applicable, may be used for this purpose:

List of names and residences of persons who assisted in running, measuring, or marking the lines and corners described in the foregoing field notes of township _____N. of Range_____, in the State of_____, viz.:

A_____B_____, a resident of_____in the county of_____and State of_____ performed the duty of chainmen and marked the corners; E_____F_____of_____ in the county of_____and State of_____and G_____H_____of_____in the county of_____and State of_____performed the duty of axe-men; and I_____K_____of _____in the county of_____and State of_____performed the duty of compass-man, under the personal supervision and direction of L_____M_____Deputy Surveyor, in running most of the lines, above referred to.

We hereby certify that we assisted L. M., Deputy Surveyor, in subdividing township_____of Range_____in the State of_____that our names and residences, and the duties that we respectively performed, are correctly set forth in the above statement, and that said township has been in every respect well and faithfully surveyed, according to the instructions of the Surveyor General.

         A_____B_____*Chainman,*
         C_____D_____*Chainman,*
         E_____F_____*Axe-man,*
         G_____H_____*Axe-man,*
         I_____K_____*Compass-man.*

Subscribed and sworn to by the above named persons, before me at_____this _____day of_____18__.

        O_____P_____*Justice of the Peace*
        (or other officer authorized to administer oaths) of the County of_____and State of_____.

49. In every field book, after the certificate above mentioned, an affidavit of the following form is to be written, and sworn to and subscribed by you before some person duly authorized to administer, oaths, viz.:

I, L_____M_____of_____in the county of_____and State of_____, a Deputy Surveyor, do solemnly swear (or affirm) that, in pursuance of a contract with C_____N_____Surveyor General of the United States, for Ohio, Indiana, and Michigan, bearing date_____day of_____18__, and in strict conformity to the laws of the United States, and the instructions of the said Surveyor General, I have faithfully and correctly surveyed township number_____of range number_____of the principal meridian, in the State of _____ and I do further solemnly swear (or affirm) that the foregoing are the true and original field notes of the said survey, executed as aforesaid.

              L_____M_____, *Deputy Surveyor.*

 Subscribed by said L_____M_____, Deputy Surveyor, and sworn to before me at_____this_____day of_____18___.

           O_____P__Y__, *Justice of the Peace,*
           (or other officer authorized to administer oaths) of_____in the county of _____and State of_____.

50. Should you employ an assistant to run random lines, an affidavit, of the following form, must be written, subscribed and sworn to by him after his field notes in each book, viz.:

 I, R_____S_____, of_____in the county of_____and State of_____do solemnly swear, that the foregoing are the true and original field notes of the random lines therein described, in township_____of range_____in the State of_____and that the said lines were carefully and accurately run by me with a good solar compass, independently of the needle, except as mentioned in said notes, and that they were measured in my presence under the direction and at the expense of L_____M_____Deputy Surveyor, while I was employed by him and paid by the month.

            R_____S__Y__, *Random Line Surveyor.*

 Subscribed by said R_____S_____random line surveyor, and sworn to before me this_____day of_____18___.

           O_____P_____, *Justice of the Peace,*
           (or other officer authorized to administer oaths) of_____in the county of _____and State of_____.

51. A printed specimen of the Field Notes of the subdivision of a township into sections, accompanies these Instructions; which will serve to illustrate both the order and method of performing the surveys, and the most approved form of keeping the Field Notes; for which purpose, it is to be regarded as a part of these General Instructions. Where the notes of the true line follow immediately after those of the random, the provisions of section 3, under the head of field notes, must be carefully adhered to. When they do not so follow, a page may embrace the notes of more than one mile, provided they do not extend to the next page.

52. Any material departure from these Instructions, or negligence in the observance thereof, will be considered as a violation of the conditions of your contract, and a forfeiture of all claim for payment. And loose, inaccurate, precipitate, or defective work, either as it respects the surveys in the field, or the notes and returns thereof on paper,—*will not be admitted.*

53. That you may better understand the responsibility under which you are acting, your attention is particularly called to the provisions of the third section of an act of Congress, approved August 8th, 1846, entitled "an act to equalize the compensation of the Surveyor General of the public lands of the United States, and for other purposes," which is as follows, viz.:

"SEC. 3. That the Surveyor General of the public lands of the United States, in addition to the oaths now authorized by law to be administered to deputies on their appointment to office, shall require each of their deputies, on the return of his surveys, to take and subscribe an oath or affrmation that the surveys have been faithfully and correctly executed, according to law and the instructions of the Surveyor General; and, on satisfactory evidence being presented to any court of competent jurisdiction, that surveys, or any part thereof, had not been thus executed, the deputy making such false oath or affirmation shall be deemed guilty of perjury, and shall suffer all the pains and penalties attached to that offense; and the district attorney of the United States for the time being, in whose district any such false, erroneous, or fraudulent surveys shall have been executed, shall upon the application of the proper Surveyor General, immediately institute suit upon the bond of such deputy; and the institution of such suit shall act as a lien upon any property owned or held by such deputy, or his sureties, at the time such suit was instituted."

The provisions of the above section will, in all cases, and in every particular, be rigidly enforced.

Surveyor General.

GENERAL INSTRUCTIONS OF 1851

OFFICE OF THE SURVEYOR GENERAL
OF WISCONSIN AND IOWA,
Dubuque, 1851

To   *Deputy Surveyor;*
SIR:

You are to survey in person, or by the assistance of some duly authorized Deputy Surveyor, acting under your immediate direction and supervision, the district assigned you under contract of_____18____, conformably to such parts of the following instructions as apply to the character of the work for which you have contracted, except so much thereof as is modified or countermanded by manuscript special instructions, hereinafter written.

SYSTEM OF SURVEY

1. The United States lands are surveyed into rectangular tracts, bounded by north and south, east and west lines. They are first surveyed into townships or tracts of six miles square, which are subdivided into thirty-six equal parts, called sections.

2. Townships and ranges number from base and meridian lines—the former bearing due east and west, and the latter intersecting them at right angles, and bearing due north and south.

3. The base line of the surveys in Wisconsin is the south boundary of so much thereof as borders the State of Illinois; that of Iowa, is located near the geographical centre of the State of Arkansas.

4. The fourth principal meridian, to which the surveys in Wisconsin relate, starts from the mouth of the Illinois River. The fifth principal meridian, to which the surveys in Iowa relate, starts from the mouth of the Arkansas River.

5. The townships, both in Wisconsin and Iowa, number from their respective base lines, northward; the ranges, in each, number from their respective meridians, both east and west.

6. Sections are numbered from east to west and from west to east progressively, commencing with the north-east corner section;

7. Correction lines provide for the error that would otherwise arise from the convergency of meridians, and arrest that arising from the inaccuracies of measurement. They are run due east and west, at stated distances, forming a base to the townships north of them. This base, for each township, is extended sufficiently to meet the convergency for a given distance.

INSTRUMENTS

Base, meridian, correction and township lines are to be run with an instrument that operates independently of the magnetic needle, which is to be employed only to show the true magnetic variation. Section, meander and all other lines interior of a township, may be run either with the same instrument, or with the

Plain Compass, provided it is of approved construction and furnished with a vernier or nonius.

Assistants—Their Oaths

You are to employ no other assistants than men of reputable character, each of whom must, before performing any duty as such, take and subscribe an oath (or affirmation) of the following form, which must be forwarded to or deposited in this office, prior to or upon the return of your field notes:

For Chainmen

I, A.B., do solemnly swear (or affirm), that I will impartially and faithfully execute the duties of chain carrier, that I will level the chain upon uneven ground, and plumb the tally-pins whether sticking or dropping the same; that I will report the true distance to all notable objects, and the true length of all lines that I assist in measuring, to the best of my skill and ability.

Sworn and subscribed before me at_____this_____18_____.
Justice of the Peace.
(or other officer authorized to administer oaths) of_____, County of_____, State (or Territory of_____.

For Flagman or Axeman

I, C.D., do solemnly swear (or affirm) that I will well and truly perform the duties of axeman or flagman, according to instructions given me, and to the best of my skill and ability.

Marking Lines, Establishing and Marking Corners

1. All lines which you actually establish are to be marked as follows: Those trees which intercept your line are to have two notches upon the side where your line intersects and leaves them, without any other mark whatever.

2. A sufficient number of those trees which approach nearest your line, to render the same conspicuous, are to be blazed upon two sides, diagonally or quartering towards the line; the blazes to approach nearer each other the farther the line passes from the blazed trees, and to be as nearly opposite—coinciding with the line—as possible, in cases where they are barely passed.

3. Corner posts are to be made only of the most durable wood found in the vicinity of your lines. Township corner posts must not be less than five, section and meander corner posts four, and quarter section posts three inches in diameter. These posts must be set firmly into the ground, by digging a hole to admit them two feet deep, and be very securely rammed with earth, also with stone when convenient. They are to appear above ground, at township corners, three feet, at section and meander corners, two and a half feet, and at quarter section corners, two feet.

4. All township and section corner posts are to be squared upon their upper ends and the angles of the square set with the cardinal points of the compass. Township corner posts must have six notches upon each of the said angles; section corner posts, upon township lines, as many notches upon one of the said angles

as they are miles distant from the township corner where the line commenced, and interior section corner posts as many notches, both upon their south and east angles, as they are miles distant from the south and east boundaries of the township, respectively.

5. Quarter section and meander corner posts are to be blazed upon two opposite sides, and set with those blazes facing the sections between which they occur.

6. A tree supplying the place of a corner post, is to be squared and marked as directed for posts.

7. All posts established at corner of sections, are to be marked upon each side of their squared part with the number of the four sections which those sides respectively face, at meander corners with the number of the sections between which such posts are set, and at quarter section corners with ¼ S. upon the two blazed sides.

8. Bearing trees are those of which you take the course and distance from a corner. They are distinguished by a large smooth blaze or chop, fronting the corner, upon which is marked, with an iron made for that purpose, the number of the range, township and section, except at quarter section corners where ¼ S. will supply the number of the section, thus:

R._____E. or W.
T._____N.
S._____or ¼ S.

The letters B. T. are also to be marked upon a smaller chop, directly under the large one, and as near the ground as practicable.

9. Witness trees are signalized and marked as above, but the course and distance to them, as well as the small chop, are omitted.

10. Trees, employed either for the purpose of bearing or witness trees, are to be alive and healthy and not less than five inches diameter.

11. From all posts established for township corners, or for section corners upon township lines, four bearing trees, if within a reasonable distance, must be taken; one to stand within each of the four sections.

12. At interior section corners four trees, one to stand within each of the four sections, are to be marked with number of township and range, as well as section in which they stand.

13. From quarter section and meander corners two bearing trees are marked, one within each of the adjoining sections.

14. Wherever bearing trees cannot be had, quadrangular mounds of earth or stone are to be raised around the corner posts, the four angles of which must coincide with the cardinal points of the compass.

15. Mounds at township corners are to have a base of five feet, a top of two feet, and a height of three feet; at section, meander and quarter section corners, they are to have a base of four feet, a top of one and a half feet, a height of two and a half feet.

16. Where mounds are made of earth the place from which it is taken is styled the *Pit*, which is to be a uniform and stated distance from the mound in all instances where the same is practicable, viz.: at township corners there are to be two pits, one ten links due north, and the other ten links due south; at section corners one pit, eight links due south; at quarter section corners one pit eight links due east, and at meander corners one pit, eight links either due north, south,

east or west. The distance of the mound and pit to be obtained by measuring from centre to centre. The mounds are to be neatly covered with sod in all cases where the same can be had.

17. Posts established in mounds for township corners are to be marked upon each side of the square, with the appropriate number of the range and township; at section corners upon township lines with the appropriate number of the range and township upon two sides thereof, and at interior section corners with the range and township within which such post stands.

18. Whenever the true place of establishing a corner is inaccessible, or unadapted to the establishment of a proper corner, except it occurs in a body of water that is to be meandered, you are to establish a witness corner as near thereto as is practicable and either due north, south, east or west of it. Such corner is to be constructed in all respects like the one for which it stands as a witness, with the addition of the letters W. C., immediately over the numbering, both upon the post and trees.

19. When a section or quarter section corner happens at the point for establishing a meander corner, the posts and trees are to be marked with the appropriate numbers for such section or quarter section corner. Or, in lieu of posts, you may at *any* corner, insert endways into the ground, to the depth of seven or eight inches, a stone, the number of cubic inches in which shall not be less than the number contained in a stone fourteen inches long, twelve inches wide and three inches thick. The edges of which must be set north and south on north and south lines; and east and west on east and west lines. The dimensions of each stone to be given in the field notes at the time of establishing the corner.

Where stone section corners are made on the range and township lines, as many notches will be distinctly cut with a pick or chisel on the two sides in the direction of the line, as the corner is sections from the nearest township corners. At township corners six notches will be cut on each edge or side toward the cardinal points. At section corners in the interior of a township, as many notches will be cut on the south edge and east sides as the corner is sections distant from the south and east boundaries of the township; and at the corners of subdivisional intersections with the north boundaries of the townships, six notches on the south edge, and at the intersection with the west boundaries six notches on the east edge; and as many notches on the east or south sides (as the case may require), as the corner is sections distant from the township corner. Quarter section corner stones will have ¼ cut on the west side on north and south lines, and on the north side on east and west lines.

Where a corner is perpetuated by a stone of the dimensions, marked and set in the manner above described, no mound need be erected.

When the closing lines to the north or west boundaries of the townships, either in subdivision or exterior work, exceed one hundred chains of length, corners for the legal subdivisions of the sections will be established at every twenty chains north or west of the quarter section corner.

Measurements and Where to Establish Meander Corners

1. Your distances are all to be noted and returned in chains and links, and to be taken with a half or two pole chain of fifty parts, each measuring seven inches and ninety-two-hundredths. The length of your chain should be adjusted

by means of a screw attached to the handle of the hind end; every tenth link should compose a swivel, and all the rings and loops should be welded or brazed. The accuracy of your chain is to be preserved by comparing it with a standard adjusted at this office.

2. Your tally-pins, eleven in number, must not exceed fourteen inches in length, must be of sufficient weight to drop plum, and are to be made of iron or seasoned wood pointed with steel.

3. The length of every line you run is to be ascertained by horizontal measurement.

4. Whenever your line is obstructed by an object over which you cannot measure with the chain, you are to pass the same by offsets, traverse or trigonometry, observing that the distance thus obtained extends no farther than is necessary to actually pass the interposing object.

5. Whenever your course is so obstructed by navigable streams, or other bodies of water which are to be meandered, you are to establish a meander corner at the intersection of your lines with both margins thereof, and also on each side of all islands which said lines may cross.

Township Lines

1. North and south lines are termed range lines; east and west, township lines. The former are styled, in the field notes, the line between certain ranges; the latter, the line between certain townships. Each mile, both of a range and township line, is particularized by the number of the sections between which it is run, thus; north between sections 31 and 36, west between sections 1 and 36.

2. Upon the base or township line forming the southern boundary of your district, township corners are established at intervals of six miles: From each of these corners you are to run range lines due north, six miles; establishing a quarter section corner at the end of the first forty, and a section corner at the end of the first eighty chains, and observing the same order and intervals of establishing quarter section and section corners to the end of the sixth mile, where you will temporarily set a township corner post.

3. You will then commence at a township corner upon the first range line east of your district, and immediately east of the township corner posts temporarily set by you, and from thence run due west across your whole district, intersecting your range lines at or within three chains and fifty links, due north or south, of your said six mile posts. At the point of intersection, if within the above limits, you will establish a township corner. Upon this township or last mentioned line, quarter section and section corners are to be established at the same distances and intervals as directed for range lines; observing that the length of each and every township line which you are to establish, is in no case to exceed or fall short of the length of the corresponding township boundary upon the south, more than three chains and fifty links. If, however, in closing your first tier of townships, and all others closing to or upon old work, you find it impossible to preserve the true course of your lines and close within the above limits, you are to resurvey and examine until you detect the real cause of discrepancy, which if not in your own work, you will report to this office, and for which you will provide in the field, in all instances where the same is practicable, by adding to, or deducting from the length of your first range line or lines. And where, in order to close a township to or upon old

work, you are compelled to employ a variation greater or less than the true magnetic variation, both must be stated.

4. After closing your first tier of townships, you are to run up and close successive tiers, to the completion of your district, by the same method of survey as directed for the first tier.

5. You are to observe and note the true magnetic variation, at least upon every mile or section line, and as much oftener as there is a change therein.

6. The bearing trees, standing upon the west side of range, and upon the north side of township lines, are to be entered first in your field notes.

7. After a township corner is established as before directed, you are to complete the notes of the corresponding range line, by inserting the said corner, with the true distance thereto, and adding or erasing the notes of any topography or other minutes, that may be included or excluded by thus adding to or deducting from the length of the range line as temporarily established.

8. With your field notes you must return a diagram, drawn upon a scale of three inches to six miles, on which you are to represent each boundary you have run with the length and variation thereof, and with all the topography thereupon that can be properly expressed upon that scale.

SUBDIVISION

Length of North and South and East and West Lines, and Where to Establish Quarter Section Posts

1. Every north and south section line, except those terminating in the north boundary, are to be one mile in length. The east and west section lines, except those terminating in the west boundary, are to be within one hundred links of eighty chains in length; and the north and south boundaries of any one section, except in the extreme western tier, are to be within one hundred links of equal length.

2. The length of the section lines closing to the north and west boundaries, are to be governed by the length of the sixth or closing miles, both of the range and township lines, and must be as nearly of the same length, or of an average thereof, as is practicable.

3. Quarter section corners, both upon north and south and upon east and west lines, are to be set equidistant from the corresponding section corners; except upon those closing to the north and west boundaries, where the quarter section corners will be established precisely forty chains north or west of the respective section corners from which those lines start.

Method of Subdividing; Random, Corrected and True Lines, and Diagram

1. The first mile, both of the south and east boundaries of each township you are to subdivide, is to be carefully traced and measured before you enter upon the subdivision thereof. This will enable you to observe any change that may have taken place in the magnetic variation, as it existed at the running of the township lines, and will also enable you to compare your chaining with that upon the township lines.

2. Any discrepancy, arising either from a change in the magnetic variation or a difference in measurement, is to be stated as directed under the head of field notes.

3. After adjusting your compass to a variation which you have thus found will retrace the eastern boundary of the township, you will commence at the corner to sections 35 and 36, on the south boundary, and run a line due north, forty chains, to the quarter section corner which you are to establish between sections 35 and 36; continuing due north forty chains further, you will establish the corner to sections 25, 26, 35 and 36.

4. From the section corner last named, run a random line, without blazing, due east for corner of sections 25 and 36, in east boundary. If you intersect exactly at the corner, you will blaze your random line back and establish it as the true line. But if your random line intersects the said range line, either north or south of the said corner, you will measure the distance of such intersection, from which you will calculate a course that will run a true line back to the corner from which your random started.

5. From the corner of sections 25, 26, 35, 36, run due north between sections 25 and 26, setting the quarter section post, as before at forty chains, and at eighty chains establishing the corner of sections 23, 24, 25, 26. Then run a random line due east for the corner of sections 24 and 25 in east boundary; correcting back in the manner directed for running the line between sections 25 and 36.

6. In this manner proceed with the survey of each successive section in the first tier, until you arrive at the north boundary of the township, which you will reach in running up a random line between sections 1 and 2. If this line should not intersect at the post established for corner to sections 1, 2, 35 and 36 upon the township line, you will note the distance that you fell east or west of the same, from which distance you will calculate a course that will run a true line south to the corner from which your random started.

7. The first tier of sections being thus laid out and surveyed, you will return to the south boundary of the township, and from the corner of sections 34 and 35 commence and survey the second tier of sections, in the same manner that you pursued in the survey of the first, closing at the section corners on the first tier.

8. In like manner proceed with the survey of each successive tier of sections, until you arrive at the fifth or last tier. From each section corner which you establish upon this tier, you are to run random lines for the corresponding corners established upon the range line forming the western boundary of your township, and in returning, establish the true line as before directed.

9. All section lines are to be right lines, regardless of the number or nature of intervening obstacles; except in the event of their intersecting a lake or pond of such diameter, at the points of intersection, as forbids their continuance by means of a trigonometrical calculation, in which case, and in cases also where a river, lake, correction line, or reservation, form a part of the boundary of a township, when the closing lines thereupon, will be *true lines*, the courses of which will have a strict reference to the variation and closing of the adjacent line; the quarter section posts upon which are to be set forty chains from the section corner at which such true lines commenced.

10. In closing upon a correction line, you are to establish a section corner at the point of your intersection therewith, stating the true distance of such intersection from the nearest corner thereon.

11. Field notes of random lines are to embrace nothing but the variation, length and closing thereof.

12. Topography of every description, line trees and corners, are to be taken

upon the corrected lines and included in the notes thereof, following which is to be written the description of the land and timber.

You will report in your general descriptions, and indicate upon your diagrams, the whole number of residences, or other edifices, and as nearly as practicable the character and extent of improvement within each township. Where you cannot determine these important facts accurately without leaving your lines, you must specify the smallest subdivision or subdivisions upon which such residence or other improvement exists.

You are to return the distance at which you strike, and that at which you leave every stream or other body of water that exceeds one hundred links of width at an ordinary stage of water; giving also the right-angled width of the same.

Chain Carriers

Your chain carriers must be reversed at every tally, so that one may be ahead upon the odd and the other upon all the even tallies. The discrepancies of measure likely to arise from unequal strength or care in chainmen, are thus rendered compensative; a check is instituted upon the accuracy of the tally, and the labor of recollecting and reporting objects is divided. As the chainmen pass each other, the pins must be, in every instance, counted by each of them.

Markers and Marking Irons

You are to provide yourself with marking irons of the most approved description, and which are to be used only by experienced and skillful markers. In the marking of your lines in timber and the establishing and marking of your corners, whether in prairie or timber, particular care is to be taken, and such parts thereof as are not executed by yourself are to be personally inspected by you. The importance of this caution will be manifest, when you reflect that it is upon this evidence alone that the settler depends in locating or entering his land.

Standard-Chain

Your chain, adjusted to the standard in this office, must be carefully guarded against all injury, and by it you will compare and adjust your measuring chain every morning after the latter has been in service, and note the difference between them in your field book, and if none, then state that fact also.

Corrections and Resurveys

Full notes of every line and part of a line which you retrace, of every one which you re-establish, of every random line which it is necessary for you to run, whether measured or not—of every corner which you re-establish, alter or perfect—of every offset—of the elements of every distance obtained by triangulation, are to be carefully entered at the time in the proper place in your field books.

Field Notes and Books

The second page in each field book must contain the names and duties of assistants then engaged upon your lines. Whenever you employ a new assistant or change the duty of one, the fact, with the cause thereof, must be given in an entry immediately preceding the notes taken under the new arrangements.

The notes which you take in the field are to be returned to this office. With this view you will enter your notes, taken as above directed, in books containing a number of pages, that will admit of their being entered in every particular in conformity to these instructions. The books must be of regular form, size and material. If after the notes of any one or more townships are thus taken, the book or books are too much worn, soiled or defaced to be returned in conformity to said instructions, you will make out and submit, *with the original*, a fair handed and neat copy of the same. You are to use no other than black ink of the best quality. No erasures are to be made. If mistakes occur, the pen may be drawn across the erroneous entry, but always in such a manner that the words can be read afterwards. No leaves are to be cut, torn or otherwise taken out of your field books, as reason is thus given for suspicion that there was something upon the missing leaves which it was not to the interest of the deputy to have known.

With these instructions you are furnished diagrams of each of the townships of your district upon a scale of two inches per mile, upon which are accurately laid down the respective boundaries of each township, the length of each of the closing lines, the magnetic variation of each mile, and at least two of the bearing trees, at all the section corners thereon, where bearings were taken. P. in M. signifies post in mound, the pits to which (unless it is otherwise stated) are in the direction and at the distance hereinbefore prescribed.

Diagrams

With your field notes you are to return a map of each township of your district, upon the scale above named, upon which is to be expressed the length and variation of each of your lines with *all* the topography neatly laid down. With a view to the completeness of these maps, you should make sketches of the topography as you progress with your lines, that you may be able to present not only the points upon your lines at which the same occurs, but also its direction and position between the lines or within each section, as every object of topography is to be properly closed or connected. These maps form the basis of all the official plats, and are carefully preserved in this office.

Swamp Lands

By an act of Congress, approved September 28th, 1850, all of the swamp and overflowed lands that are unfit for cultivation, which were unsold at the date of the passage of the said act, were granted to the State or Territory in which said lands are located. In order that the field notes of surveys may hereafter clearly present the quantity and locality of the lands thus granted, you will, in addition to the objects of topography required by the foregoing instructions, note the point upon which you enter and leave all lands which are clearly the subject of the above grant, stating the character of the land thus noted, and whether it is a swamp or marsh, or subject from other cause to inundation, to an extent that would in the absence of artificial means render it uncultivable. The depth of inundation, if in timber, may be easily determined from the marks upon the trees, and its frequency may be ascertained, either from your knowledge of the general character of the stream which overflows, or from the testimony of those residing upon or near the locality under examination. The usual phraseology for entering or leaving a swamp or marsh may be employed with the addition of "unfit for cultivation"; but if the margin of bottom, swamp or marsh in which uncultivable land exists is not identical with the margin of such uncultivable land, then a separate entry must be made for each opposite the marginal distance at which they respectively occur.

Lands Overflowed by Artificial Means

When lands are overflowed by artificial means (say by dams for milling, logging or other purposes) you will in no instance set meander posts, but continue your lines across said overflowed tract, in the manner directed in the foregoing instructions, stating particularly in your notes the depth of water and how the overflow is caused.

Errors in Town Lines

Should you find a manifest error in the measurement or course of any of the township lines of your district, you are to correct the same by resurveying and re-establishing such line or lines, from the point where the error was detected, to the north or west thereof, noting your intersection with each one of the erroneous corners as you progress, which you are to demolish and deface with all evidences thereof. Of such remeasurement and corrections you are to take full and complete field notes, in a separate book, to be returned to the Surveyor General's office, with the field notes of your subdivision.

How and What to Meander

1. In subdividing any one township, you are to meander as hereinafter directed, any lake or lakes, pond or ponds, lying entirely within the boundaries thereof, of the area of forty acres and upwards, and which cannot be drained and are not likely to fill up, or from any cause to become dry.

2. Whenever required by special instructions, to meander any stream or body of water, passing through or lying within your district, you are also to meander all islands situated therein.

3. Standing with your face towards the mouth of the stream, the bank on your left hand, is termed the *left bank*, and that upon your right hand, the *right bank*. These terms are to be universally used to distinguish the two banks of a river, both in running lines and meandering.

4. In meandering rivers, you are to commence at a meander corner in the township boundary, and take the course and distance of the bank upon which you commence, to a meander corner upon the same or another boundary of the same township, carefully noting your intersection with all intermediate meander corners. By the same method you are to meander the opposite bank of the same river.

5. In meandering lakes, ponds or bayous, you are to commence at a meander corner upon the township line and proceed as above directed for the banks of a

navigable stream, except where a lake, pond or bayou lies entirely within the township boundaries, when you will commence at a meander corner established in subdividing, and from thence take the course and distance of the entire margin thereof.

6. To meander a pond, lying entirely within the boundaries of a section, you will run a random line thereto from the nearest section or quarter section corner. At the point where this random line intersects the margin of such pond, you will establish a witness point, by fixing a post in the ground and raising a mound or taking bearings, as at a meander corner, except that the post and the large face upon the bearing trees will be marked with the letter W. only.

7. In meandering islands, you are to proceed as directed in sections 5 and 6 of this chapter, except that where there are no meander corners established upon an island, you are to take the course and distance of your starting point from the nearest meander corner, instead of section or quarter section corner.

8. The meanders of each fractional section, or between any two meander posts, or of a pond or island interior of a section, must close within one chain and fifty links.

9. Your field notes of meanders in any one township, are to follow immediately after the notes of the subdivision thereof. They are to state and describe, particularly, the meander corner from which they commenced, each one with which they close, and are to exhibit the meanders of each fractional section separately; following and composing a part of which, will be given a description of the land, timber, depth of inundation to which the bottom is subject, and the banks, current and bottom of the stream or body of water you are meandering.

10. To furnish data that will enable this office to fix their exact location, you will note in the proper place in the meanders of each fractional section the exact position and extent of all falls and rapids, fords portages and mill sites existing in, or connected with the river or other body of water which you are meandering.

11. No blazes or marks of any description are to be made upon your meander lines, though the utmost care must be taken to pass no object of topography, *or change, therein*, without giving a particular description thereof in its proper place in your meander notes.

Field Notes

1. Your field notes are to form a full and perfect history of your operations in the field.

2. The field notes of the subdivision of every township, whether fractional or not, are to be written in a separate book.

3. Description of the timber, undergrowth, surface, soil and minerals, upon each section line, is to follow the notes thereof, and not to be mixed with them.

4. The language of your field notes must be so concise and clear, the hand in which they are written so plain and legible, that no doubt can exist as to your figures, letters, words and meaning.

5. No *abbreviations* are to be made in your field notes, except such as relate to course, to express which, the proper combinations of the capital letters, N. S. E. and W. are to be used; except when a course is exactly to a cardinal point, in which case it is to be written in full.

6. The description of each mile must be independent, and *not refer to a preceding description*.

7. The date of each day's work must follow immediately after the notes thereof.

8. All rivers, creeks, and other streams, lakes, ponds, prairies, swamps, marshes, groves, hills, bluffs, windfalls, roads and trails, are to be distinguished in your field notes by their original and received names only, and where such names cannot be ascertained or do not exist your imagination is not to supply them.

9. Your field notes must be kept in the exact form of the specimen herewith furnished you.

Objects and Data to Be Embraced in Your Field Notes

You are to enter in their proper places in the field notes of your survey, a particular description and the exact location of the following objects:

1. The length and variation or variations of every line you run.
2. The name and diameter of all bearing trees, with the course and distance of the same from their respective corners.
3. The name of the material of which you construct mounds, with the course and distance to the pits.
4. The name, diameter and exact distance to all those trees which your lines intersect.
5. At what distance you enter, and at what distance you leave every river, creek or other "bottom," prairie, swamp, marsh, grove or windfall, with the course of the same at both points of intersection.
6. The surface, whether level, rolling, broken or hilly.
7. The soil, whether first, second, or third rate.
8. The several kinds of timber and undergrowth, naming the timber in the order of its prevalency.
9. All rivers, creeks and smaller streams of water, with their actual or right angled widths, course, banks, current and bed, at the points where your lines cross.
10. A description of all bottom lands—whether wet or dry, and if subject to inundation, state to what depth.
11. All springs of water, and whether fresh, saline or mineral, with the course and width of the stream flowing from them.
12. All lakes and ponds, describing their banks and the depth and quality of their water.
13. All coal banks, precipices, caves, sink-holes, quarries and ledges with the character and quality of the same.
14. All water-falls and mill sites.
15. All towns and villages, houses, cabins, fields and sugar camps, factories, furnaces and other improvements.
16. All metalliferous minerals or ores, and all diggings therefor, with particular descriptions of both, that may come to your knowledge, whether intersected by your lines or not.
17. All roads and trails, with the course they bear.
18. All offsets or calculations by which you obtain the length of such parts of your lines as cannot be measured with the chain.
19. The precise course and distance of all witness corners from the true corners which they represent.

Affidavit

1. Following the field notes and general descriptions, in each of your field books, an affidavit of the following form is to be written, and to be signed by yourself and each of your assistants in the field:

I, A. B., Deputy Surveyor, do solemnly swear (or affirm) that, in pursuance of a contract with C. D., Surveyor General of the United States for Wisconsin and Iowa, bearing date the_____day of_____, 18____, and in strict conformity to the laws of the United States, and the instructions of the said Surveyor General, I have regularly surveyed_____ principal meridian (State or Territory) of_____and I do further solemnly swear (or affirm) that the foregoing are the true and original field notes of the said survey, executed as aforesaid.

A. B., *Deputy Surveyor*

G. H. ⎱
J. K. ⎰ *Chainmen*
L. M., *Marker*
N. O., *Flagman*

Subscribed by said A. B., Deputy Surveyor, and sworn before me_____ at_____this_____day of_____, 18_____.

P. Q., *Justice of the Peace*
(or other officer authorized to adminis-
ter oaths) of_____in the county of
_____State (or Territory of_____).

2. Your attention is directed to the following section of an act of Congress, approved, August 8th, 1846, entitled "an act to equalize the compensation of Surveyors General of the public lands of the United States, and for other purposes."

3. "That the Surveyors General of the public lands of the United States, in "addition to the oath now authorized by law to be administered to deputies on "their appointment to office, shall require each of their deputies, on the return of "his surveys, to take and subscribe an oath or affirmation that those surveys have "been faithfully and correctly executed, according to law and the instructions of "the Surveyor General; and, on satisfactory evidence being presented to any court "of competent jurisdiction that such surveys, or any part *thereof*, had not been thus "executed, the deputy making such false oath or affirmation shall be deemed guilty "of perjury, and shall suffer all the pains and penalties attached to that offense; "and the district attorney of the United States for the time being, in whose district "any such false, erroneous, or fraudulent surveys shall have been executed, shall, "upon the application of the proper Surveyor General, immediately institute suit "upon the bond of such deputy; and the institution of such suit shall act as a lien "upon any property owned or held by such deputy, or his sureties, at the time such "suit was instituted."

The above section of the said law applies to the foregoing affidavit, and will be in all particular and in every instance, rigidly enforced.

General Remarks

Your attention is particularly directed to the following specimen of field notes, which will illustrate the order and method of performing the work, and the manner in which your field notes are to be returned, and is to be regarded, therefore, as a part of these general instructions, any departure from which, without special authority, will be considered a violation of your contract and oath, and a forfeiture to all claim of payment. As your work will be rigidly examined in the field, by a deputy appointed by this office for the special purpose, any neglect on your part cannot fail to be reported, and the penalty, however disagreeable, will certainly be enforced.

It will be seen from the variations in the instructions up to this point that those responsible for the United States land surveys were gradually perfecting a system which could be followed without great change in future surveys. The instructions of 1855 which follow were the guide book for practically all surveys from that time until the end of the contract system in 1910. From time to time as equipment improved modernization changes were authorized. It can be assumed, however, that no great changes were made in the rules under which the surveys were conducted during the next half century. Familiarity, then, with the instructions of 1855 is probably more important to the surveyor in the public land states where the surveys were conducted after 1855 than any knowledge he may acquire of the more recent and more refined methods used since 1910.

For those surveys completed before 1855 it is very important to compare the survey record as preserved in the original plats and field notes with the current original instructions of the same date as the survey.

No amount of reading of the present day instructions can account for the multiple corners on all sides of the townships in eastern Iowa and in important areas of those other states where surveys were made when true lines were required to be run to closing corners on north, east and west boundaries of all townships. See instructions of 1843, page 41 of this book.

The remarks of W. D. Jones which follow the 1855 instructions are intended to call attention to the principal variations in the instructions as they were developed.

The excess length given to the south boundary of section 31 on the standard parallel was included in William Burt's special instructions of 1836. Of course, when the final scheme of subdivision into 24-mile checks was developed this excess length was no longer necessary to keep convergence shortages within reasonable bounds.

Diagram A[1]

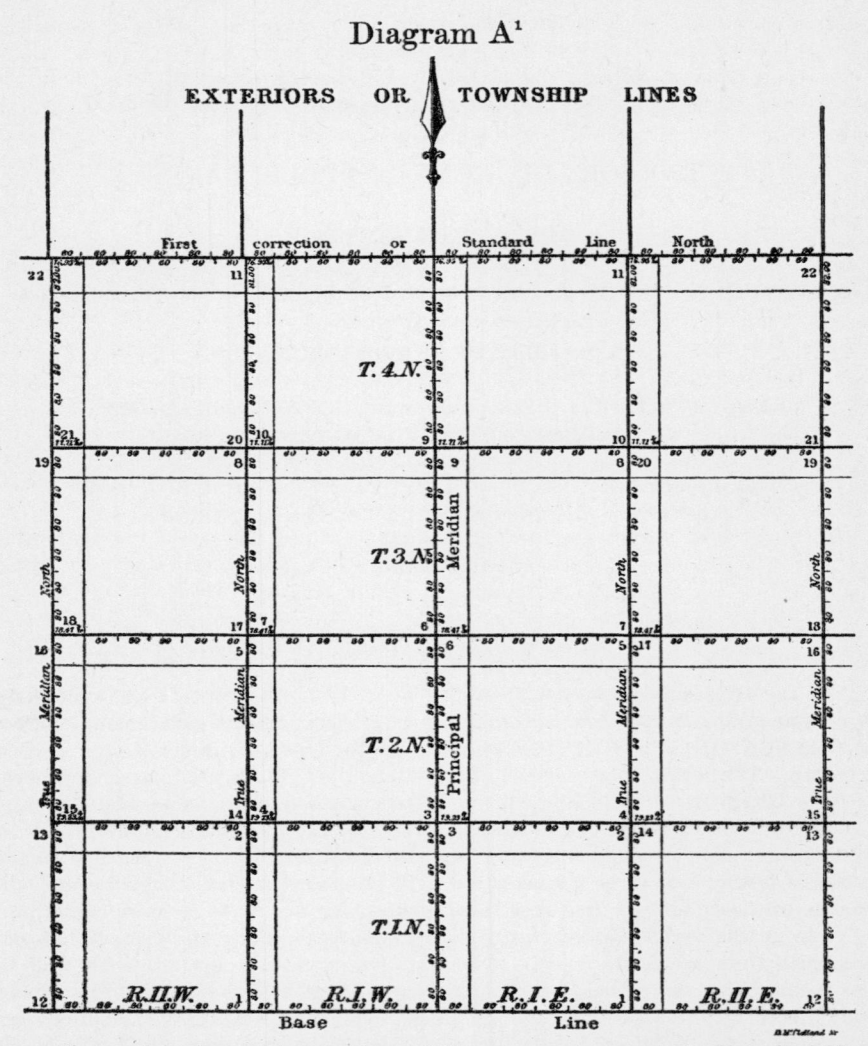

EXTERIORS OR TOWNSHIP LINES

The upright figures (made thus 1.2.3) commencing near the Principal Meridian and Base line with No. 1, indicate the perambulations of the Surveyor in running the Townships and Correction lines.

The Correction or Standard lines North of the Base are every 4 townships, and South of the Base every 5 townships.

The excess or deficiency of measurement on northern and southern boundaries is thrown on the westernmost half mile.

The measurements between Meridian lines will, of course, always vary according to the latitude of the survey, besides being liable to be rendered inexact where the country is very hilly or broken. The convergency of the range lines as shown by the measurements on this diagram, is according to calculation, as it exists between the parallels of 46° and 47° N. L.

[1] This reproduction of the beautifully lithographed original, folded and tipped at the back of the 1855 Instructions, is referred to on pp. 104 and 120, q.v.

INSTRUCTIONS
TO THE
SURVEYORS GENERAL OF PUBLIC LANDS
of
THE UNITED STATES
FOR THOSE
SURVEYING DISTRICTS ESTABLISHED IN AND SINCE THE YEAR 1850;
CONTAINING ALSO,
A MANUAL OF INSTRUCTIONS
To
REGULATE FIELD OPERATIONS OF DEPUTY SURVEYORS,
ILLUSTRATED BY DIAGRAMS

Prescribed, according to law, by the principal clerk of surveys, pursuant to order of the commissioner of the General Land Office.

WASHINGTON:
A. O. P. NICHOLSON, Public Printer.
1855

By the direction of the COMMISSIONER OF THE GENERAL LAND OFFICE, the accompanying instructions are prescribed for your official government, including a MANUAL OF INSTRUCTIONS to regulate the field operations of your deputy surveyors. The latter is a revision of the Manual of Surveying Instructions prepared for OREGON in 1851, (the edition of which is now exhausted,) and presents, in some respects, more copious illustrations, both in the specimen field notes and in the diagrams, than could be furnished amidst the pressure of the exigency under which the former had to be prepared. It will be observed that, in the former edition, the township and section lines south of the base are made to start therefrom, and close on the first standard parallel south; whereas, under the present instructions, such lines are made to start from the first standard parallel south, and to close to the north on the base: and thus there will be closing corners and starting corners, both on the base and standard lines. Such modification is introduced for the sake of entire uniformity of method in new fields of survey, and will not, of course, affect any past operations under the original instructions.

The starting corners on the base line and on the standards will, of course, be common to two townships or to two sections lying on the north of such lines; and the closing corners on such lines, from the south, should be carefully connected with the former by measurements to be noted in the field book.

Where STONE can be had to perpetuate corner boundaries, such, for obvious reasons, should always be preferred for that purpose, and the dimensions of the stone, as herein prescribed, (on page 9), are to be regarded as the *minimum size*; but in localities where it is found practicable to obtain a stone of *increased dimensions*, it is always desirable to do so, particularly for TOWNSHIP CORNERS, and especially for those on base, meridian, and standard lines; and to such purport the deputy surveyor is to be specially instructed.

Prior to entering upon duty, the deputy surveyor is to make himself thoroughly acquainted with the official requirements in regard to field operations in all the details herein set forth, and to be apprized of the weighty moral and legal responsibilities under which he will act.

Unfaithfulness in the execution of the public surveys will be detected by special examinations of the work to be made for that purpose, and, when detected, will immediately subject the delinquent deputy and his bondsmen to be sued by the district attorney of the United States, at the instance of the proper surveyor general—the institution of which suit will act at once as a lien upon any property owned by him or them at that time; and such delinquency, moreover, is an offence punishable by the statute, with all the pains and penalties of perjury, (see act of 1846, quoted on pages 19 and 20 hereof,) and will of necessity debar the offending deputy from future employment in like capacity. Hence, in the execution of contracts for surveying public lands, there is every incentive to fidelity that can address itself either to the moral sense, or to motives of private interest.

By order of the Commissioner:

JOHN M. MOORE,
Principal Clerk of Surveys.

GENERAL LAND OFFICE,
February 22, 1855.

TABLE OF CONTENTS

	PAGE.
System of rectangular surveying; range, township, and section lines; mode of numbering townships and sections. Standard parallels	1, 2
Of measurements, chaining, and marking; tally pins; process of chaining; levelling the chain and plumbing the pins	2, 3, 4
Marking lines; of trial or random lines	4
Insuperable objects on line; witness points; marking irons	4, 5
Establishing corner boundaries; at what points for township, section, quarter section, and meander corners, respectively	5, 6
Manner of establishing corners by means of posts	6, 7
Notching corner posts	7
Bearing trees; how many at the difference corners, and how to be marked	7, 8
Stones for corner boundaries; minimum size; marking same	8, 9
Mounds around posts, of earth or stone; how to be constructed and conditioned	9, 10
Mound memorials—witness mounds to corners	10, 11
Double corners only on base and standard parallels	11
Meandering navigable streams, lakes, and deep ponds	12, 13
Field books for deputy surveyors	13, 14, 15
Summary of objects and data to be noted in field books	15, 16, 17
Swamp lands granted to the State by act of 28th of September, 1850; their outlines to be specially noted by the deputy surveyor	17

Noting of settlers' claims in OREGON, WASHINGTON and NEW MEXICO ... 18
Affidavits to field notes, and provisions of act of 8th August, 1846, respecting the same. Pains and penalties which attach to false surveys ... 18, 19
Forms of official oaths, prior to entering upon duty, for a deputy and his assistants ... 19
Exteriors or township lines; and limitations within which they must close ... 20, 21
Method of subdividing ... 21, 22
Limitations within which section and meander lines must close ... 22
Of Diagram A, showing a body of township exteriors ... 23
Of Diagram B, showing the subdivisions of a township into sections ... 23
Of Diagram C, illustrating the mode of making mound, stake, and stone corners ... 23
Subdivisions of fractional sections into forty-acre lots are to be made by the surveyor general on the township plats, and to be designated by special numbers, where they cannot be described as quarter-quarters ... 23, 24
Township plats to be prepared by the surveyor general in *triplicate* ... 24
Township plats to be furnished to the General Land Office and to the district land offices. Details to be shown thereon, respectively ... 24
"Descriptive notes," showing the quality of soil and kind of timber found on the surveyed lines in each township, and describing each corner boundary, are to accompany the plat of the same, to be furnished by the surveyor general to the district land office ... 24
The original field books of surveys, bearing the written approval of the surveyor general, to be retained in his office ... 24
Certified transcripts of field books to be furnished to General Land Office ... 24
Meander corners to be numbered on township plats ... 24, 25
Variation of the needle, and mode of ascertaining the same ... 26, 27, 28
Specimen field notes A and B—the former of the exterior lines of a township, and the latter of the subdivision of the same—constitute a separate series of pages from 1 to 53 inclusive; and they are preceded by an INDEX referring the township, section, closing and meander lines, as shown on diagram B, to their corresponding pages in the notes A and B ... 1-53
The "General description" of the character of public land in the township follows the subdivisional notes, with a "list of names" of assistants, and the mode of authenicating the survey, under the provisions of the act of 8th August, 1846, and form for certifying copies of field notes to be transmitted to the General Land Office ... 54, 55, 56
Conclusion. "Table showing the difference of latitude and departure in running 80 chains, at any course from 1 to 60 minutes" ... 56

SYSTEM
of
RECTANGULAR SURVEYING.

1. The public lands of the United States are ordinarily surveyed into rectangular tracts, bounded by lines conforming to the cardinal points.

2. The public lands are laid off, in the first place, into bodies of land of six miles square, called *Townships*, containing as near as may be 23,040 acres. The

townships are subdivided into thirty-six tracts called *Sections*, of a mile square, each containing as near as may be 640 acres. Any number or series of contiguous townships, situated north or south of each other, constitute a *Range*.

The law requires that the lines of the public surveys shall be governed by the true meridian, and that the townships shall be *six miles square*,—two things involving in connexion a mathematical impossibility—for, strictly to conform to the meridian, necessarily throws the township out of square, by reason of the convergency of meridians, and hence by adhering to the true meridian, results the necessity of departing from the strict requirements of law, as respects the precise area of townships and the subdivisional parts, thereof, the township assuming something of a trapezoidal form, which inequality develops itself more and more as such the higher the latitude of the surveys. It is doubtless in view of these circumstances that the law provides (see sec. 2 of the act of May 18, 1796) that the sections of a mile square shall contain the quantity of 640 acres, *as nearly as may be;* and moreover, provides (see sec. 3 of the act of 10th May, 1800) in the following words: "And in all cases where the exterior lines of the townships thus to be subdivided into sections or half sections, shall exceed, or shall not extend six miles, the excess or deficiency shall be specially noted, and added to or deducted from the western or northern ranges of sections or half sections in such township, according as the error may be in running the lines from east to west, or from south to north; the sections and half sections bounded on the northern and western lines of such townships shall be sold as containing only the quantity expressed in the returns and plats, respectively, and all others as containing the complete legal quantity."

The accompanying diagram, marked A, [p. 100] will serve to illustrate the method of running out the exterior lines of townships, as well on the *north* as on the *south* side of the base line: and the order and mode of subdividing townships will be found illustrated in the accompanying specimen field notes, conforming with the township diagram B. The method here presented is designed to insure as full a compliance with all the requirements, meaning, and intent of the surveying laws as, it is believed, is practicable.

The section lines are surveyed from *south* to north on true meridians, and from *east* to west, in order to throw the excess or deficiencies in measurements on the north and west sides of the township, as required by law.

3. The townships are to bear numbers in respect to the base line either north or south of it; and the tiers of townships called "Ranges," will bear numbers in respect to the meridian line according to their relative position to it, either on the east or west.

4. The thirty-six sections into which a township is subdivided are numbered, commencing with number *one* at the *northeast* angle of the township, and proceeding west to number six, and thence proceeding east to number twelve, and so on, alternately, until the number thirty-six in the southeast angle.

5. STANDARD PARALLELS (usually called correction lines) are established at stated intervals to provide for or counteract the error that otherwise would result from the convergency of meridians, and also to arrest error arising from inaccuracies in measurements on meridian lines, which, however, must ever be studiously avoided. On the *north* of the principal base line it is proposed to have these standards run at distances of every *four* townships, or twenty-four miles, and on the *south* of the principal base, at distances of every *five* townships, or thirty miles.

OF MEASUREMENTS, CHAINING, AND MARKING.

1. Where uniformity in the variation of the needle is not found, the public surveys must be made with an instrument operating independently of the magnetic needle. Burt's *improved solar compass*, or other instrument of equal utility, must be used of necessity in such case; and it is deemed best that such instrument should be used under all circumstances. Where the needle can be relied on, however, the ordinary compass may be used in subdividing and meandering.

2. The township lines, and the subdivision lines, will usually be measured by a two-pole chain of thirty-three feet in length, consisting of fifty links, and each link being seven inches and ninety-two hundredths of an inch long. On uniform and level ground, however, the four-pole chain may be used. Your measurements will, however, always be represented according to the four-pole chain of one hundred links. The deputy surveyor must also have with him a measure of the standard chain, wherewith to compare and adjust the chain in use, from day to day, with punctuality and carefulness; and must return such standard chain to the Surveyor General's office for examination when his work is completed.

OF TALLY PINS.

3. You will use eleven tally pins made of steel, not exceeding fourteen inches in length, weighty enough towards the point to make them drop perpendicularly, and having a ring at the top, in which is to be fixed a piece of red cloth, or something else of conspicuous color, to make them readily seen when stuck in the ground.

PROCESS OF CHAINING.

4. In measuring lines with a two-pole chain, every *five* chains are called "*a tally*," because at that distance the last of the ten tally pins with which the forward chainman set out will have been stuck. He then cries "tally", which cry is repeated by the other chainman, and each registers the distance by slipping a thimble, button, or ring of leather, or something of the kind, on a belt worn for that purpose or by some other convenient method. The hind chainman then comes up, and having counted in the presence of his fellow the tally pins which he has taken up, so that both may be assured that none of the pins have been lost, he then takes the forward end of the chain, and proceeds to set the pins. Thus the chainmen alternately change places, each setting the pins that he has taken up, so that one is forward in all the odd, and the other in all the even tallies. Such procedure, it is believed, tends to insure accuracy in measurement, facilitates the recollection of the distances to objects on the line, and renders a mis-tally almost impossible.

LEVELLING THE CHAIN AND PLUMBING THE PINS.

5. The length of every line you run is to be ascertained by precise horizontal measurement, as nearly approximating to an air line as is possible in practice on the earth's surface This all important object can only be attained by a rigid adherence to the three following observances:

1. Ever keeping the chain *stretched* to the utmost degree of tension on even ground.
2. On uneven ground, keeping the chain not only stretched as aforesaid, but

horizontally *levelled*. And when ascending and descending steep ground, hills, or mountains, the chain will have to be *shortened* to one-half its length, (and sometimes more,) in order accurately to obtain the true horizontal measure.

3. The careful plumbing of the tally pins, so as to attain precisely the *spot* where they should be stuck. The more uneven the surface, the greater the caution needed to set the pins.

MARKING LINES.

6. All lines on which are to be established the legal corner boundaries are to be marked after this method, viz.: Those trees which may intercept your line must have two chops or notches cut on each side of them without any other marks whatever. These are called *"sight trees," "line trees,"* or *"station trees."*

A sufficient number of other trees standing nearest to your line, on either side of it, are to be *blazed* on two sides diagonally, or quartering towards the line, in order to render the line conspicuous, and readily to be traced, the blazes to be opposite each other, coinciding in direction with the line where the trees stand very near it, and to approach nearer each other the further the line passes from the blazed trees. Due care must ever be taken to have the lines so well marked as to be readily followed.

ON TRIAL, OR RANDOM LINES,

the trees are not to be blazed, unless occasionally from indispensable necessity, and then it must be done so guardedly as to prevent the possibility of confounding the marks of the trial line with the *true*. But bushes and limbs of trees may be lopped, and *stakes set* on the trial, or random line, at every *ten* chains, to enable the surveyor on his return to follow and correct the trial line, and establish therefrom the *true line*. To prevent confusion, the temporary stakes set on the trial, or random lines, must be *pulled up* when the surveyor returns to establish the true line.

INSUPERABLE OBJECTS ON LINE—WITNESS POINTS.

7. Under circumstances where your course is obstructed by impassable obstacles, such as ponds, swamps, marshes, lakes, rivers, creeks, &c., you will prolong the line across such obstacles by taking the necessary right angle offsets; or, if such be inconvenient, by a traverse or trigonometrical operation, until you regain the line on the opposite side. And in case a north and south, or a true east and west, line is regained in advance of any such obstacle, you will prolong and mark the line back to the obstacle so passed, and state all the particulars in relation thereto in your field book. And at the intersection of lines with both margins of impassable obstacles, you will establish a *Witness Point*, (for the purpose of perpetuating the intersections therewith) by setting a post, and giving in your field book the course and distance therefrom to two trees on opposite sides of the line, each of which trees you will mark with a blaze and notch facing the post; but on the margins of navigable water courses, or navigable lakes, you will mark the trees with the proper number of the fractional section, township, and range.

The best marking tools adapted to the purpose must be provided for marking neatly and *distinctly* all the letters and figures required to be made at corners; and the deputy is to have always at hand the necessary implements for keeping his marking irons in order; for which purpose a rat-tail file and a small whetstone will be found indispensable.

ESTABLISHING CORNER BOUNDARIES.

To procure the faithful execution of this portion of a surveyor's duty is a matter of the utmost importance. After a true coursing, and most exact measurements, the corner boundary is the consummation of the work, for which all the previous pains and expenditures have been incurred. If, therefore, the corner boundary be not perpetuated in a permanent and workmanlike manner, the *great aim* of the surveying service will not have been attained. A boundary corner, in a timbered country, is to be a *tree*, if one be found at the precise spot; and if not, a *post* is to be planted thereat; and the position of the corner post is to be indicated by trees adjacent, the angular bearings and distances of which from the corner are facts to be ascertained and registered in your field book. (See article, "Bearing trees.") [p. 109]

In a region where stone abounds the corner boundary will be a small *monument of stones* along side of a single marked stone for a township corner, and a single stone for all other corners.

In a region where timber is not near, and stone not found, the corner will be a *mound of earth*, of prescribed size, varying to suit the case.

The following are the different points for perpetuating corners, viz.:

1. For township boundaries, at intervals of every six miles.
2. For section boundaries, at intervals of every mile, or 80 chains.
3. For quarter section boundaries, at intervals of every half mile, or 40 chains. Exceptions, however, occur on east and west lines, as explained hereafter.

(The half quarter section boundary is not marked in the field, but is regarded by the law as a point intermediate between the half mile or quarter section corners. See act of 24th April, 1820, entitled "An act making further provision for the sale of the public lands," which act refers to the act of Congress passed on the 11th of February, 1805, entitled "An act concerning the mode of surveying the public lands of the United States," for the manner of ascertaining the corners and contents of half quarter sectons.)*

4. MEANDER CORNER POSTS are planted at all those points where the township or section lines intersect the banks of such rivers, bayous, lakes, or islands, as are by law directed to be meandered.

The course and distances on meandered navigable streams govern the calculations wherefrom are ascertained the true areas of the tracts of land (sections, quarter sections, &c.) known to the law as *fractional* and binding on such streams.

MANNER OF ESTABLISHING CORNERS BY MEANS OF POSTS.

Township, sectional, or mile corners, and quarter sectional or half mile corners, will be perpetuated by planting a post at the place of the corner, to be formed of the most durable wood of the forest at hand.

The posts must be set in the earth by digging a hole to admit them *two feet* deep, and must be very securely rammed in with earth, and also with stone, if any

---

* The subdivision of the half-quarter section into quarter-quarter sections is authorized by "An act supplementary to the several laws for the sale of the public lands," approved April 5, 1832.

be found at hand. The portion of the post which protrudes above the earth must be *squared* off sufficiently smooth to admit of receiving the marks thereon, to be made with appropriate marking irons, indicating what it stands for. Thus the sides of *township corner posts* should square at least *four* inches, (the post itself being *five* inches in diameter.) and must protrude *two feet* at least above the ground; the sides of *section corner posts* must square at least *three inches*, (the post itself being *four* inches in diameter,) and protrude *two feet* from the ground; and the *quarter section corner posts and meander corner posts* must be *three* inches *wide,* presenting *flattened* surfaces, and protruding *two feet* from the ground.

Where a township post is a corner common to *four* townships, it is to be set in the earth *diagonally,* thus:

<pre>
        N
    W - E
        S
</pre>

On each surface of the post is to be marked the number of the particular township, and its range, which it *faces.* Thus, if the post be a common boundary to four tounship—say *one* and *two,* south of the base line, of range *one,* west of the meridian; also to townships *one* and *two,* south of the base line, of range *two,* west of the meridian, it is to be marked thus.

<pre>
                (R. 1 W.)   (1 W.)
    From N. to E. (T. 1 S.) from E. to S. (2 S.)
                (S. 31   )   (6   )
                (2 W.)   (2 W.)
    From N. to W. (1 S.) from W. to S. (2 S.)
                (36   )   (1   )
</pre>

These marks are not only to be distinctly but *neatly* cut into the wood, at least the eighth of an inch deep; and to make them yet more *conspicuous* to the eye of the anxious explorer, the deputy must apply to all of them a *streak of red chalk.*

Section or mile posts, being corners of sections, and where such are common to *four* sections, are to be set *diagonally* in the earth, (in the manner provided for township corner posts;) and on each side of the squared surfaces (made smooth, as aforesaid, to receive the marks) is to be marked the appropriate *number* of the particular one of the *four sections,* respectively, which such side *faces;* also on one side thereof are to be *marked* the numbers of its *township* and *range;* and to make such marks yet more *conspicuous,* in manner aforesaid, a streak of *red chalk* is to be applied.

In every township, subdivided into thirty-six sections, there are twenty-five interior section corners, each of which will be *common* to *four* sections.

A quarter section, or half mile post, is to have no other mark on it than ¼ S., to indicate what it stands for.

NOTCHING CORNER POSTS.

Township corner posts, common to four townships, are to be notched with *six* notches on each of the four angles of the squared part set to the cardinal points.

All mile posts on *township lines* must have as many notches on them, on two opposite *angles* thereof, as they are miles distant from the township corners, respectively. Each of the posts at the corners of sections in the *interior* of a township must indicate, by a number of notches on each of its four corners directed to the cardinal points, the corresponding number of miles that it stands from the *outlines* of the township. The four sides of the post will indicate the number of the section they respectively *face*. Should a tree be found at the place of any corner, it will be marked and notched as aforesaid, and answer for the corner in lieu of a post, the kind of tree and its diameter being given in the field notes.

BEARING TREES.

The position of all corner posts, or corner trees, of whatever description, that may be established, is to be evidenced in the following manner, viz. From such post or tree the courses must be taken and the distances measured to two or more adjacent trees in opposite directions, as nearly as may be, and these called "bearing trees." Such are to be distinguished by a large *smooth blaze*, with a *notch* at its lower end, facing the corner, and in the blaze is to be marked the number of the *range, township*, and *section;* but at quarter section corners nothing but ¼ S. need be marked. The letters B.T. (bearing tree) are also to be marked upon a smaller blaze directly under the large one, and as near the ground as practicable.

At all township corners, and at all section corners, on range or township lines, *four* bearing trees are to be marked in this manner, one in each of the adjoining sections.

At interior section corners *four* trees, one to stand within each of the four sections to which such corner is common, are to be marked in manner aforesaid, if such be found.

A tree supplying the place of a corner post is to be marked in the manner directed for posts; but if such tree should be a beech, or other *smooth* bark tree, the marks may be made on the bark, and the tree notched.

From quarter section and meander corners two bearing trees are to be marked, one within each of the adjoining sections.

Where the requisite number of "bearing trees" is not to be found at convenient and suitable distances, such as are found are to be marked as herein directed; but in all such cases of deficiency in the number of bearing trees, (unless, indeed, the boundary itself be a *tree*,) a *quadrangular trench*, with side of *five* feet, and with the angles to the cardinal points must be spaded up outside the corner, as a centre, and the earth carefully thrown on the inside, so as to form a range of earth, which will become covered with grass, and present a small square elevation, which in aftertime will serve to mark, unmistakably, the spot of the corner.

CORNER STONES.

Where it is deemed best to use STONES for boundaries, in lieu of posts, you may at *any* corner, insert endwise into the ground, to the depth of 7 or 8 inches, a stone, the number of cubic inches in which shall not be less than the number contained in a stone 14 inches long, 12 inches wide, and 3 inches thick—equal to 504 cubic inches—the edges of which must be set north and south, on north and south lines, and east and west on east and west lines; the dimensions of each stone to be given in the field notes at the time of establishing the corner. The kind of stone should also be stated.

MARKING CORNER STONES.

Stones at township corners, common to four townships, must have *six* notches, cut with a pick or chisel on each edge or side towards the cardinal points; and where used as section corners on the range and township lines, or as section corners in the interior of a township, they will also be notched, to correspond with the directions given for notching posts similarly situated.

Posts or stones at township corners on the base and standard lines, and which are common to two townships on the north side thereof, will have *six* notches on each of the *west, north* and *east* sides or edges; and where such stones or posts are set for corners to two townships *south* of the base or standard, *six* notches will be cut on each of the west, *south*, and east sides or edges.

Stones, when used for quarter section corners, will have ¼ cut on them-on the west side on north and south lines, and on the north side on east and west lines.

MOUNDS.

Whenever bearing trees are not found, mounds of earth, or stone, are to be raised *around posts* on which corners are to be marked in the manner aforesaid. Wherever a mound of earth is adopted, the same will present a conical shape; but at its base, on the earth's surface a *quadrangular trench* will be dug; by the "trench" (heremeant) is to be understood a *spade deep* of earth thrown up from the four sides of the line, *outside* the trench, so as to form a *continuous elevation along its outer edge*. In mounds of earth, common to *four* townships or to *four* sections, they will present the *angles* of the quadrangular trench (*diagonally*) towards the cardinal points. In mounds, common only to *two* townships or *two* sections, the *sides* of the quadrangular trench will *face* the cardinal points. The sides of the quadrangular trench at the base of a township mound are to be *six* feet, the height of mound *three* feet.

At section, quarter section, and meander corners, the sides of the quadrangular trench at base of mounds are to be *five* feet, and the conical height *two and a half feet*.

Prior to piling up the earth to construct a mound, there is to be dug a spadeful or two of earth from the corner boundary point, and in the cavity so formed is to be deposited a *marked stone*, or a portion of *charcoal*, (the quantity whereof is to be noted in the field book;) or in lieu of charcoal or marked stone, a *charred stake* is to be driven twelve inches down into such centre point: either of those will be a *witness* for the future, and whichever is adopted, the fact is to be noted in the field book.

When mounds are formed of *earth*, the spot from which the earth is taken is called the *"pit"*, the centre of which ought to be, wherever practicable, at a uniform distance and in a uniform direction from the centre of the mound. There is to be a *"pit"* on *each* side of every mound, distant eighteen inches outside of the trench. The trench may be expected hereafter to be covered by tufts of grass, and thus to indicate the place of the mound, when the mound itself may have become obliterated by time or accident.

At meander corners the "pit" is to be directly on the line, *eight links* further from the water than the mound. Wherever necessity is found for deviating from these rules in respect to the "pits," the course and distance to each is to be stated in the field books.

Perpetuity in the mound is a great desideratum. In forming it with light alluvial soil, the surveyor may find it necessary to make due allowance for the future settling of the earth, and thus making the mound more elevated than would be necessary in a more compact and tenacious soil, and increasing the base of it. In so doing, the relative proportions between the township mound and other mounds is to be preserved as nearly as may be.

The earth is to be pressed down with the shovel during the process of piling it up. Mounds are to be *covered* with sod, grass side up, where sod is to be had: but, in forming a mound, *sod* is NEVER to be *wrought up* with the earth, because sod decays, and in the process of decomposing it will cause the mound to become porous, and therefore liable to premature destruction.

POSTS IN MOUNDS

must show above the top of the mound ten or twelve inches, and be notched and marked precisely as they would be for the same corner without the mound.

MOUND MEMORIALS.

Besides the *charcoal*, marked *stone* or *charred stake*, one or the other of which must be lodged in the earth at the point of the corner, the deputy surveyor is recommended to plant *midway* between each pit and the trench seeds of some tree, (those of fruit trees adapted to the climate being always to be preferred,) so that, in course of time, should such take root, a small clump of trees may possibly hereafter note the place of the corner. The facts of planting such seed, and the kind thereof, are matters to be truthfully noted in the field book.

WITNESS MOUNDS TO TOWNSHIP OR SECTION CORNERS.

If a township or section corner, in a situation where bearing or witness trees are not found within a reasonable distance therefrom, shall fall within a ravine, or in any other situation where the nature of the ground, or the circumstances of its locality, shall be such as may prevent, or prove unfavorable to, the erection of a mound, will perpetuate such corner by selecting in the immediate vicinity thereof a suitable plot of ground as a site for a bearing or *witness mound*, and erect thereon a mound of earth in the same manner and conditioned in every respect, with *charcoal, stone,* or *charred stake* deposited beneath, as before directed; and measure and state in your field book the distance and course from the position of the true corner of the bearing or witness mound so placed and erected.

DOUBLE CORNERS.

Such corners are to be nowhere except on the base and standard lines, whereon are to appear both the corners which mark the intersections of the lines which close thereon, and those from which the surveys start on the north. On these lines, and at the time of running the same, the township, section, and quarter section corners are to be planted, and each of these is a corner common to *two*, (whether township or section corners,) on the north side of the line, and must be so marked.

The corners which are established on the standard parallel, at the time of running it, are to be known as *"standard corners,"* and, in addition to all the *ordinary* marks, (as herein prescribed,) they will be marked with the letters S. C. Closing corners will be marked with the letters C. C. in addition to other marks.

The standard parallels are designed to be run in *advance* of the contiguous surveys on the south of them, but circumstances may exist which will *impede* or temporarily delay the *due* extension of the standard; and when, from uncontrollable causes, the *contiguous townships* must be surveyed, in advance of the time of extending the standard, in any such event it will become the duty of the deputy who shall afterwards survey any such standard to plant thereon the *double set* of corners, to wit; the standard corners, to be marked S. C., and the closing ones which are to be marked C. C.; and to make such measurements as may be necessary to connect the closing corners and complete the unfinished meridianal lines of such contiguous and prior surveys, on the principles herein set forth, under the different heads of "exterior or township lines," and of "diagram B."

You will recollect that the corners, (whether township or section corners,) which are *common* to *two*, (two townships or two sections,) are not to be planted *diagonally* like those which are common to *four*, but with the flat sides facing the cardinal points, and on which the marks and notches are made as usual. This, it will be perceived, will serve yet more fully to distinguish the standard parrallels from all other lines.

THE MEANDERING OF NAVIGABLE STREAMS.

1. Standing with the face looking *down* stream, the bank on the *left* hand is termed the "left bank," and that on the *right* hand the "right bank." These terms are to be universally used to distinguish the two banks of a river or stream.

2. Both banks of *navigable* rivers are to be meandered by taking the courses and distances of their sinuosities, and the same are to be entered in the field book.

At those points where either the township or section lines intersect the banks of a navigable stream, POSTS, or, where necessary, MOUNDS of *earth* or *stone*, are to be established at the time of running these lines. They are called "meander corners;" and in meandering you are to commence at one of those corners on the township line, coursing the banks, and measuring the distance of each course from your commencing corner to the next "meander corner," upon the same or another boundary of the same township, carefully noting your intersection with all intermediate meander corners. By the same method you are to meander the opposite bank of the same river.

The crossing distance *between* the MEANDER CORNERS on same line is to be ascertained by triangulation, in order that the river may be protracted with entire accuracy. The particulars to be given in the field notes.

3. You are also to meander, in manner aforesaid, all *lakes* and deep ponds of area of twenty-five acres and upwards; also navigable bayous; *shallow* ponds, readily to be drained, or likely to dry up, are not to be meandered.

You will notice all streams of water falling into the river, lake, or bayou you are surveying, stating the width of the same at their mouth; also all springs, noting the size thereof and depth, and whether the water be pure or mineral; also the head and mouth of all bayous; and all islands, rapids, and bars are to be noticed, with intersections to their upper and lower points to establish their exact situation. You will also note the elevation of the banks of rivers and streams, the heights of falls and cascades, and the length of rapids.

4. The precise relative position of islands, in a township made fractional by the river in which the same are situated, is to be determined trigonometrically —sighting to a flag or other fixed object on the island, from a special and carefully

measured base line, connected with the surveyed line, on or near the river bank, you are to form connexion between the meander corners on the river to points corresponding thereto, in direct line, on the bank of the island, and there establish the proper meander corners, and calculate the distance across.

5. In meandering lakes, ponds, or bayous, you are to commence at a meander corner upon the township line, and proceed as above directed for the banks of a navigable stream. But where a lake, pond, or bayou lies entirely within the township boundaries, you will commence at a meander corner established in subdividing, and from thence take the courses and distances of the entire margin of the same, noting the intersection with all the meander corners previously established thereon.

6. To meander a pond lying entirely within the boundaries of a section, you will run and measure *two* lines thereunto from the nearest section or quarter section corner on *opposite* sides of such pond, giving the courses of such lines. At *each* of the points where such lines shall intersect the margin of such pond, you will establish a *witness point*, by fixing a post in the ground, and taking bearings to any adjacent trees, or, if necessary, raising a mound.

The relative position of these points being thus definitely fixed in the section, the meandering will commence at one of them, and be continued to the other, noting the intersection, and thence to the beginning. The proceedings are to be fully entered in the field book.

7. In taking the connexion of an island with the main land, when there is no meander corner in line, opposite thereto, to sight from you will measure a special base from the meander corner nearest to such island, and from such base you will triangulate to some fixed point on the shore of the island, ascertain the distance across, and there establish a *special* meander corner, wherefrom you will commence to meander the island.

The field notes of meanders will be set forth in the body of the field book according to the dates when the work is performed, as illustrated in the specimen notes annexed. They are to state and describe particularly the meander corner from which they commenced, each one with which they close, and are to exhibit the meanders of each fractional section separately; following, and composing a part of such notes, will be given a description of the land, timber, depth of inundation to which the bottom is subject, and the banks, current, and bottom of the stream or body of water you are meandering.

9. No blazes or marks of any description are to be made on the lines meandered between the established corners, but the utmost care must be taken to pass no object of topography, or *change therein*, without giving a particular description thereof in its proper place in your meander notes.

OF FIELD BOOKS.

The FIELD NOTES afford the elements from which the plats and calculations in relation to the public surveys are made. They are the sources wherefrom the description and evidence of locations and boundaries are officially delineated and set forth. They therefore must be a faithful, distinct and minute record of everything officially done and observed by the surveyor and his assistants, pursuant to instructions, in relation to running, measuring, and marking lines, establishing boundary corners, &c; and present, so far as possible, a full and complete *topographical description* of the country surveyed, as to every matter of useful information, or likely to gratify public curiosity.

There will be sundry separate and distinct field books of surveys, as follows:

Field notes of the MERIDIAN AND BASE lines, showing the establishment of the *township, section*, or mile, and *quarter section* or half mile, boundary corners thereon; with the crossings of streams, ravines, hills, and mountains, character of soil, timber, minerals, &c.

Field notes of the "STANDARD PARALLELS, or correction lines," will show the establishment of the township, section, and quarter section corners, besides exhibiting the topography of the country on line, as required on the base and meridian lines.

Field notes of the EXTERIOR lines of TOWNSHIPS, showing the establishment of corners on lines, and the topography, as aforesaid.

Field notes of the SUBDIVISIONS of TOWNSHIPS into sections and quarter sections.

The field notes must in all cases be taken precisely in the order in which the work is done on the ground, and the *date* of each day's work must follow immediately after the notes thereof. The *variation of the needle* must always occupy a *separate line* preceding the notes of measurements on line.

The exhibition of every mile of surveying, whether on township or subdivisional lines, must be *complete in itself*, and be separated by a black line drawn across the paper.

The description of the surface, soil, minerals, timber, undergrowth, &c., on *each mile* of line, is to follow the notes of survey of such line, and not be mixed up with them.

No abbreviations of words are allowable, except of such words as are *constantly* occurring, such as "*sec.*" for "*section*," "*in. diam.*" for *inches diameter;* "*chs.*" for "*chains;*" "*lks.*" for "*links;*" "*dist.*" for "*distant*," etc. Proper names must never be abbreviated, however often their recurrence.

The nature of the subject-matter of the field-book is to form its title page, showing the State or Territory where such survey lies, by whom surveyed, and the dates of commencement and completion of the work. The second page is to contain the names and duties of assistants. Whenever a new assistant is employed, or the duties of any one of them are changed, such facts with the reasons therefor, are to be stated in an appropriate entry immediately preceding the notes taken under such changed arrangements. With the notes of the *exterior* lines of townships, the deputy is to submit a plat of the lines run, on a scale of two inches to the mile, on which are to be noted all the objects of topography on line necessary to illustrate the notes, viz: the distances on line at the crossings of streams, so far as such can be noted on the paper, and the direction of each by an arrowhead pointing downstream; also the intersection of line by prairies, marshes, swamps, ravines, ponds, lakes, hills, mountains, and all other matters indicated by the notes, to the fullest extent practicable.

With the instructions for making subdivisional surveys of townships into sections, the deputy will be furnished by the Surveyor-General with a diagram of the *exterior* lines of the townships to be subdivided, on the above scale, upon which are carefully to be laid down the measurements of each of the section lines on such boundaries whereon he is to close, the magnetic variation of each mile, and the particular description of each corner. "P. in M." signifies post in mound. And on such diagram the deputy who subdivides will make appropriate sketches of the various objects of topography as they occur on his lines, so as to exhibit not only the points on line at which the same occur, but also the direction and position of each between the lines, or within each section, so that every object of topography may be properly completed or connected in the showing.

These notes must be distinctly written out, in language precise and clear, and their figures, letters, words, and meaning are always to be unmistakable. No leaf is to be cut or mutilated, and none to be taken out, whereby suspicion might be created that the missing leaf contained matter which the deputy believed it to be his interest to conceal.

Summary of Objects and Data Required to be Noted

1. The precise length of every line run, noting all necessary offsets therefrom, with the reason and mode thereof.

2. The kind and diameter of all *"bearing trees,"* with the course and distance of the same from their respective corners; and the precise relative position of *witness corners* to the *true corners*.

3. The kind of materials, (earth or stone) of which *mounds* are constructed —the fact of their being conditioned according to instructions—with the course and distance of the "pits," from the center of the mound, where necessity exists for deviating from the *general* rule.

4. *Trees on line.* The name, diameter, and distance on line to all trees which it intersects.

5. Intersections by line of *land objects.* The distance at which the line first intersects and then leaves every *settlers claim and improvement;* prairie, river, creek or other "bottom"; or swamp, marsh, grove, and windfall, with the course of the same at both points of intersection; also the distances at which you begin to ascend, arrive at the top, begin to descend and reach the foot of all remarkable hills and ridges, with their courses, and estimated height, in feet, above the level land of the surrounding country, or above the bottom lands, ravines, or waters near which they are situated.

6. Intersections by line of *water objects.* All rivers, creeks, and smaller streams of water which the line crosses; the distance on line at the points of intersection, and their widths on line. In cases of navigable streams, their width will be ascertained between the meander corners, as set forth under the proper head.

7. *The land's Surface*—Whether level, rolling, broken, or hilly.

8. The *soil.*—Whether first, second, or third rate.

9. *Timber.*—The several kinds of timber and undergrowth, in the order in which they predominate.

10. *Bottom lands.*—To be described as wet or dry, and if the subject to inundation, state to what depth.

11. *Springs of water.*—Whether fresh, saline, or mineral, with the course of the stream flowing from them.

12. *Lakes and Ponds.*—Describing their banks and giving their height, and also the depth of water, and whether it be pure or stagnant.

13. *Improvements.*—Towns and villages; Indian towns and wigwams; houses or cabins; fields or other improvements; sugar tree groves, sugar camps; mill seats; forges ,and factories.

14. *Coal* banks or beds; *peat* or turf grounds; *minerals* and *ores*, with particular description of the same as to quality and extent, and all *diggings* therefor; also, *salt* springs and licks. All reliable information you can obtain respecting these objects whether they be on your immediate line or not, is to appear in the general description to be given at the end of the notes.

15. *Roads and trails*, with their directions, whence and whither.

16. Rapids, cataracts, cascades, or falls of water, with the height of their fall in feet.

17. Precipices, caves, sink-holes, ravines, stone quarries, ledges of rock, with the kind of stone they afford.

18. *Natural curiosities*, interesting fossils, petrifications, organic remains, etc.; also, all ancient works of art, such as mounds, fortifications, embankments, ditches, or objects of like nature.

19. The *variation* of the needle must be noted at all points or places on the lines where there is found any material *change* of variation, and the position of such points must be perfectly identified in the notes.

20. Besides the ordinary notes taken on line, (and which must always be written down on the spot, leaving nothing to be supplied by memory,) the deputy will subjoin, at the conclusion of his book, such further description or information touching any matter or thing connected with the township, (or other survey), which he may be able to afford, and may deem useful or necessary to be known—with a *general description* of the township in the *aggregate*, as respects the face of the country, its soil and geological features, timber minerals, water, etc.

Swamp Lands.

By the act of Congress, approved, September 28, 1850, swamp and overflowed lands, "unfit for cultivation," are granted to the State in which they are situated. In order clearly to define the quantity and locality of such lands, the field notes of surveys, in addition to the other objects of topography required to be noted, are to indicate the points at which you enter all lands which are evidently subject to such grant, and to show the distinctive character of the land so noted; whether it is a swamp or marsh, or otherwise subject to inundation to an extent that, without artificial means, would render it "unfit for cultivation." The depth of inundation is to be stated, as determined from indications on the trees where timber exists; and its frequency is to be set forth as accurately as may be, either from your own knowledge of the general character of the stream which overflows, or from reliable information to be obtained from others. The words "unfit for cultivation," are to be employed in addition to the usual phraseology in regard to entering or leaving such swamps, marshy or overflowed lands. It may be that sometimes the margin of bottom, swamp, or marsh, in which such uncultivable land exists, is not identical with the margin of the body of land "unfit for cultivation;" and in such cases a separate entry must be made for each, opposite the marginal distance at which they respectively occur.

But in case where lands are overflowed by *artificial* means (say by dams for milling, logging, or other purposes,) you are not officially to regard such overflow, but will continue your lines across the same without setting meander posts, stating particularly in the notes the depth of the water, and how the overflow was caused.

SPECIAL INSTRUCTION RESPECTING THE NOTING OF SETTLERS' CLAIMS IN OREGON, WASHINGTON, AND NEW MEXICO

The law requires that such claims should be laid down temporarily on the township plats, in order to do which, it is indispensably necessary to obtain, to some extent, connexions of these claims with the lines of survey. Under the head of "intersection by line of land objects," the deputy is required to note the *points* in line *whereat* it may be intersected by such claims; but, in addition thereto, there must be obtained at least *one angle* of each claim, with its course and distance either from the point of intersection, or from an established corner boundary, so that its connexion with the regular survey will be legally determined. If the settler's *dwelling* or barn is visible from line, the bearings thereof should be carefully taken from *two* points noted on line, and set forth in the feld notes.

AFFIDAVITS TO FIELD NOTES.

At the close of the notes and the *general description* is to follow an affidavit, a form for which is given; and to enable the deputy surveyor fully to understand and appreciate the responsibility under which he is acting, his attention is invited to the provisions of the second section of the act of Congress, approved August 8th, 1846, entitled "An act to equalize the compensation of the surveyors general of the public lands of the United States, and for other purposes," and which is as follows:

"Sec. 2. That the surveyors general of the public lands of the United States, in addition to the oath now authorized by law to be administered to deputies on their appointment to office, shall require each of their deputies, on the return of his surveys, to take and subscribe an oath or affirmation that those surveys have been faithfully and correctly executed according to law and the instructions of the surveyor general; and on satisfactory evidence being presented to any court of competent jurisdiction, that such surveys, or any part thereof, had not been thus executed, the deputy making such false oath or affirmation shall be deemed guilty of perjury, and shall suffer all the pains and penalties attached to that offence; and the district attorney of the United States for the time being, in whose district any such false erroneous, or fraudulent surveys shall have been executed, shall, upon the application of the proper surveyor general, immediately institute suit upon the bond of such deputy; and the institution of such suit shall act as a lien upon any property owned or held by such deputy, or his sureties, at the time such suit was instituted."

Following the "general description" of the township is to be "A list of the names of the individuals employed to assist in running, measuring and marking the lines and corners described in the foregoing field notes of township No. ——— of the BASE LINE of range No. ——— of the ——— MERIDIAN, showing the respective capacities in which they acted."

FORM OF OFFICIAL OATHS TO BE TAKEN PRIOR TO ENTERING UPON DUTY.

For a deputy surveyor.

I, A. B., having been appointed a deputy surveyor of the lands of the United

States in ———, do solemnly swear (or affirm) that I will well and faithfully, and to the best of my skill and ability, execute the duties confided to me pursuant to a contract with C. D., surveyor general of public lands in ———, bearing date the _____ day of _____, 185__, according to the laws of the United States and the instructions received from the said surveyor general.

(To be sworn and subscribed before a justice of the peace, or other officer authorized to administer oaths.)

For chairman.

I, E. F., do solemnly swear (or affirm) that I will faithfully execute the duties of chain carrier; that I will level the chain upon uneven ground, and plumb the tally pins, whether by sticking or dropping the same; that I will report the true distance to all notable objects, and the true length of all lines that I assist in measuring, to the best of my skill and ability.

(To be sworn and subscribed as above.)

For flagman or axeman.

I, G. H., do solemnly swear (or affirm) that I will well and truly perform the duties of ———, according to instructions given me, and to the best of my skill and ability.

(To be sworn and subscribed as above.)

Exteriors or Township Lines.

The principal meridian, the base line and the standard parallels having been first run, measured, and marked, and the corner boundaries thereon established, according to instructions, the process of running, measuring, and marking the exterior lines of townships will be as follows:

Townships situated north of the base line, and west of the principal Meridian.

Commencing at No. 1, (see figures on diagram A), being the southwest corner of township 1, north, range 1, west, as established on the base line, thence north, on a true meridian line, four hundred and eighty chains, establishing the section and quarter-section corners thereon, as per instructions, to No. 2, whereat establish the corner of townships 1 and 2, north, ranges 1 and 2, west; thence east, on a random or trial line, setting *temporary* section and quarter section stakes, to No. 3, where measure and note the distance at which the line intersects the eastern boundary, north or south of the true or established corner. Run and measure westward, on the true line, (taking care to note all the land and water crossings, etc., as per instructions,) to No. 4, which is identical with No. 2, establishing the section and quarter-section *permanent corners* on said line. Should it happen, however, that such random line falls short, or overruns in length, or intersects the eastern boundary of the township at more than three chains and fifty links distance from the *true corner* thereon, as compared with the corresponding boundary on the south, (either of which would indicate an important error in the surveying,) the lines must be *retraced*, even if found necessary to remeasure the meridianal boundaries of the township, (especially the western boundary,) so as to discover and correct the error; in doing which, the *true corners* must be established and marked, and the *false ones* destroyed and obliterated to prevent confusion in future; and *all the facts* must be distinctly set forth in the notes. Thence proceed in a similar manner from No. 4 to No. 5, No. 5 to No. 6, No. 6 to No. 7, and so on to No. 10, the southwest corner of T. 4 N.—R. 1 W. Thence north, still on a true meridian line, establishing the mile and half-mile corners until reaching the STANDARD PARALLEL of correction line; throwing the *excess* over, or *deficiency* under *four hundred* and *eighty chains*, on the *last* half-mile, according to law, and at the intersection establishing the "CLOSING CORNER," the distance of which *from* the standard corner must be measured and noted as required by the instructions. But should it ever so happen that some impassable barrier will have prevented or delayed the extension of the standard parallel along and above the field of present survey, then the deputy will plant, in place, the corner of the township, subject to correction thereafter, should such parallel be extended.

NORTH of the base line, and EAST of the principal meridian.

Commence at No. 1, being the *southeast* corner of T. 1 N.—R. 1 E., and proceed as with townships situated "north and west," except that the *random* or trial lines will be run and measured *west*, and the *true* lines east, throwing the excess over or deficiency under four hundred and eighty chains on the *west end* of the line, as required by law; wherefore the surveyor will commence his measurement with the length of the deficient or excessive half section boundary on the west of the township, and thus the remaining measurements will all be *even* miles and half-miles.

METHOD OF SUBDIVIDING

1. The first mile, both of the south and east boundaries of each township you are required to subdivide, is to be carefully traced and measured before you enter upon the subdivision thereof. This will enable you to observe any change that may have taken place in the magnetic variation, as it existed at the time of running the township lines, and will also enable you to compare your chaining with that upon the township lines.

2. Any discrepancy, arising either from a change in the magnetic variation or a difference in measurement, is to be carefully noted in the field notes.

3. After adjusting your compass to a variation which you have thus found will retrace the eastern boundary of the township, you will commence at the corner to sections 35 and 36, on the south boundary, and run a line due north, forty chains, to the quarter section corner which you are to establish between sections 35 and 36; continuing due north forty chains further, you will establish the corner to sections 25, 26, 35 and 36.

4. From the section corner last named, run a *random* line, without blazing, *due east*, for corner of sections 25 and 36, in east boundary, and at forty chains from the starting point set a post for *temporary* quarter section corner. If you intersect exactly at the corner, you will blaze your random line back, and establish it as the *true* line; but if your random line intersects the said east boundary, either north or south of said corner, you will measure the distance of such intersection, from which you will calculate a course that will run a *true* line back to the corner from which your random started. You will establish the *permanent* quarter section corner at a point equidistant from the two terminations of the *true* line.

5. From the corner of sections 25, 26, 35, 36, run due north between section 25 and 26, setting the quarter section post, as before, at forty chains, and at eighty chains establishing the corner of sections 23, 24, 25, 26. Then run a random *due east* from the corner of sections 24 and 25 in east boundary; setting temporary quarter section post at forty chains; correcting back, and establishing *permanent* quarter section corner at the equidistant point on the *true* line, in the manner directed on the line between section 25 and 36.

6. In this manner you will proceed with the survey of each successive section in the first tier, until you arrive at the north boundary of the township, which you will reach in running up a random line between sections 1 and 2. If this random line should not intersect at the corner established for section 1, 2, 35 and 36, upon the township line, you will note the distance that you fall east or west of the same, from which distance you will calculate a course that will run a true line south to the corner from which your random started. Where the closing corner is on the base or standard line, a deviation from the general rule is explained under the head of "Diagram B."

7. The first tier of sections being thus laid out and surveyed, you will return to the south boundary of the township, and from the corner of sections 34 and 35 commence and survey the second tier of sections in the same manner that you pursued in the survey of the first, closing at the section corners on the first tier.

8. In like manner proceed with the survey of each successive tier of sections, until you arrive at the fifth tier; and from each section corner which you establish upon this tier, you are to run random lines to the corresponding corners established upon the range line forming the western boundary of the township; setting, as you proceed, each *temporary* quarter section post at forty chains from the interior section corner, so as to throw the excess or deficiency of measurement on the extreme tier of quarter sections contiguous to the township boundary; and on returning, establish the *true* line, and establish thereon the *permanent* quarter section corner.

QUARTER SECTION CORNERS, both upon north and south and upon east and west lines, are to be established at a point *equidistant* from the corresponding section corners, *except* upon the lines closing on the north and west boundaries of the township, and in those situations the quarter section corners will always be established at precisely *forty* chains to the north or west (as the case may be) of the respective section corners from which those lines respectively *start*, by which procedure the excess or deficiency in the measurements will be thrown, according to law, on the extreme tier of quarter sections.

Every north and south section line, except those terminating in the north boundary of the township, is to be eighty chains in length. The east and west section lines, except those terminating on the west boundary of the township, are to be within one hundred links of eighty chains in length; and the north and south boundaries of any one section, except in the extreme western tier, are to be within one hundred links of equal length. The meanders within each fractional section, or between any two meander posts, or of a pond or island in the interior of a section, must close within one chain and fifty links.

DIAGRAM A [p. 100] illustrates the mode of laying off "township exteriors *north* of the BASE line, and EAST and WEST of the principal MERIDIAN, whether between the base and first standard, or between any two standards; and the same general principles will equally apply to townships south of the base line and east and west of the meridian and between any two standards *south*, where the distances between the base and first standard, and between the standards themselves, are five townships or thirty miles.

DIAGRAM B indicates the mode of laying off a TOWNSHIP into sections and quarter sections, and the accompanying set of the field notes (marked B) critically illustrates the mode and order of conducting the survey under every variety of circumstance shown by the topography on the diagram. In townships lying *south* of and contiguous to the base or to any standard parallel, the lines between the northern tier of sections will be run *north*, and to be made to close as *true* lines; quarter section corners will be set at forty chains, and section corners established at the intersection of such lines with the base or standard, (as the case may be,) and the distance is to be measured and entered in the field book to the nearest corner on such standard or base.

DIAGRAM C illustrates the mode of making mound, stake, or stone corner boundaries for townships, sections, and quarter sections. [See p. 170].

The mode and order of surveying the *exterior* boundaries of a township are illustrated by the specimen field notes marked A; and the mode and order of *subdividing* a township into sections and quarter sections are illustrated by the specimen field notes marked B. The attention of the deputy is particularly directed to these specimens, as indicating not only the method in which his work is to be conducted, but also the order, manner, language, &c., in which his field notes are required to be returned to the Surveyor General's office; and such specimens are to be deemed part of these instructions, and any *departure* from their details, without special authority, in cases where the circumstances are analogous in practice, *will be regarded as a violation of his contract and oath.*

The subdivisions of fractional sections into forty acre lots, (as near as may be,) are to be so laid down on the official township plat in *red* lines, as to admit of giving to each a specific designation, if possible, according to its relative position in the fractional section, as per examples afforded by diagram B, as well as by a number, in all cases where the lot cannot properly be designated as a quarter-quarter. Those fractional subdivision lots which are not susceptible of being described according to relative local position, are to be numbered in regular series No. 1 being (wherever practicable, and as a general rule) either the northeastern or the most easterly fractional lot, and proceeding from east to west and from west to east, alternately, to the end of the series; but such general rule is departed from under circumstances given as examples in fractional sections 4, 7, 19 and 30, where No. 1 is the interior lot of the northern and western tiers of the quarter sections to which there is a corresponding No. 2 given to the exterior lot, and the series of numbers is in continuation of the latter. The lots in the extreme northern and western tiers of quarter sections, containing either more or less than the regular quantity, are always to be numbered as per example. Interior lots in such extreme tiers are to be *twenty* chains wide, and the excess or deficiency of measurement is always to be thrown on the exterior lots; elsewhere, the assumed subdivisional corner will always be a point equidistant from the established corners.

The official township plat to be returned to the General Land Office is to show on its face, on the right hand margin, the meanders of navigable streams, islands, and lakes. Such details are wanted in the adjustment of the surveying accounts, but may be omitted in the copy of the township plat to be furnished to the district land office by the surveyor general. A suitable margin for *binding* is to be preserved on the left hand side of each plat. Each plat is to be certified with table annexed, according to the forms subjoined to "diagram B," and is to show the areas of public land, of private surveys, and of water, with the aggregate area as shown on the diagram.

Each township plat is to be prepared in *triplicate*: one for the General Land Office, one for the district office, and the third to be retained as the record in the office of the Surveyor General.

The original field books, each bearing the *written approval* of the Surveyor General, are to be substantially bound into volumes of suitable size, and retained in the surveyor general's office, and certified *transcripts* of such field books (to be of foolscap size) are to be prepared and forwarded, from time to time, to the General Land Office.

With the copy of each township plat furnished to a district land office, the surveyor general is required by law to furnish *descriptive notes* as to the character and quality of the soil and timber found on and in the vicinity of each surveyed line, and giving a description of each corner boundary.

Printed blank forms for such notes will be furnished by the General Land Office. The forms provide eighteen spaces for *meander corners*, which, in most cases, will be sufficient; but when the number shall exceed eighteen, the residue will have to be inserted on the face of the township plat, to be furnished to the register of the district land office. There is shown a series of meander corners on diagram B., viz: from No. 1 to No. 22, on the river and islands; 23 to 28 being on Island lake; 29 and 30 on Clear lake; and 31 and 32 on lake in section 26.

There is also a distinct series of numbers, 1 to 7, to designate corners of D. Reed's private survey, and to fractional sections, made such thereby: and the same series is continued from 8 to 14 inclusive, to designate corners to S. William's private survey, and to fractional sections made such thereby. These are numberings on the plat merely for the purpose of ready reference to the descriptions of such corners to be furnished to the registers.

The *letters* on "diagram B," at the "corners" on the township boundaries, are referred to in the descriptive notes to be furnished to the district land office, but are not required to be inserted on the official plat to be returned to the General Land Office.

The following chapter, on the subject of the variation of the magnetic needle, is extracted from the revised edition of the work on surveying by CHARLES DAVIES, L. L. D., a graduate of the Military Academy at West Point. The work itself will be a valuable acquisition to the deputy surveyor; and his attention is particularly invited to the following chapter, which sets forth the modes by which the variation may be ascertained.

VARIATION OF THE NEEDLE

1. The angle which the magnetic meridian makes the true meridian, at any

place on the surface of the earth, is called the *variation of the needle* at that place, and is east or west, according as the north end of the needle lies on the east or west side of the true meridian.

2. The variation is difference at different places, and even at the same place it does not remain constant for any length of time. The variation is ascertained by comparing the magnetic with the true meridian.

3. If we suppose a line to be traced through those points on the surface of the earth, where the needle points directly north, such a line is called the *line of no variation*. At all places lying on the east of this line, the variation of the needle is west; at all places lying on the west of it, the variation is east.

4. The public is much indebted to Professor Loomis for the valuable results of many observations and much scientific research on the dip and variation of the needle, contained in the 39th and 42d volumes of Silliman's Journal.

The variation at each place was ascertained for the year 1840; and by a comparison of previous observations and the application of known formulas, the annual motion, or change in variation, at each place, was also ascertained, and both are contained in the table which follows.

5. If the annual motion was correctly found, and continues uniform, the variation at any subsequent period can be ascertained by simply multiplying the annual motion of the number of years, and adding the product, in the algebraic sense, to the variation in 1840. It will be observed, that all variations west are designated by the plus sign; and all variations east, by the minus sign. The annual motions being all west, have all the plus sign.

6. Our first object will be to mark the line, as it was in 1840, of *no variation*. For this purpose we shall make a table of places lying near this line.

PLACES NEAR THE LINE OF NO VARIATION

Places	Latitude	Longitude	Variation	Annual Motion
A point	40° 53'	80° 13'	0° 00'	+4.4'
Cleveland, Ohio	41 31	81 45	−0 19	4.4
Detroit, Mich	42 24	82 58	−1 56	4
Mackinaw	45 51	84 41	−2 08	3.9
Marietta, Ohio	39 30	81 28	−1 24	4.3
Charlottesville, Va	39 02	78 30	+0 19	3.7
Charleston, S. C	32 42	80 04	−2 44	1.3

At the point whose latitude is 40° 53' longitude 80° 13', the variation of the needle was nothing in the year 1840, and the direction of the line of no variation, traced north, was N. 24° 35' west. The line of no variation, prolonged, passed a little to the east at Cleveland, in Ohio—the variation there being 19 minutes east. Detroit lay still further to the west of this line, the variation there being 1° 56' east; and Mackinaw still further to the west, as the variation at that place was 2° 08' east.

The course of the line of no variation, prolonged southerly, was S. 24° 35' E. Marietta, Ohio, was west of this line—the variation there being 1° 24' east. Charlottesville, in Virginia, was a little to the east of it—the variation there being 19' west; whilst Charleston, in South Carolina, was on the west—the variation there being 2° 44' east.

From these results, it will be easy to see about where the line of no variation is traced in our own country.

7. We shall give two additional tables:

PLACES WHERE THE VARIATION WAS WEST

Places	Latitude	Longitude	Variation	Annual Motion
Angle of Maine	48° 00'	67° 37'	+19° 30'	+8.8'
Waterville, Me.	44 27	69 32	12 36	5.7
Montreal	45 31	73 35	10 18	5.7
Keesville, N. Y.	44 28	73 32	8 51	5.3
Burlington, Vt.	44 27	73 10	9 27	5.3
Hanover, N. H.	43 42	72 14	9 20	5.2
Cambridge, Mass.	42 22	71 08	9 12	5
Hartford, Ct.	41 46	72 41	6 58	5
Newport, R. I.	41 28	71 21	7 45	5
Geneva, N. Y.	42 52	77 03	4 18	4.1
West Point	41 25	74 00	6 52	4
New York City	40 43	71 01	5 34	3.6
Philadelphia	39 57	75 11	4 08	3.2
Buffalo, N. Y.	42 53	79 06	1 37	4.1

PLACES WHERE THE VARIATION WAS EAST

Places	Latitude	Longitude	Variation	Annual Motion
Mouth of Columbia River	46° 12'	123° 30'	−21° 40'	Unknown
Jacksonville, Ill.	39 43	90 20	8 28	+2.5'
St. Louis, Mo.	38 37	90 17	8 37	2.3
Nashville, Tenn.	36 10	86 52	6 42	2
Louisiana, at.	29 40	94 00	8 41	1.4
Mobile, Ala.	30 42	86 16	7 05	1.4
Tuscaloosa, Ala.	33 12	87 43	7 26	1.6
Columbus, Geo.	32 28	85 11	5 28	2
Milledgeville, Geo.	33 07	83 24	5 07	2.4
Savannah, Geo.	32 05	81 12	4 13	2.7
Tallahassee, Fla.	30 26	84 27	5 03	1.8
Pensacola, Fla.	30 24	87 23	5 53	1.4
Logansport, Ind.	40 45	86 22	5 24	2.7
Cincinnati, Ohio	39 06	84 27	4 46	3.1

METHODS OF ASCERTAINING THE VARIATION

8. The best practical method of determining the true meridian of a place is by observing the north star. If this star were precisely at the point in which the axis of the earth, prolonged, pierces the heavens, then the intersection of the vertical plane passing through it and the place, with the surface of the earth, would be the true meridian. But the star being at a distance from the pole equal to 1° 30' nearly, it performs a revolution about the pole in a circle, the polar distance of which is 1° 30': the time of revolution is 23 h. and 56 min.

To the eye of an observer this star is continually in motion, and is due north but twice in 23 h. 56 min.; and is then said to be on the meridian. Now, when it departs from the meridian it apparently moves east or west for 5 h. and 59 m., and then returns to the meridian again. When at its greatest distance from the meridian, east or west, it is said to be at its greatest *eastern* or *western* elongation.

The following tables show the times of its greatest eastern and western elongations.

Eastern elongations.

Days	April	May	June	July	August	Sept.
	h. m.	h. m.	h. m.	h. m.	h. m.	h. m.
1	18 18	16 26	14 24	12 20	10 16	8 20
7	17 56	16 03	14 00	11 55	9 53	7 58
13	17 34	15 40	13 35	11 31	9 30	7 36
19	17 12	15 17	13 10	11 07	9 08	7 15
25	16 49	14 53	12 45	10 43	8 45	6 53

Western elongations.

Days	Oct.	Nov.	Dec	Jan.	Feb.	March
	h. m.	h. m.	h. m.	h. m.	h. m.	h. m.
1	18 18	16 22	14 02	12 02	9 50	8 01
7	17 56	15 59	13 53	11 36	9 26	7 38
13	17 34	15 35	13 27	11 10	9 02	7 16
19	17 12	15 10	13 00	10 44	8 39	6 54
25	16 49	14 45	12 34	10 18	8 16	6 33

The eastern elongations are put down from the first of April to the first of October; and the western from the first of October to the first of April; the time is computed from 12 at noon. The western elongations in the first case, and the eastern in the second, occurring in the daytime, cannot be used. Some of those put down are also invisible, occurring in the evening, before it is dark, or after daylight in the morning. In such case, if it be necessary to determine the meridian at that particular season of the year, let 5 h. and 59 m. be added to, or subtracted from, the time of greatest eastern or western elongation, and the observation be made at night, when the star is on the meridian.

9. The following table exhibits the angle which the meridian plane makes with the vertical plane passing through the pole-star, when at its greatest eastern or western elongation: such angle is called the *azimuth*. The mean angle only is put down, being calculated for the first of July of each year:

Azimuth table.

Year	Lat. 32° Azimuth	Lat. 34° Azimuth	Lat. 36° Azimuth	Lat. 38° Azimuth	Lat. 40° Azimuth	Lat. 42° Azimuth	Lat. 44° Azimuth
1851	1°45½'	1°48'	1°50½'	1°53½'	1°56¾'	2°00¼'	2°04¼'
1852	1°45'	1°47½'	1°50'	1°53'	1°56¼'	1°59¾'	2°03¾'
1853	1°44½'	1°47'	1°49¾'	1°52½'	1°55¾'	1°59¼'	2°03¼'
1854	1°44¼'	1°46½'	1°49¼'	1°52'	1°55¼'	1°59'	2°02¾'
1855	1°43¾'	1°46¼'	1°48¾'	1°51¾'	1°54¾'	1°58½'	2°02¼'
1856	1°43¼'	1°45¾'	1°48¼'	1°51¼'	1°54½'	1°58'	2°01¾'
1857	1°43'	1°45¼'	1°48'	1°50¾'	1°54'	1°57½'	2°01¼'
1858	1°42½'	1°44¾'	1°47½'	1°50¼'	1°53½'	1°57'	2°00¾'
1859	1°42'	1°44½'	1°47'	1°49¾'	1°53'	1°56½'	2°00¼'
1860	1°41¾'	1°44'	1°46½'	1°49½'	1°52½'	1°56'	2°00'
1861	1°41¼'	1°43¾'	1°46¼'	1°49'	1°52¼'	1°55¾'	1°59½'

The use of the above tables, in finding the true meridian, will soon appear.

To Find the True Meridian with the Theodolite.

10. Take a board, of about one foot square, paste white paper upon it, and perforate it through the center; the diameter of the hole being somewhat larger than the diameter of the telescope of the theodolite. Let this board be so fixed to a vertical staff as to slide up and down freely; and let a small piece of board, about three inches square, be nailed to the lower edge of it, for the purpose of holding a candle.

About twenty-five minutes before the time of the greatest eastern or western elongation of the pole-star, as shown by the tables of elongations, let the theodolite be placed at a convenient point and leveled. Let the board be placed about one foot in front of the theodolite, a lamp or candle placed on the shelf at its lower edge; and let the board be slipped up or down, until the pole-star can be seen through the hole. The light reflected from the paper will show the cross hairs in the telescope of the theodolite.

Then, let the vertical spider's line be brought exactly upon the pole-star, and, if it is an eastern elongation that is to be observed, and the star has not yet reached the most easterly point, it will move from the line toward the east, and the reverse when the elongation is west.

At the time the star attains its greatest elongation, it will appear to coincide with the vertical spider's line for some time, and then leave it, in the direction contrary to its former motion.

As the star moves toward the point of greatest elongation, the telescope must be continually directed to it, by means of the tangent-screw of the vernier plate; and when the star has attained its greatest elongation, great care should be taken that the instrument be not afterward moved.

Now, if it be not convenient to leave the instrument in its place until daylight, let a staff, with a candle or small lamp upon its upper extremity, be arranged at thirty or forty yards from the theodolite, and in the same vertical plane with the axis of the telescope. This is easily effected, by revolving the vertical limb about its horizontal axis without moving the vernier plate, and aligning the staff to coincide with the vertical hair. Then mark the point directly under the theodolite; the line passing through this point and the staff, makes an angle with the true meridian equal to the azimuth of the pole-star.

From the table of azimuths, take the azimuth corresponding to the year and nearest latitude. If the observed elongation was east, the true meridian lies on the west of the line which has been found, and makes with it an angle equal to the azimuth. If the elongation was west, the true meridian lies on the east of the line, and, in either case, laying off the azimuth angle with the theodolite, gives the true meridian.

To Find the True Meridian with the Compass.

11. 1. Drive two posts firmly into the ground, in a line nearly east and west; the uppermost ends, after the posts are driven, being about three feet above the surface, and the posts about four feet apart; then lay a plank, or piece of timber three or four inches in width, and smooth on the upper side, upon the posts, and let it be pinned or nailed, to hold it firmly.

2. Prepare a piece of board four or five inches square, and smooth on the under side. Let one of the compass-sights be placed at right angles to the upper surface of the board, and let a nail be driven through the board, so that it can be tacked to the timber resting on the posts.

3. At about twelve feet from the stakes, and in the direction of the pole-star, let a plumb be suspended from the top of an inclined stake or pole. The top of the pole should be of such a height that the pole star will appear about six inches below it; and the plumb should be swung in a vessel of water to prevent it from vibrating.

This being done, about twenty minutes before the time of elongation, place the board to which the compass-sight is fastened on the horizontal plank, and slide it east or west, until the aperture of the compass-sight, the plumb-line, and the star are brought into the same range. Then if the star depart from the plumb-line, move the compass-sight east or west along the timber, as the case may be, until the star shall attain its greatest elongation, when it will continue behind the plumb-line for several minutes, and will then recede from it in the direction contrary to its motion before it became stationary. Let the compass-sight be now fastened to the horizontal plank. During this observation it will be necessary to have the plumb-line lighted: this may be done by an assistant holding a candle near it.

Let now a staff, with a candle or lamp upon it, be placed at a distance of thirty or forty yards from the plumb-line, and in the same direction with it and the compass-sight. The line so determined makes, with the true meridian, an angle equal to the azimuth of the pole star; and from this line the variation of the needle is readily determined, even without tracing the true meridian on the ground.

Place the compass upon this line, turn the sights in the direction of it, and note the angle shown by the needle. Now, if the elongation at the time of observation was west, and the north end of the needle is on the west side of the line, the azimuth, plus the angle shown by the needle, is the true variation. But should the north end of the needle be found on the east side of the line, the elongation being west, the difference between the azimuth and the angle would show the variation, and the reverse when the elongation is east.

1. Elongation west, azimuth _____ 2° 04'
   North end of the needle on the west, angle _____ 4° 06'
   Variation _____ 6° 10' west.

2. Elongation west, azimuth _____ 1° 59'
   North end of the needle on the east, angle _____ 4° 50'
   Variation _____ 2° 51' east.

3. Elongation east, azimuth _____ 2° 05'
   North end of the needle on the west, angle _____ 8° 30'
   Variation _____ 6° 25' west.

4. Elongation east, azimuth _____ 1° 57'
   North end of the needle on the east, angle _____ 8° 40'
   Variation _____ 10° 37' east.

REMARK I.—The variation at West Point, in September, 1835, was 6° 32' west.

REMARK II.—The variation of the needle should always be noted on every survey made with the compass, and then if the land be surveyed at a future time, the old lines can always be re-run.

12. It has been found by observation, that heat and cold sensibly affect the magnetic needle, and that the same needle will at the same place indicate different lines at different hours of the day.

If the magnetic meridian be observed early in the morning, and again at different hours of the day, it will be found that the needle will continue to recede from the meridian as the day advances, until about the time of the highest temperature, when it will begin to return, and at evening will make the same line as in the morning. This change is called the *diurnal variation*, and varies, during the summer season, from one-fourth to one-fifth of a degree.

13. A very near approximation to a true meridian, and consequently to the variation, may be had, by remembering that the pole star very nearly reaches the true meridian, when it is in the same vertical plane with the star Alioth in the tail of the Great Bear, which lies nearest the four stars forming the quadrilateral.

The vertical position can be ascertained by means of a plumb-line. To see the spider's lines in the field of the telescope at the same time with the star, a faint light should be placed near the object-glass. When the plumb-line, the star Alioth, and the north star, fall on the vertical spider's line, the horizontal limb is firmly clamped, and the telescope brought down to the horizon; a light, seen through a small aperture in a board, and held at some distance by an assistant, is then moved according to signals, until it is covered by the intersection of the spider's lines. A picket driven into the ground, under the light, serves to mark the meridian line for reference by day, when the angle formed by it and the magnetic meridian may be measured.

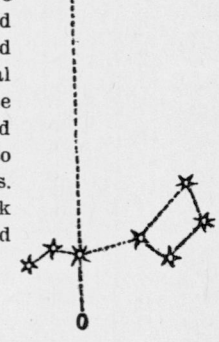

INDEX.

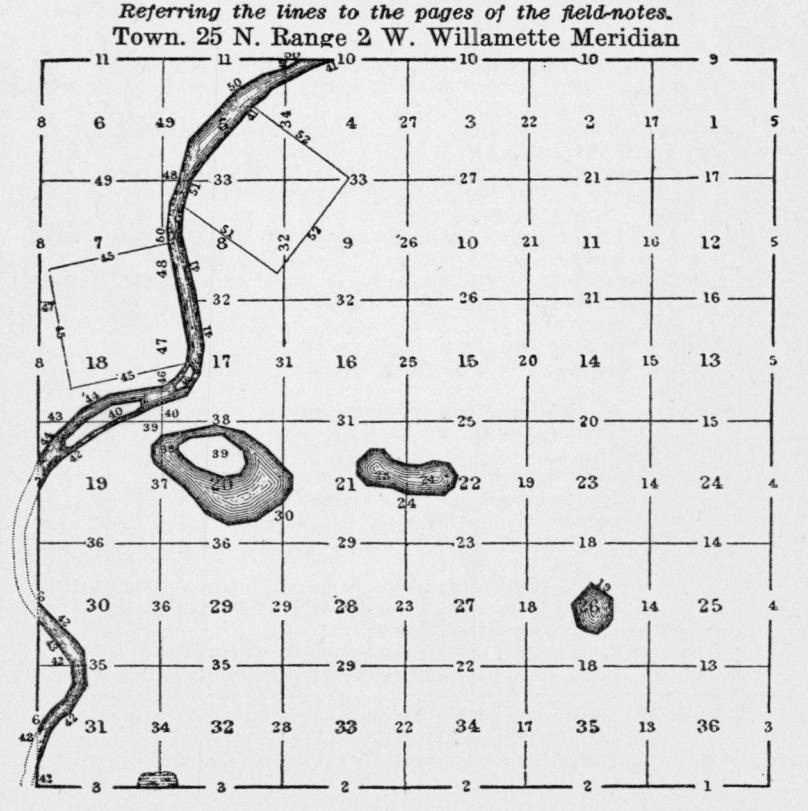

Referring the lines to the pages of the field-notes.
Town. 25 N. Range 2 W. Willamette Meridian

GENERAL INSTRUCTIONS OF 1855 129

A.

FIELD-NOTES OF THE SURVEY OF THE EXTERIOR BOUNDARIES OF TOWNSHIP 25 NORTH, OF RANGE 2 WEST, OF THE WILLAMETTE MERIDIAN, IN THE TERRITORY OF OREGON, BY ROBERT ACRES, DEPUTY SURVEYOR, UNDER HIS CONTRACT NO. 1, BEARING DATE THE 2D DAY OF JANUARY, 1854.

South boundary, T. 25 N., R. 2 W., Willamette meridian.

Chains.	
	Begin at the post, the established corner to townships 24 and 25 north, ranges 2 and 3 west. The witness trees all standing, and agree with the description furnished me by the office, viz:
	A black oak, 20 in. dia., N. 37 E. 27 links;
	A bur oak, 24 in. dia., N. 43 W 35 links;
	A maple, 18 in. dia., S. 27 W. 39 links;
	A white oak, 15 in. dia., S. 47 E. 41 links.
	East, on a random line on the south boundaries of sections 31, 32, 33, 34, 35, and 36.
	Variation by Burt's improved solar compass, 18° 41' E.,
	I set temporary half-mile and mile posts at every 40 and 80 chains; and at 5 miles 74 chains 53 links, to a point 2 chains and 20 links north of the corner to townships 24 and 25 north, ranges 1 and 2 W., (Therefore the correction will be 5 chains 47 links *west* and 37 links *south* per mile.)
	I find the corner post standing, and the witness trees to agree with the description furnished me by the surveyor general's office, viz:
	A bur oak, 17 in. dia., bears N. 44 E. 31 links;
	A white oak, 16 in. dia., N. 26 W. 21 links;
	A lynn, 20 in. dia., S. 42 W. 15 links;
	A black oak, 24 in. dia., S. 27 E. 14 links.
	From the corner to townships 24 and 25 N., ranges 1 and 2 west, I run at a variation of 18° 25' east)
	West, on a *true* line along the south boundary of section 36,
40.00	Set a post for quarter-section corner, from which
	A beech, 24 in. dia., bears N. 11 E., 38 links dist.;
	A beech, 9 in. dia., bears S. 9 E., 17 links dist.
62.50	A brook, 6 links wide, runs north.
80.00	Set a post for corner to sections 35 and 36, 1 and 2, from which
	A beech, 9 in. dia., bears N. 22 E., 16 links dist.;
	A beech, 8 in. dia., bears N. 19 W., 14 links dist.;
	A white oak, 10 in. dia., bears S. 52 W., 7 links dist.;
	A black oak, 14 in. dia., bears S. 46 E., 8 links dist.
	Land level, good soil, fit for cultivation.
	Timber, beech; various kinds of oak, ash, and hickory.
	West, on a *true* line along the south boundary of section 35, Variation 18° 25' east,
40.00	Set a post for quarter-section corner, from which
	A beech, 8 in. dia., bears N. 20 E., 8 links dist.
	No other tree convenient; made trench around post.
65.00	Begin to ascend a moderate hill; bears N. and S.
80.00	Set a post with trench for corner of sections 34 and 35, 2 and 3, from which
	A beech, 10 in. dia., bears N. 56 W., 9 links dist.;
	A beech, 10 in. dia., bears S. 51 E., 13 links dist.
	No other trees convenient to mark.
	Land level, or gently rolling, and good for farming.
	Timber, beech, oak, ash, and hickory; some walnut and poplar.
	West, on a *true* line along the south boundary of section 34, Variation 18° 25' east,
40.00	Set a quarter-section post with trench, from which

South boundary, T. 25 N., R. 2 W., Willamette meridian—Continued.

Chains.	

80.00	A black oak, 10 in. dia., bears N. 2 E., 635 links dist.
	No other tree convenient to mark.
	To point for corner of sections 33, 34, 3 and 4,
	Drove charred stakes, raised mounds with trenches, as per **instructions**, from which
	    A bur oak, 16 in. dia., bears N. 31 E. 344 links; and
	    A hickory, 12 in. dia., bears S. 43 W. 231 links.
	No other trees convenient to mark.
	Land level, rich, and good for farming.
	Timber, some scattering oak and walnut.

	West, on a *true* line along the south boundary of section 33, Variation 18° 25' east,
37.51	A black oak, 24 in. dia.

40.00	Set a post for quarter-section corner, from which
	    A black oak, 18 in. dia., bears N. 25 E., 32 links dist.;
	    A white oak, 15 in. dia., bears N. 43 W., 22 links dist.

62.00	To foot of steep hill, bears N. E. and S. W.

80.00	Set a post for corner to sections 32, 33, 4 and 5, from which
	    A white oak, 15 in. dia., bears N. 23 E., 27 links dist.:
	    A black oak, 20 in. dia., bears N. 82 W., 75 links dist.:
	    A bur oak, 20 in. dia., bears S. 37 W., 92 links dist.
	    A white oak, 24 in. dia., bears S. 26 E., 42 links dist.
	Land gently rolling; good rich land for farming.
	Timber, black and white oak, hickory, and ash.

	West, on a *true* line along the south boundary of section 32. Variation 18° 25' east.
37.50	A creek, 20 links wide, runs north.

40.00	Set a granite stone, 14 in. long, 10 in. wide, and 4 in. thick, for quarter-section corner, from which
	    A maple, 20 in. dia., bears N. 41 E., 25 links dist.:
	    A birch, 24 in. dia., bears N. 35 W., 22 links dist.

76.00	To S. E. edge of swamp. As it is impossible to establish *permanently* the corner to sections 31, 32, 5, and 6 in the swamp, I therefore at this point, 400 chains east of the true point for said section cor., raise a witness mound with trench, as per instructions, from which A black oak, 20 in. dia., bears N. 51 E. 115 links.
80.00	A point in deep swamp for corner to sections 31, 32, 5, and 6. Land, rich bottom; *west* of creek part wet; *east* of creek good for farming. Timber, good; oak, hickory, and walnut.
	West, on a *true* line along the south boundary of section 31. Variation 18° 25' east.
11.00	Leave swamp and rise bluff 30 feet high; bears N. and S.

40.00	Set post for quarter-section corner, from which
	    A sugar tree, 27 in. dia., bears S. 81 W., 42 links dist.:
	    A beech, 24 in. dia., bears S. 71 E. 24.

54.00	Foot of rocky bluff, 30 feet high; bears N. E. and S. W.
57.50	A spring branch comes out at the foot of the bluff 5 links wide; runs N. W. into swamp.
61.00	Enter swamp; bears N. and S.
70.00	Leave swamp; bears N. S. The swamp contains about 15 acres, the greater part in section 31.
74.73	The corner to townships 24 and 25 N., ranges 2 and 3 W. Land, except the swamp, rolling, good, rich soil. Timber, sugar tree, beech, and maple. *January* 25, 1854.

GENERAL INSTRUCTIONS OF 1855 131

Between ranges 1 and 2 W., T. 25 N., Willamette meridian.

Chains.	
	Between ranges 1 and 2 west, T. 25 N., Willamette meridian. From the corner to townships 24 and 25 N., ranges 1 and 2 W., I run North, along the east boundary of section 36. Variation 17° 51′ E.,
1	A brook 5 links wide, runs N. W.
18.00	To foot of hill, bearing N. W. and S. E.
20.00	To rocky bluff 50 feet high, bears N. W. and S. E.
40.00	Set a post for quarter-section corner, from which A beech 13 in. dia., bears N. 36 E., 22 links dist.; A poplar, 20 in. dia., bears S. 39 E., 42 links dist.
55.00	To top of rocky bluff 40 feet high; bears N. W. and S. E.
57.00	To foot of bluff, enter level, rich land.
72.50	A brook 10 links wide, runs N. W.
80.00	Set a post for corner to sections 25, 36, 30, and 31, from which A birch, 24 in. dia., bears N. 20 E., 49 links dist.; A sugar tree, 12 in. dia., bears N. 81 W., 25 links dist.; A white oak, 9 in. dia., bears S. 40 W., 60 links dist.; A poplar, 15 in. dia., bears S. 38 E., 12 links dist. Land, north and south parts rich and good for farming; middle part broken, 3d rate. Timber, beech, sugar tree, poplar, and white oak.
	North, on the east boundary of section 25, Variation 18° east,
5.51	A maple, 20 in. dia.
6.00	To foot of hill, rises moderately; bears E. and N. W.
40.00	Set quarter-section stone, (a rose quartz,) 15 inches long, 12 inches wide, and 3 inches thick, (on steep side hill, slopes west,) from which A poplar, 40 in. dia., bears N. 40 W., 10 links dist.; A beech, 9 in. dia., bears S. 42 W., 11 links dist.
73.21	A white oak, 20 in. dia.
80.00	Set a post for corner of sections 24, 25, 19, and 30, from which A beech, 20 in. dia., bears N. 64 E., 41 links dist.; A white oak, 10 in. dia., bears N. 30 W., 13 links dist.; A beech, 12 in. dia., bears S. 32 W., 26 links dist.; A white oak, 11 in. dia., bears S. 34 E., 48 links dist. Land rolling; good soil; nearly 1st rate. Timber, sugar tree, beech, walnut, elm, and white oak.
	North, on the east boundary of section 24, Variation 17° 55′ east,
21.17	A white walnut, 20 in. dia.
40.00	Set a quarter-section post, from which A buckeye, 14 in. dia., bears N. 39 E., 27 links dist.; A buckeye, 10 in. dia., bears S. 48 W., 6 links dist.
44.00	The road (at the foot of the bluff) from Williamsburg to Astoria, bears east and west
49.00	Elk Creek, 150 links wide, gentle current, runs west.
57.10	A brook, 10 links wide, runs S. W.
59.67	A black oak, 24 in. dia.
65.50	Leave creek bottom and enter upland, bears E. and W.
80.00	Set a limestone, 16 in. long, 14 wide, and 3 in. thick, for corner to sections 13, 24, 18, and 19, from which A beech, 12 in. dia., bears N. 30 E., 50 links dist.; A walnut, 9 in. dia., bears N. 18 W., 29 links dist.; A walnut, 8 in. dia., bears S. 8 W., 51 links dist.; A beech, 6 in. dia., bears S. 20 E., 40 links dist. Land, except creek bottom, rolling; good rich soil. The bottom dry and rich, not subject to inundation. Timber, good: walnut, beech, maple, ash, and hickory.

Between ranges 1 and 2 W., T. 25 N., Willamette meridian—Continued.

Chains.	
	North, on the east boundary of section 13, Variation 17° 55' east,
14.00	A white oak, 24 in. dia.
21.00	Enter high, broken ridges, bearing east and N. W.

40.00	Set a post for quarter-section corner, from which
	    A cherry, 10 in. dia., bears N. 35 W., 2 links dist.;
	    A cherry, 10 in. dia., bears S. 52 E., 21 links dist.

43.71	A bur oak, 30 in. dia.

80.00	Set a post for corner to sections 12, 13, 7 and 18, from which
	    A hickory, 15 in. dia., bears N. 40 E., 14 links dist.;
	    A hickory, 20 in. dia., bears N. 39 W., 38 links dist.;
	    A beech, 12 in. dia., bears S. 36 W., 16 links dist.;
	    A sugar tree, 10 in. dia., bears S. 42 E., 23 links dist.
	Land (except 21.00 chains, south part) high, broken, and mountainous.
	Timber, beech, hickory, sugar tree, and blackjack.

	North, on the east boundary of section 12, Variation 17° 55' east,
7.26	A black oak, 24 in. dia.

40.00	Set a post for quarter-section corner, from which
	    A white ash, 10 in. dia., bears N. 35 W., 15 links dist.;
	    An elm, 10 in. dia., bears S. 83 E., 2 links dist.

68.00	The foot of the mountain bears east and N. W.

80.00	Set a post on the top of eastern extremity of mountain, 300 feet high, for corner to sections 1, 12, 6 and 7, from which
	    An elm, 12 in. dia., bears N. 46 E., 30 links dist.;
	    A beech, 10 in. dia., bears N. 40 W., 28 links dist.;
	    A hickory, 10 in. dia., bears S. 55 W., 40 links dist.;
	    A beech, 10 in. dia., bears S. 40 E., 6 links dist.
	Land mountainous and broken.
	Timber, hickory, white oak, black oak, beech, and ash.

	North, on the east boundary of section 1, Variation 17° 55' east,
9.00	The foot of mountain bears east and west,
25.37	A white oak, 16 in. dia.

40.00	Set a post, in deep ravine bearing S. W., for quarter-section corner, from which
	    A poplar, 9 in. dia., bears N. 76 E., 7 links dist.;
	    A sugar tree, 9 in. dia., bears S. 22 E., 15 links dist.

44.00	Leave timber and enter prairie; bears E. and N. W.
80.00	To a point for corner to townships 25 and 26 N., ranges 1 and 2 W. Drove charred stake, and raised a mound with trench, as per instructions, and planted N. W. 4 chestnuts, S. W. 2 hickory nuts, N .E. 4 cherry stones, and S. E. 4 white-oak acorns. Land, south of prairie, mountainous and broken; prairie good for farming. Timber, sugar tree, cedar, and pine.

January 26, 1854.

	From the corner to townships 24 and 25 N., ranges 2 and 3 west, I run North, on the range line between sections 31 and 36, Variation 18° 56' east,

8.56	Set a post on the left bank of Chickeeles River for corner to fractional sections 31 and 36, from which
	    A hackberry, 11 in. dia., bears N. 50 E., 11 links dist.;
	    A sycamore, 60 in. dia., bears S. 15 W., 24 links dist.

GENERAL INSTRUCTIONS OF 1855 133

Between ranges 2 and 3 W., T. 25 N., Willamette meridian—Continued.

Chains.	
	I now cause a flag to be set on the *right* bank of the river, and in the line between sections 31 and 36. I now cross the river, and from a point on the right bank thereof, *west* of the corner just established on the left bank, I run *north*, on an offset line, 25 chains and 94 links, to a point 8 chains and 56 links *west* of the flag. I now set a post, in the place of the flag, for corner to fractional sections 31 and 36, from which
	A beech, 10 in. dia., bears N. 2 E., 12 links dist.;
	A black oak, 12 in. dia., bears N. 80 W., 16 links dist.
34.50	The corner above described.
40.00	Set a post for quarter-section corner, from which
	A bur oak, 20 in. dia., bears N. 37 E., 26 links dist.;
	A black oak, 24 in. dia., bears S. 75 W., 21 links dist.
43.41	A black walnut, 30 in. dia.
80.00	Set a post for corner to sections 30, 31, 25 and 36, from which
	A beech, 14 in. dia., bears N. 20 E., 14 links dist.;
	A hickory, 9 in. dia., bears N. 25 W., 12 links dist.;
	A beech, 16 in. dia., bears S. 40 W., 16 links dist.;
	A white oak, 10 in. dia., bears S. 44 E., 20 links dist.
	Land level; rich bottom; not subject to inundation.
	Timber, white and black oak, beech, hickory, and ash.
	North, between sections 25 and 30, Variation 18° 50′ east,
27.73	Set a post, for corner to fractional sections 25 and 30, on the right bank of Chickeeles River, a navigable stream, which here runs S. E., from which
	A willow, 6 in. dia., bears S. 37 W., 55 links dist.;
	A maple, 20 in. dia., bears S. 30 E., 11 links dist.
	I now cause a flag to be set on the left bank of the river, and in the line between sections 25 and 30. From the above corner I run west **3.33** chains, to a point from which the flag bears N. 16° 30′ E., which gives for the distance across the river on the line 11.27 chains; to which add 27.73, makes
39.00	To the flag on the bank. I here set a post for corner to fractional sections 25 and 30, from which
	A hickory, 8 in. dia., bears N. 44 E., 17 links dist.;
	A white oak, 8 in. dia., bears N. 15 W., 8 links dist.
40.00	Set a post for quarter-section corner, from which
	A hickory, 9 in. dia., bears N. 16 E., 16 links dist.;
	A buckeye, 10 in. dia., bears S. 16 E., 18 links dist.
43.71	A hickory, 24 in. dia.
80.00	Set a post for corner to sections 19, 30, 24, 25, from which
	An elm, 6 in. dia., bears N. 82 E., 25 links dist.;
	A sugar tree, 14 in. dia., bears N. 49 W., 4 links, dist.;
	An elm, 9 in. dia., bears S. 42 W., 30 links dist.;
	A sugar tree, 10 in. dia., bears S. 55 E., 45 links dist.
	Land good; rich bottom; 1st rate.
	Timber, hickory, elm, buckeye, sugar tree, and ash.
	North, between sections 19 and 24, Variation 18° 50′ east,
32.50	A hickory, 20 in. dia., on the left bank of Chickeeles River, marks it for corner to fractional sections 19 and 24, from which
	A hackberry, 20 in. diam., bears S. 13 W., 27 links dist.;
	A black oak, 24 in. dia., bears S. 27 E., 31 links dist.

Between ranges 2 and 3 W., T. 25 N., Willamette meridian—Continued.

Chains.	
	I now cause a flag to be set on the right bank of the river, and in the line between sections 19 and 24, and from the corner run a *base* east 5.90 chains, to a point from which the flag bears N. 17 W.; continue the base east to a point 9.00 chains *east* of the corner of the river bank, from which the flag bears N. 25° 15′ W., which gives, by calculation, as the mean result of the two observations, for the distance across the river, on the line between sections 19 and 24, 19.30 chains, to which add 32.50 chains, the distance to the river, makes
51.80	To the flag on the right bank of the river. I here set a post for corner to fractional sections 19 and 24, from which
	A beech, 12 in. dia., bears N. 24 E. 39 links dist.;
	A beech, 14 in. dia., bears S. 55 W., 120 links dist.
	NOTE.—The point for quarter-section corner falling in the river, it cannot, therefore be established.
55.74	A black oak, 30 inches diameter.
80.00	Set a post for corner to sections 18, 19, 13, and 24, from which
	A white oak, 18 in. dia., bears N. 55 E. 24 links dist.;
	A white oak, 17 in. dia., bears N. 64 W., 18 links dist.;
	A red oak, 27 in. dia., bears S. 26 W., 20 links dist.;
	A red oak, 15 in. dia., bears S. 29 E., 40 links dist.
	Land good; rich bottom; not subject to inundation.
	Timber, various kinds of oak, beech, hickory, and ash; undergrowth, same and vines.
	North, between sections 13 and 18,
	Variations 18° 53′ east,
5.00	Leave bottom and enter upland; bears N. E. and S. W.
21.88	A red oak, 20 in. dia.
38.60	A white oak, 24 in. dia.
40.00	Set a post for quarter-section corner, from which
	A white oak, 22 in. dia., bears N. 27 W., 27 links dist.;
	A white oak, 23 in. dia., bears S. 28 E., 92 links dist.
46.50	A road from Williamsburg bears east and west.
68.37	A black walnut, 21 in. dia.
80.00	Set a post for corner to sections 7, 18, 12, and 13, from which
	A white oak, 12 in. dia., bears N. 55 E. 68 links dist.;
	A black oak, 8 in. dia., bears N. 53 W., 40 links dist.;
	A black oak, 16 in. dia., bears S. 40 W., 55 links dist.;
	A red oak, 10 in. dia., bears S. 44 E., 50 links dist.
	Land rolling, and next the bottom broken; soil 2d rate.
	Timber good; various kinds of oak and hickory.
	North, between sections 7 and 12,
	Variation 18° 53′ east,
15.18	A white oak, 15 in. dia.
30.26	A white oak, 21 in. dia.
40.00	Set a post for quarter-section corner, from which
	A white oak, 12 in. dia., bears S. 13 W., 60 links dist.;
	A white oak, 15 in. dia., bears S. 35 E., 55 links dist.
68.37	A black walnut, 21 in. dia.
80.00	Set a post for corner to section 6, 7, 1, 12, from which
	A white oak, 17 in. dia., bears N. 58 E., 60 links dist.;
	A white oak, 18 in. dia., bears N. 54 W., 51 links dist.;
	A white oak, 18 in. dia., bears S. 51 W., 20 links dist.;
	A hickory, 14 in. dia., bears S. 64 E., 42 links dist.
	Land gently rolling; 2d rate.
	Timber, oak and hickory; undergrowth, oak and hazel.

Between ranges 2 and 3 W., T. 25 N., Willamette meridian—Continued.

Chains.	
	North, between sections 1 and 6, Variation 18° 53′ east,
3.00	Enter *stony* barrens; timber scattering; bears E. and W.
25.31	A blackjack, 12 in. dia.

40.00	Set a quartz stone, 13 in. long, 12 in. wide, and 4 in. thick, for quarter-section corner, with trench, as per instructions, from which
	     A blackjack, 20 in. dia., bears S. 44 E., 95 links dist.
	     No other tree convenient to mark.

45.00	Leave *stony* barrens; bears E. and W.
61.11	A hickory, 10 in. dia. Here leave timber and enter prairie, bearing W. and N. E.
80.00	Set a granite stone 18 in. long, 12 in. wide, and 6 in. thick, for corner to townships 25 and 26 north, ranges 2 and 3 west; raise a stone mound, with trench, as per instructions. Land broken and stony; too poor for cultivation. Timber, scattering and poor; blackjack and hickory. *January* 27, 1851.
	From the corner to townships 25 and 26 N., ranges 2 and 3 west, I run East, on a *random* line between said townships, the variation of my compass being 18° 41′ E., I set temporary half-mile and mile posts at 40.00 and 80.00 chains. At 160.09 intersected the right bank of Chickeeles River, a navigable stream, where set a temporary post; obtain the distance across the river on the line by causing my flag to be set on the left bank of the river, in said line. From the temporary post on the right bank, I run north, 7 chains 63 links to a point, thence east, on an offset line, and at 30.00 chains, a point north of the flag standing on the left bank of the river, set a temporary post in the place of the flag. I find the township line to be 5 miles 76 chains 53 links, and the falling to be 25 links north of the township corner. The correction for the true line will therefore be 3 chains 47 links west and 4.2 links south per mile.
	From the corner to townships 25 and 26 north, ranges 1 and 2 west, I run West, on a *true* line between sections 1 and 36, Variation 18° 39′ east,
20.00	Leave prairie and enter scattering timber; bears N. and S.

40.00	Set a post for quarter-section corner, from which
	     A beech, 24 in. dia., bears N. 11 E., 38 links dist.;
	     A beech, 9 in. dia., bears S. 9 W., 19 links dist.

43.71	A black walnut, 30 in. dia.

80.00	Set a sandstone, 16 in. long, 12 in. wide, and 3 in. thick, for corner to sections 1, 2, 35, and 36, from which
	     A buckeye, 9 in. dia., bears N. 66 E., 15 links dist.;
	     An elm, 20 in. dia., bears N. 4 W., 10 links dist.;
	     An elm, 36 in. dia., bears S. 65 W., 8 links dist.;
	     A buckeye, 10 in. dia., bears S. 40 E., 20 links dist.
	 Land level, or gently rolling and 1st rate.
	 Timber, scattering next the prairies; elm, buckeye, beech, walnut, and oak.

	West, on a *true* line between sections 2 and 35, Variation 18° 39′ east,
27.13	A white oak, 24 in. dia.
40.00	Set a post for quarter-section corner, from which A white oak, 9 in. dia., bears N. 24 E., 28 links dist.;

Between townships 25 and 26 N., R. 2 W., Willamette meridian—Continued.

Chains.	
75.59	A buckeye, 12 in. dia., bears S. 48 W., 9 links dist.
	A black oak, 24 in. dia.
80.00	Set a post for corner to sections 2, 3, 34, and 35, from which
	A sugar tree, 15 in. dia., bears N. 46 E., 15 links dist.
	No tree convenient in section 34.
	A beech, 16 in. dia., bears S. 35 W., 16 links dist.;
	A sugar tree, 14 in. dia., bears S. 30 E., 14 links dist.
	Land gently rolling, and 1st rate.
	Timber, good; elm, buckeye, beech, walnut, and oak.

West, on a *true* line between sections 3 and 34,
Variation 18° 39′ east.

9.00	Enter wet prairie; bears N. and S.
16.00	A beautiful spring branch, 5 links wide, runs S. W.
22.00	Leave prairie; bears N. E. and S. W.
31.27	A black oak, 20 in. dia.
40.00	Set a post for quarter-section corner from which
	A white walnut, 16 in. dia., bears N. 64 E., 7 links dist.;
	A white walnut, 12 in dia., bears S. 73 W., 31 links dist.
41.33	A white oak, 30 in. dia.
74.52	A point 4 links south of a black oak, 24 in. dia.; mark it by cutting 2 notches south side.
75.00	Leave timber and enter narrow strip of prairie; bears N. W. and S. E.
80.00	A point for corner to sections 3, 4, 33, and 34, drove a charred stake, and raised a mound, with trench, as per instructions, from which
	A white oak, 20 in. dia., bears N. 73 E., 540 links dist.;
	A black oak, 30 in. dia., bears N. 76 E., 613 links dist.
	Land gently rolling; 1st rate.
	Timber, white and black oak, walnut, and sugar tree.

West, on a *true* line between sections 4 and 33,
Variation 18° 39′ east.

7.50	Leave prairie; bears N. W. and S. E.
21.50	A spring branch, 15 links wide, runs N. W.
40.00	A black walnut, 30 in. dia.; mark it for quarter-section corner, from which
	A buckeye, 9 in. dia., bears S. 45 E., 11 links dist.;
	A black walnut, 20 in. dia., bears N. 29 W., 25 links dist.
41.40	Leave upland and enter river bottom; bears N. E. and S. W.
46.44	Set a post on the left bank of Chickeeles River, for corner to fractional sections 4 and 33, from which
	An elm, 8 in. dia., bears N. 71 E., 5 links dist.;
	An elm, 10 in. dia., bears S. 19 W., 6 links dist.
	The line running in the river, the distance on the *random* line was obtained on an offset by running *north* from the temporary post on the right bank 7 chains 63 links to a point, thence *east* 30.00 chains, and coming back to *true* line on the left bank of the river.
76.44	Set a post on the right bank of the river for corner to fractional sections 4 and 33, from which
	A cherry, 6 in. dia., bears N. 61 E., 17 links dist.;
	A sugar tree, 20 in. dia., bears S. 75 W., 20 links dist.
76.64	A sugar tree, 23 in. dia.
80.00	Set a post for corner to sections 4, 5, 32, and 33, from which
	A hackberry, 7 in. dia., bears N. 67 E., 17 links dist.;
	A sugar tree, 20 in. dia., bears N. 71 W., 43 links dist.;

Between townships 25 and 26 N., R. 2 W., Willamette meridian—Continued.

Chains.	
	A locust, 14 in. dia., bears S. 30 W., 16 links dist.;
	A beech, 20 in. dia., bears S. 20 E., 50 links dist.
	Land, east of bottom, rolling; good soil; the bottom subject to inundation 4 feet.
	Timber, on upland, oak; in bottom, sugar, cherry, and hackberry.

	West, on a *true* line between sections 5 and 32, Variation 18° 39' east,
24.40	A white oak, 16 in. dia. Here leave bottom and enter hills; bears N. E. and S. W.
40.00	Set a post for quarter-section corner, from which
	A hickory, 18 in. dia., bears N. 88 E., 40 links dist.
	A mulberry, 14 in. dia., bears S. 69 W., 103 links dist.
42.73	A black ash, 15 in. dia.
80.00	Set a post for corner to sections 5, 6, 31, and 32, from which
	A sugar tree, 20 in. dia., bears N. 89 E., 60 links dist.;
	An elm, 14 in dia., bears N. 12 W., 24 links dist.;
	An elm, 15 in. dia., bears S. 14 W., 23 links dist.;
	A sugar tree, 16 in. dia., bears S. 15 E., 26 links dist.
	Land gently rolling, and 1st rate; the bottom level.
	Timber, sugar tree, walnut, and oak; undergrowth same, and spice.

	West, on a *true* line between sections 6 and 31, Variation 18° 39' east,
8.00	To swamp of about 15 acres; bears N. E. and S. W.
18.00	Leave swamp; bears N. E. and S. W.; the line passes through the middle of the swamp.
18.26	A red oak, 30 in. dia., on N. W. bank of swamp.
34.30	A hickory, 18 in. dia.
40.00	Set a post for quarter-section corner, from which
	A bur oak, 27 in. dia., bears N. 49 E., 46 links dist.;
	A sugar tree, 20 in. dia., bears N. 56 W., 60 links dist.
	No tree convenient *south* of the line.
48.65	A stream, 14 links wide, runs south.
57.40	A white oak, 28 in. dia.
61.00	Enter prairie; bears N. E. and S. W.
76.53	To the established corner to townships 25 and 26 N., ranges 2 and 3 west.
	Land level; 1st rate for farming.
	Timber, good; various kinds of oak, hickory, and sugar tree; undergrowth, hazel, hickory, and vines.

GENERAL DESCRIPTION.

This township contains a large amount of first-rate land for farming. It is well timbered with the various kinds of oak, hickory, sugar tree, walnut, beech, and ash.

Chickeeles River is navigable for small boats in low water, and does not often overflow its banks, which are from ten to fifteen feet high.

The township will admit of a large settlement, and should therefore be subdivided.

B.

FIELD-NOTES OF THE SUBDIVISION LINES AND MEANDERS OF CHICKEELES RIVER, IN TOWNSHIP 25 NORTH, RANGE 2 WEST, WILLAMETTE MERIDIAN.

Township 25 N., range 2 W., Willamette meridian.

Chains.	
	To determine the proper adjustment of my compass for subdividing this township, I commence at the corner to townships 24 and 25 N., R. 1 and 2 W., and run
	North, on a blank line along the east boundary of section 36,
	Variation 17° 51' east,
40.05	To a point 5 links west of the quarter-section corner,
80.09	To a point 12 links west of the corner to sections 25 and 36.
	To retrace this line or run parallel thereto, my compass must be adjusted to a variation of 17° 46' east.
	Subdivision commenced February 1, 1854.
	From the corner to sections 1, 2, 35, and 36, on the south boundary of the township, I run
	North, between sections 35 and 36,
	Variation 17° 46' east,
9.19	A beech, 30 in. dia.
29.97	A beech, 30 in. dia.
40.00	Set a post for quarter-section corner, from which
	A beech, 8 in. dia., bears N. 23 W., 45 links dist.;
	A beech, 15 in. dia., bears S. 48 E., 12 links dist.
51.00	A beech, 18 in. dia.
76.00	A sugar tree, 30 in. dia.
80.00	Set a post for corner to sections 25, 26, 35, and 36, from which
	A beech, 28 in. dia., bears N. 60 E., 45 links dist.;
	A beech, 24 in. dia., bears N. 62 W., 17 links dist.;
	A poplar, 20 in. dia., bears S. 70 W., 50 links dist.;
	A poplar, 36 in. dia., bears S. 66 E., 34 links dist.
	Land level; 2d rate.
	Timber, poplar, beech, sugar tree, and some oak; undergrowth, same and hazel.
	East, on a *random* line between sections 25 and 36,
	Variation 17° 46' east,
9.00	A brook, 20 links wide, runs north.
15.00	To foot of hills, bear N. and S.
40.00	Set a post for temporary quarter-section corner.
55.00	To opposite foot of hill, bears N. and S.
72.00	A brook, 15 links wide, runs north.
80.00	Intersected east boundary at post corner to sections 25 and 36, from which corner I run
	West, on a *true* line between sections 25 and 36,
	Variation 17° 46' east,
40.00	Set a post on top of hill, bears N. and S., from which
	A hickory, 14 in. dia., bears N. 60 E., 27 links dist.;
	A beech, 15 in. dia., bears S. 74 W., 9 links dist.
80.00	The corner to sections 25 and 26, 35 and 36.
	Land, east and west parts, level, 1st rate; middle part broken, 3d rate.
	Timber, beech, oak, ash, &c.; undergrowth, same and spice in the branch bottoms.
	North, between sections 25 and 26,
	Variation 17° 46' east,
7.00	A poplar, 40 in. dia.
17.20	A brook, 25 links wide, runs N. W.
18.05	A walnut, 30 in. dia.
23.44	A brook, 25 links wide, runs N. E.
40.00	Set a post for quarter-section corner, from which

GENERAL INSTRUCTIONS OF 1855 139

Township 25 *N., range* 2 *W., Willamette meridian—Continued.*

Chains.	
	A bur oak, 36 in. dia., bears N. 42 E., 18 links dist.;
	A beech, 30 in. dia., bears S. 72 W., 9 links dist.
60.15	A beech, 30 in. dia.
80.00	Set a post for corner to sections 23, 24, 25, and 26, from which
	A white oak, 14 in. dia., bears N. 50 E., 40 links;
	A sugar tree, 12 in. dia., bears N. 14 W., 31 links dist.;
	A white oak, 13 in. dia., bears S. 38 W., 32 links dist.;
	A sugar tree, 12 in. dia., bears S. 42 E., 14 links dist.
	Land level on the line, high ridge of hills through the middle of section 25 running N. and S.
	Timber, beech, walnut, ash, sugar tree, &c.
	East, on a *random* line between sections 24 and 25,
	Variation 17° 46' east,
8.90	A stream, 30 links wide, rapid current, runs N. W.
12.00	To foot of hill, bears south and N. E.
40.00	Set a post for temporary quarter-section corner.
48.00	To opposite foot of hill, bears south and N. W.
60.50	A stream, 30 links wide, runs N.; soon turns N. W.
73.00	To foot of hill, rises moderately, bears S. and N. W.
80.12	Intersected east boundary of the township at the post corner to sections 24 and 25, from which corner I run
	West, on a *true* line between sections 24 and 25,
	Variation 17° 46' east,
40.06	Set a post for quarter-section corner, from which
	A beech, 18 in. dia., bears N. 74 W., 26 links dist.;
	A beech, 16 in. dia., bears S. 73 E., 22 links dist.
80.12	The corner to sections 23, 24, 25, 26.
	Land rolling between the branches; good, 2d rate; branch bottoms level, 1st rate.
	Timber, walnut, beech, elm, and oak; undergrowth, same and spice.
	North, between sections 23 and 24,
	Variation 17° 46' east,
6.70	A white oak, 20 in. dia.
9.65	A stream, 25 links wide, runs N. W.
13.50	Same stream, 25 links wide, runs N. E.
16.00	Same stream, 25 links wide, runs N. W.
40.00	Set a post near the south bank of a stream for quarter-section corner, from which
	A cottonwood, 18 in. dia., bears S. 7 W., 7 links dist.;
	A white walnut, 24 in. dia., bears S. 22 E., 4 links dist.
40.35	Elk Creek, 125 links wide, runs N. W.; general course, west.
	John Jones has a field on the north side of the creek and west of the line; his house is 2 chains south of the road and 2 chains east of the line.
54.00	To the road from Astoria to Williamsburg; bears E. and W.
58.00	Enter wet prairie; bears east and west.
68.00	Leave prairie and enter timber bearing east and west.
	This prairie extends *east* into section 24 and about 30 chains.
75.12	A white oak, 30 in. dia.
75.00	Leave creek bottom and enter hills bearing east and west.
80.00	Set a post for corner to sections 13, 14, 23, 24, from which
	A white walnut, 16 in. dia., bears N. 42 E., 15 links dist.;
	A white walnut, 24 in. dia., bears N. 59 W., 27 links dist.;
	An elm, 8 in. dia., bears S. 67 W., 16 links dist.;
	A black oak, 14 in. dia., bears S. 38 E., 17 links dist.
	Land mostly level; 1st rate soil.
	Timber, walnut, various kinds of oak, buckeye, and hickory; undergrowth, same and spice. *February* 1, 1854.

Township 25 N., range 2 W., Willamette meridian—Continued.

Chains.	
	East, on a *random* line between sections 13 and 24, Variation 17° 46' east,
40.00	Set a post for temporary quarter-section corner.
80.10	Intersected the east boundary of township, 16 links south of post corner, to sections 13 and 24, from which corner I run West, on a *true* line between sections 13 and 24, Variation 17° 53' east,
40.05	Set a post for quarter-section corner, from which A sugar tree, 30 in. dia., bears N. 80 W., 22 links dist.; A white oak, 16 in. dia., bears S. 53 E., 20 links dist.
80.10	The corner to sections 13, 14, 23, 24. Land mostly rolling; good rich soil; 1st rate. Timber, walnut, sugar tree, oak, elm, and buckeye; undergrowth, same and spice.
	North, between sections 13 and 14, Variation 17° 46' east,
6.17	A white oak, 30 in. dia.
22.15	A beech, 30 in. dia.
40.00	Set a post for quarter-section corner, from which A beech, 24 in. dia., bears N. 66 W., 6 links dist.; A beech, 20 in. dia., bears S. 45 E., 40 links dist.
52.25	A beech, 24 in. dia.
62.61	A bur oak, 30 in. dia.
80.00	Set a post for corner to sections 11, 12, 13, 14, from which A black oak, 26 in. dia., bears N. 53 E., 10 links dist.; A black oak, 21 in. dia., bears N. 20 W., 35 links dist.; A sugar tree, 30 in. dia., bears S. 32 W., 25 links dist.; A white oak, 20 in. dia., bears S. 24 E., 20 links dist. Land gently rolling; good, 2d rate. Timber, beech, oak, and ash; undergrowth, same and hazel.
	East, on a *random* line between sections 12 and 13, Variation 17° 46' east,
20.50	Foot of hills, and enter broken ridges bearing north and south.
40.00	Set a post for temporary quarter-section corner,
80.10	Intersected east boundary 13 links north of post corner to sections 12 and 13, from which corner I run West, on a *true* line between sections 12 and 13, Variation 17° 46' east,
40.05	Set a post for quarter-section corner, from which An elm, 24 in. dia., bears N. 51 E., 50 links dist.; A beech, 18 in. dia., bears S. 51 W., 29 links dist.
80.10	The corner to sections 11, 12, 13, 14. Land west 20 chains; gently rolling; good, 2d rate; the balance high, broken ridges. Timber, beech, black oak, and white oak; undergrowth, same and hazel.
	North, between sections 11 and 12, Variation 17° 46' east,
10.81	An elm, 15 in. dia.
40.00	Set a post for quarter-section corner, from which A beech, 30 in. dia., bears N. 33 W., 9 links dist.; A beech, 20 in. dia., bears S. 64 W., 20 links dist.
52.25	A beech, 24 in. dia.
62.61	A black oak, 30 in. dia.
75.40	A spring branch, 10 links wide, runs west.
80.00	Set a post for corner to sections 1, 2, 11, and 12, from which A poplar, 32 in. dia., bears N. 41 E., 30 links dist.; A poplar, 36 in. dia., bears N. 43 W., 25 links dist.;

Township 25 N., range 2 W., Willamette meridian—Continued.

Chains.	
	A sugar tree, 30 in. dia., bears S. 32 W., 25 links dist.;
	A sugar tree, 21 in. dia., bears S. 35 E., 40 links dist.
	Land level; good, 2d rate.
	Timber, sugar tree, poplar, walnut, and oak; undergrowth, same and hazel.
	East, on a *random* line between sections 1 and 12,
	Variation 17° 46' east,
23.00	Enter high, broken ridges, bearing N. E. and south.
40.00	Set a post for temporary quarter-section corner.
42.50	A spring branch, 10 links wide, runs S. W.
63.00	To foot of high mountain; bears north and south.
80.24	Intersected the east boundary of the township 13 links north of post corner to sections 1 and 12, from which corner I run
	West, on a *true* line between sections 1 and 12,
	Variation 17° 40' east,
40.12	Set a post on top of narrow ridge, bearing north and south, for quarter-section corner, from which
	A sugar tree, 20 in. dia., bears N. 20 E., 32 links dist.;
	A sugar tree, 24 in. dia., bears S. 56 W., 25 links dist.
80.24	The corner to sections 1, 2, 11, 12.
	Land very broken and mountainous.
	Timber, sugar tree, beech; various kinds of oak and hickory.
	☞On this line, and toward the foot of the mountain, we discovered gold dust; and throughout the line we observed many specimens of what appeared to be rich auriferous quartz.
	North, on a *random* line between sections 1 and 2,
	Variation 17° 46' east,
40.00	Set a post for temporary quarter-section corner.
80.11	Intersected the north boundary 32 links east of corner to sections 1 and 2, from which corner I run
	South, on a *true* line between sections 1 and 2,
	Variation 18° 00' east,
40.11	Set a post for quarter-section corner, from which
	A white oak, 20 in. dia., bears N. 31 W., 65 links dist.;
	A sugar tree, 14 in. dia., bears S. 49 E., 32 links dist.
80.11	The corner to sections 1, 2, 11, 12.
	Land level; good, rich, soil.
	Timber, walnut, sugar tree, beech, and various kinds of oak; open woods.
	February 2, 1854.
	North, between sections 34 and 35,
	Variation 17° 46' east,
6.56	A hickory, 36 in dia.
23.00	To foot of hill; bears east and west.
34.58	A walnut, 38 in. dia.
40.00	Set a post for quarter-section corner, from which
	A beech, 16 in. dia., bears S. 18 E., 13 links dist.;
	A beech, 10 in. dia., bears N. 69 W., 40 links dist.
50.00	A maple, 24 in. dia.
75.86	An ash, 24 in dia.
80.00	Set a post for corner to sections 26, 27, 34, and 35, from which
	An ash, 30 in. dia., bears N. 30 E., 24 links dist.;
	An ash, 36 in. dia., bears N. 52 W., 19 links dist.;
	A beech, 16 in. dia., bears S. 69 W., 41 links dist.;
	A beech, 14 in. dia., bears S. 67 E., 12 links dist.
	Land, south 23 chains, broken; the balance level, rich soil.
	Timber, ash, beech, oak, and hickory; undergrowth, same and spice.

Township 25 N., range 2 W., Willamette meridian—Continued.

Chains.	
	East, on a *random* line between sections 26 and 35.
	Variation 17° 46' east,
40.00	Set a post for temporary quarter-section corner.
80.08	Intersected N. and S. line 20 links north of the corner to sections 25, 26, 35, and 36, from which corner I run
	West, on a *true* line between sections 26 and 35,
	Variation 17° 37' east,
40.04	Set a post for quarter-section corner, from which
	A beech, 14 in. dia., bears N. 56 E., 12 links dist.;
	A beech, 12 in. dia., bears S. 32 W., 32 links dist.
80.08	The corner to sections 26, 27, 34, and 35.
	Land level; good, rich soil.
	Timber, beech, elm, ash, and walnut.
	North, between sections 26 and 27,
	Variation 17° 46' east,
8.47	An elm, 20 in. dia.;
29.18	A lynn, 34 in. dia.
40.00	Set a post for quarter-section corner, from which
	A sugar tree, 14 in. dia., bears N. 54 E., 27 links dist.;
	A beech, 12 in. dia., bears S. 13 W., 31 links dist.
46.37	A poplar, 40 in. dia.;
60.48	A black oak, 36 in. dia.
80.00	Set a post for corner to sections 22, 23, 26, 27, from which
	A white oak, 30 in. dia., bears N. 50 E., 13 links dist.;
	A walnut, 30 in. dia., bears N. 36 W., 14 links dist.;
	A walnut, 24 in. dia., bears S. 24 W., 16 links dist.;
	An ironwood, 8 in. dia., bears S. 32 E., 24 links dist.
	Land, south half, 2d rate; north half, 1st rate.
	Timber, walnut, poplar, white oak, beech, and hickory.
	☞About 10 chains from this corner on the S. W., and on the left bank of Elk Creek, we discovered evidences of extensive ancient works, supposed to be fortifications, with many ancient mounds in the vicinity.
	East, on a *random* line between sections 23 and 26,
	Variation 17° 46' east,
40.00	Set a post for temporary quarter-section corner.
48.00	A stream, 12 links wide, outlet to a lake in the middle of section 26, runs N. W.
80.00	Intersected north and south line 15 links north of post corner to sections 23, 24, 25, 26, from which corner I run
	West, on a *true* line between sections 23 tnd 26,
	Variation 17° 40' east,
40.00	Set a post for quarter-section corner, from which
	A beech, 16 in. dia., bears N. 72 W., 18 links dist.;
	A beech, 10 in. dia., bears S. 72 W., 16 links dist.
80.00	The corner to sections 22, 23, 26, 27.
	Land level, good; 2d rate soil.
	Timber, beech, sugar tree, elm, and hickory.
	Notes of the meanders of a small lake in section 26
	Begin at the quarter-section corner on the line between sections 23 and 26, and run thence south,
24.00	To the north margin of the lake, where set a post for meander corner, from which
	A beech, 14 in. dia., bears N. 45 E., 10 links dist.;
	A beech, 9 in. dia., bears N. 15 W., 14 links dist.
	Thence meander around the lake as follows:
	S. 53° E., 17.75. At 75 links cross outlet to lake, 10 links wide, runs N. E.
	S. 3° E., 13.00,
	S. 30' W., 8.00,

General Instructions of 1855

Township 25 N., range 2 W., Willamette meridian—Continued.

Chains.	
	S. 65° W., 12.00, to a point previously determined 20.30 chains *north* of the quarter-section corner, on the line between sections 26 and 35, Set post meander corner, maple, 16 in. dia., bears S. 15 W., 20 links dist. Ash, 12 in. dia., bears S. 21 E., 15 links dist.
	N. 63° W., 10.00 { In this vicinity we discovered remarkable fossil remains of animals well worthy the attention of naturalists.
	N. 13° W., 21.00
	N. 52° E., 17.30, to the place of beginning.
	This is a beautiful lake, with well-defined banks from 6 to 10 feet high. Land, 1st rate.
	North, between sections 22 and 23, Variation 17° 46' east,
8.00	Elk Creek, 150 links wide, runs S. W.
24.20	Same creek, rapid current, rocky bed and banks, 150 links wide, runs S. E.
40.00	Set a post for quarter-section corner, from which
	A black oak, 20 in. dia., bears N. 34 E., 48 links;
	A black oak, 20 in. dia., bears S. 9 W. 45 links.
41.60	Same creek, 150 links wide, rocky bed and banks, runs west.
	About 500 chains below the crossing of the line, a stream 20 links wide comes in from the north.
	Two chains below the mouth of this stream the creek turns south.
	Here is a very fine mill seat, the fall in the river being about 6 feet in the distance of three chains. Both banks of the creek about 10 feet high, composed principally of limestone of excellent quality.
47.00	Enter wet prairie near the west end, bearing N. W. and east.
65.00	Leave wet prairie, bearing east and west.
68.00	The road from Astoria to Williamsburg, bearing S. 80 E., and N. 60 W.
69.92	A white oak, 18 in. dia.
70.50	Enter high, rolling land, bearing east and west.
80.00	Set a post for corner to sections 14, 15, 22, and 23, from which
	An elm, 16 in. dia., bears N. 27 E., 50 links dist.;
	An elm, 24 in. dia., bears N. 34 W., 45 links dist.;
	A sugar tree, 18 in. dia., bears S. 60 W., 42 links dist.;
	A sugar tree, 24 in. dia., bears S. 52 E., 23 links dist.
	Land, south of wet prairie at 47 chains, broken, 3d rate; the balance part wet, 2d rate.
	Timber, elm, sugar tree, oak, and hickory.
	February 3, 1854.
	East, on a *random* line between sections 14 and 23, Variation 17° 46' east,
40.00	Set a post for temporary quarter-section corner.
80.14	Intersected north and south line 14 links north of the corner to sections 13, 14, 23, and 24, from which corner I run
	West, on a *true* line between sections 14 and 23, Variation 17° 40' east,
40.07	Set a post for quarter-section corner, from which
	A sugar tree, 30 in. dia., bears N. 39 E., 31 links dist.;
	A mulberry, 12 in. dia., bears S. 26 W., 4 links dist.
80.14	To corner to sections 14, 15, 22, 23.
	Land gently rolling; good soil.
	Timber, elm, sugar tree, oak, and mulberry.
	North, between sections 14 and 15, Variation 17° 46' east,
14.14	A sugar tree, 14 in. dia.
34.13	A white oak, 22 in. dia.
40.00	Set a post for quarter-section corner, from which
	A beech, 24 in. dia., bears N. 45 W., 37 links dist.;

Township 25 N., range 2 W., Willamette meridian—Continued.

Chains.	
	A sugar tree, 20 in. dia., bears S. 43 E., 74 links dist.
47.20	A walnut, 27 in. dia.
61.84	A white oak, 36 in. dia.
77.72	A stream, 25 links wide, rapid current, runs S. W.
80.00	Set a post for corner to sections 10, 11, 14, 15, from which
	A bur oak, 28 in. dia., bears N. 16 E., 40 links dist.;
	A black oak, 30 in. dia., bears N. 17 W., 32 links dist.;
	A white oak, 14 in. dia., bears S. 15 W., 38 links dist.;
	A hickory, 15 in. dia., bears S. 12 E. 36.
	Land gently rolling; 2d rate.
	Timber, various kinds of oak, beech, and walnut; open woods.
	East, on a *random* line between sections 11 and 14,
	Variation 17° 46' east,
8.25	A stream, 25 links wide, runs S. W.
13.00	A stream, 10 links wide, runs N. W.
40.00	Set a post for temporary quarter-section corner.
80.16	Intersected N. and S. line 20 links north of post corner to sections 11, 12, 13, 14, from which corner I run
	West, on a *true line* between sections 11 and 14,
	Variation 17° 37' east,
40.08	Set a post for quarter-section corner, from which
	A sugar tree, 16 in. dia., bears N. 66 E., 35 links dist.;
	A sugar tree, 14 in. dia., bears S. 44 W., 13 links dist.
80.16	To corner to sections 10, 11, 14, 15.
	Land rolling, but not broken; good soil.
	Timber, good; various kinds of oak, beech, sugar tree, elm, and ash.
	North, between sections 10 and 11,
	Variation 17° 40' east,
5.29	A white oak, 24 in. dia.
39.16	A white oak, 36 in. dia.
40.00	Set a post for quarter-section corner, from which
	A beech, 15 in. dia., bears N. 18 W., 42 links dist.;
	A beech, 18 in. dia., bears S. 62 E., 12 links dist.
45.17	A sugar tree, 27 in. dia.,
63.79	A sugar tree, 30 in. dia.
71.12	A brook, 20 links wide, rapid current, gravelly bottom, runs west; soon turns south.
80.00	Set a post for corner to sections 2, 3, 10, 11, from which
	A sugar tree, 18 in. dia., bears N. 13 E., 61 links dist.;
	A beech, 24 in. dia. bears N. 48 W., 26 links dist.;
	A white oak, 13 in. dia., bears S. 39 W., 40 links dist.
	No tree in section 11 convenient to mark.
	Land gently rolling, good, 2d rate.
	Timber, various kinds of oak, beech, walnut; open woods.
	East, on a *random* line between sections 2 and 11,
	Variation 17° 40' east,
18.36	A brook, 20 links wide, runs S. W.
40.00	Set a post for temporary quarter-section corner.
80.10	Intersected N. and S. line 12 links north of the corner to sections 1, 2, 11, 12, from which corner I run
	West, on a *true* line between sections 2 and 11,
	Variation 17° 35' east,
40.05	Set a post for quarter-section corner, from which
	A beech, 18 in. dia., bears N. 35 W., 5 links dist.;
	A beech, 14 in. dia., bears S. 47 E., 49 links dist.
80.10	The corner to sections 2, 3, 10, 11.
	Land gently rolling; soil good. [open woods.
	Timber, beech, sugar tree, elm, and oak; west part brushy; east part

GENERAL INSTRUCTIONS OF 1855   145

Township 25 *N., range* 2 *W., Willamette meridian—Continued.*

Chains.	
	North, on a *random* line between sections 2 and 3, Variation 17° 30' east,
40.00	Set a post for temporary quarter-section corner.
80.00	Intersected the north boundary of the township 25 links east of the corner to sections 2 and 3, from which corner I run South, on a *true* line bethween sections 2 and 3, Variation 17° 51' east,
40.00	Set a post for quarter-section corner, from which An elm, 8 in. dia., bears N. 35 W., 5 links dist.; A hickory, 10 in. dia., bears S. 75 E., 18 links dist.
80.00	The corner to sections 2, 3, 10, 11. Land gently rolling; good, 2d rate. Timber, various kinds of oak, beech, elm, and hickory; open woods. *February* 4, 1854.
	North, between sections 33 and 34, Variation 17° 46' east,
5.61	An ash, 22 in. dia.
13.20	An elm, 15 in. dia.
40.00	Set a sand stone, 15 in. long, 12 in. wide, and 4 in. thick, for quarter-section corner, from which A beech, 15 in. dia., bears N. 22 E., 18 links dist.; A beech, 24 in. dia., bears S. 78 W., 15 links dist.
49.10	A black oak, 36 in. dia.
71.04	An elm, 30 in. dia.
80.00	Set a post on high ridge bearing N. S. for corner to sections 27, 28, 33, 34, from which A white oak, 14 in. dia., bears N. 22 E., 18 links dist.; A beech, 8 in. dia., bears N. 48 W., 14 links dist.; An elm, 12 in. dia., bears S. 16 W., 42 links dist.; A beech, 10 in. dia., bears S. 74 E., 14 links dist. Land broken, poor soil, not fit for cultivation. Timber, beech, oak, sugar tree, and elm.
	East, on a *random* line between sections 27 and 34, Variation 17° 46' east,
18.00	To foot of hill bearing north and S. E.
40.00	Set a post for temporary quarter-section corner.
48.20	A brook, 20 links wide, runs north.
50.20	A brook, 15 links wide, runs N. W.
79.90	Intersected N. and S. line 14 links north of the corner to sections 26, 27, 34, and 35, from which corner I run West, on a *true* line between sections 27 and 34, Variation 17° 40' east,
39.95	Set a post for quarter-section corner, from which A sugar tree, 15 in. dia., bears N. 32 W., 32 links dist.; A sugar tree, 15 in. dia., bears S. 52 E., 26 links dist.
79.90	The corners to sections 27, 28, 33, and 34. Land east of hill gently rolling; good soil. Timber, sugar tree, elm, oak, and ash.
	North, between sections 27 and 28. Variation 17° 46' east.
2.11	A black oak, 30 in. dia.
20.42	An elm, 36 in. dia.
34.00	To foot of hill bearing S. W. and S. E.
40.00	Set a post for quarter-section corner, from which A buckeye, 10 in. dia., bears N. 30 W., 6 links dist.; A poplar, 36 in. dia., bears S. 15 E., 38 links dist.
62.16	A sugar tree, 24 in. dia.
64.20	Elk Creek, 200 links wide, rapid current; bluff bank 20 feet high; south

Township 25 *N., range* 2 *W., Willamette meridian—Continued.*

Chains.	

80.00	side runs west; enter bottom after crossing creek.
	Set a sandstone, 16 in long, 12 in. wide, and 6 in. thick, for corner to sections 21, 22, 27, 28, from which
	    An elm, 15 in. dia., N. 31 E., 14 links dist.;
	    A beech, 14 in. dia., bears N. 43 W., 37 links dist.;
	    An elm, 20 in. dia., bears S. 24 W., 24 links dist.;
	    A beech, 24 in. dia., bears S. 20 E., 52 links dist.
	Land, south of creek, broken and rolling, 3d rate; north of creek rich bottom.
	Timber, beech, elm, various kinds of oak and hickory.

	East, on a *random* line between sections 22 and 27, Variation 17° 46′ east,
40.00	Set a post for temporary quarter-section corner.
75.70	Elk Creek, 200 links wide, gentle current, gravelly bottom, runs S. W.
80.06	Intersected north and south line 15 links north of the corner to sections 22, 23, 26, and 27, from which corner I run West, on a *true* line between sections 22 and 27, Variation 17° 40′ east,

40.03	Set a post for quarter-section corner, from which
	    An elm, 14 in. dia., bears N. 50 E., 16 links dist.;
	    A mulberry, 10 in. dia., bears S. 87 W., 43 links dist.

80.06	The corner to sections 21, 22, 27, 28. Land level; rich bottom; 2d rate. Timber, elm, beech, oak, and hickory.
	North, between sections 21 and 22, Variation 17° 46′ east,
3.15	A walnut, 18 in. dia.
32.32	An ash, 24 in. dia.

33.50	Set a post on the south bank of a lake of deep, clear water for corner to fractional sections 21 and 22, from which
	    A maple, 16 in. dia., bears S. 33 W., 21 links dist.;
	    An ash, 12 in. dia., bears S. 21 E., 34 links dist.
	To obtain the distance across the lake, I send my flagman around the west end thereof, who sets the flag on its north bank, and in the line between sections 21 and 22.
	I now run a base *west* (from the corner on south bank) 5.60 chains, to a point from which the flag bears N. 16° 15′ E., and continue said base line west; and at 9 chains and 6 links, a point from which said flag bears N. 25° 15′ E., and taking the mean between the results so ascertained, find for the distance across the lake, on the line between sections 21 and 22, 19 chains and 20 links, to which add 33.50 chains, makes

52.70	To the flag on the north bank of the lake.
	Here set a post for corner to fractional sections 21 and 22, from which
	    An ash, 16 in. dia., bears N. 21 E., 15 links dist.;
	    An elm, 14 in. dia., bears N. 71 W., 23 links dist.
	The point for quarter-section corner, being in the lake, cannot be established.

56.11	An elm, 36 in. dia.

80.00	Set a post for corner to sections 15, 16, 21, 22, from which
	    A black oak, 12 in. dia., bears N. 83 E., 23 links dist.;
	    A buckeye, 10 in. dia., bears N. 82 W., 17 links dist.;
	    A white oak, 14 in. dia., bears S. 14 W., 14 links dist.;
	    A black oak, 15 in. dia., bears S. 28 E., 24 links dist.
	Land level; rich bottom; not subject to inundation.
	Timber, elm, oak, hickory and ash.

GENERAL INSTRUCTIONS OF 1855   147

Township 25 N., range 2 W., Willamette meridian—Continued.

Chains.	
	Field-notes of the meanders of Clear Lake.
	Begin at the corner to fractional sections 21 and 22, on the north bank, and run thence, in section 22, as follows:
	East 10.00 chains; thence
	N. 80 E. 12.00 chains; thence
	S. 75 E. 5.00 chains; thence
	S. 60 E. 5.00 chains; thence
	S. 30 E. 5.00 chains; thence
	S. 10 W. 6.00 chains; thence
	S. 36 W. 8.00 chains; thence
	S. 82 W. 10.00 chains; thence
	West 10.00 chains; thence
	N. 89 W. 8.55 chains, to the corner to fractional sections 21 and 22, on the south bank of the lake; thence, in section 21,
	N. 75 W., 9.00 chains, thence
	N. 87 W., 10.50 chains, thence
	N. 62 W., 8.00 chains, thence ⎫ At 1.50 chains outlet to lake 20 links
	N. 43 W., 5.50 chains, thence ⎬ wide, runs southwest.
	N. 34 W., 4.20 chains, thence ⎭
	North, 5.00 chains, thence
	N. 35 E., 7.00 chains, thence
	N. 55 E., 8.00 chains, thence
	East, 5.00 chains, thence
	S. 75 E., 3.00 chains, thence
	S. 35 E., 6.50 chains, thence
	S. 67½ E., 11.10 chains, to the corner to fractional sections 21 and 22, on the north bank of the lake, and place of beginning.
	Land, around this lake, good, rich soil; banks from 8 to 10 feet high, except at the western part, as far *south* as the outlet, where the land is level and wet.
	Timber, good black oak, hickory, and ash.
	MONDAY, *February* 6, 1854.
	☞ If the deputy should find it more convenient to meander the lake before continuing the line north of it, he will do so.
	East, on a *random* line between sections 15 and 22,
	Variation 17° 46' east,
40.00	Set a post for temporary quarter-section corner.
58.00	The road from Astoria to Williamsburg bearing N. W. and S. E.
65.50	A stream, 20 links wide, runs south.
79.94	Intersected north and south line 12 links north of the corner to sections 14, 15, 22, and 23, from which corner I run
	West, on a *true* line between sections 15 and 22,
	Variation 17° 41' east,
39.97	Set a post for quarter-section corner, from which
	A sugar tree, 20 in. dia., bears N. 35 W., 21 links dist.;
	A lynn, 13 in. dia., bears S. 28 E., 81 links dist.
79.94	The corner to sections 15, 16, 21, 22.
	Land, gently rolling; good, rich soil.
	Timber, good; various kinds of oak, hickory, ash, and sugar tree.
	North, between sections 15 and 16,
	Variation 17° 46' east,
4.68	An elm, 24 in. dia.
13.00	Leave timber and enter high rolling prairie, bearing east and west.
16.75	The road from Astoria to Williamsburg bears N. 80 W., and S. 80 E.
40.00	Set a hard flint stone, which cannot be marked, for quarter-section corner; said stone is 16 in. long, 12 in. wide, and 8 in. thick, and from

Township 25 N., range 2 W., Willamette meridian—Continued.

Chains.	
	which a cone white oak, 16 in. dia., bears N. 42 W., 351 links dist. No other tree convenient to mark.
50.00	Enter John Orr's field, bearing N. W. and S. E.
55.00	A point 3 chains west of Orr's house;
61.00	Leave field bearing N. W. and S. E. This field contains about 10 acres; the line passing through the middle.
80.00	Set a post in mound, with trench, as per instructions, for corner to sections 9, 10, 15, 16, from which corner a granite boulder, four feet in diameter at the surface of the ground, and three feet high, bears N. 72 E., 257 links distant. I cut a cross near the top, facing the corner; the cross-marks being four inches long, and one-fourth of an inch deep. Land high, rolling prairie; good soil; not stony, but occasional boulders appear above the natural surface.

	East, on a *random* line between sections 10 and 15, Variation 17° 46′ east,
40.00	Set a post for temporary quarter-section corner.
46.50	Leave prairie and enter timber, bearing north, and S. 40 E.
61.40	A stream, 25 links wide, gentle current, muddy bottom, runs south.
79.86	Intersected N. and S. line at the post corner to sections 10, 11, 14, 15, from which corner I run West, on a *true* line between sections 10 and 15, Variation 17° 46′ east,
39.93	Set a sandstone, 20 in. long, 12 in. wide, and 4 in. thick for quarter-section corner, raise a mound 2 feet high, west side of stone. From the stone a bur oak, 16 in. dia., in the eastern edge of the timber, bears N. 75 E., 674 links distant.
79.86	The corner to sections 9, 10, 15, 16. Land; the prairie rolling; good soil; timber land level; 1st rate. Timber, oak, hickory, and ash.

	North, between sections 9 and 10, Variation 17° 46′ east,
40.00	Set a post for quarter-section corner, raise a mound with trench, as per instructions. A lone bur oak, 10 in. dia., bears S. 75 E., 530 links distant; no other tree near. This corner about 10 chains *west* of a grove of oak and hickory of about 15 acres. From this corner Jacob Fry's house, in the north end of grove, bears N. 45 E.
51.25	A point from which Fry's house bears east, a field of about 10 acres north of the house.
80.00	Deposited a quart of charcoal, and set a post for corner to sections, 3, 4, 9, 10, and raised a mound, as per instructions, and planted N. W. 4 white-oak acorns, S. W. wild cherry stones, N. E. beech nuts, and S. E. a butter nut. Land high, rolling prairie; good rich soil, fit for cultivation.

	East, on a *random* line between sections 3 and 10, Variation 17° 46′ east,
40.00	Set a post for temporary quarter-section corner.
55.00	Leave prairie and enter timber, bearing N. and S.
79.90	Intersected N. and S. line 14 links south of the corner to sections 2, 3, 10, 11, from which corner I run West, on a *true* line between sections 3 and 10, Variation 17° 52′ east,
39.95	Set a sand stone, 16 in. long, 12 in. wide, and 4 in. thick, for quarter-section corner, from which a granite boulder, 4 feet long E. and W., by 3½ feet wide N. and S., and 2 feet high above ground, and marked ¼ with a pick, bears N. 31 E., 153 links distant; no other boulder in

Township 25 N., range 2 W., Willamette meridian—Continued.

Chains.	
79.90	sight of this corner. The corner to sections 3, 4, 9, 10. Land level; good rich soil. Timber, elm, beech, maple, and ash.
	North, on a *random* line between sections 3 and 4, Variation 17° 46' east,
40.00	Set a post for temporary quarter-section corner.
42.00	Leave prairie and enter timber, bearing S. E. and S. W.
55.15	A spring branch, 10 links wide, runs N. W.
66.50	Enter prairie, bearing N. W. and S. E.
79.95	Intersected the north boundary of the township 30 links east of the corner to sections 3 and 4, from which corner I run South, on a *true* line between sections 3 and 4, Variation 17° 59' east,

39.95	Set a mulberry post, 6 in. diameter, in the north point of prairie, from which
	    A white oak, 16 in. dia., bears N. 41 E. 195 links;
	    A black oak, 20 in. dia., bears N. 37 W. 205 links.

79.95	The corner to sections 3, 4, 9, 10. Land level, good rich soil, fit for cultivation. Timber, oak, hickory, and elm. *February* 7, 1854.
	All traces of the corner to sections 4, 5, 32 and 33, on the south boundary of the township, having disappeared, I restore and reëstablish said corner in the following manner, viz: Begin at the quarter-section corner the line between sections 4 and 33. One of the witness trees to this corner has fallen down, and the post is gone. The black oak, 18 in. dia., bearing N. 25 E. 32 links, standing and sound. I find also the black-oak station tree, 24 in. dia., called for at 37.51 chains; and at 2.49 chains west of the quarter-section corner set a *new* post at the point for quarter-section corner, and mark for witness tree a white oak, 20 in. dia., bears N. 34 W., 37 links dist. West, with the *old* marked line, Variation 18° 25' east,
40.00	Set a post for temporary corner to sections 4, 5, 32, and 33.
80.06	To a point 7 links south of the quarter-section corner on the line between sections 5 and 32. This corner agrees with its description, and from which I run East, on the *true* line between sections 5 and 32, Variation 18° 22' east,

40.03	Set a lime stone, 18 in. long, 12 in. wide, and 3 in. thick, for *re-established* corner to sections 4, 5, 32 and 33, from which
	    A white oak, 12 in. dia., bears N. 21 E., 41 links dist.;
	    A white oak, 16 in. dia., bears N. 41 W., 21 links dist.;
	    A black oak, 18 in. dia., bears S. 17 W., 32 links dist.;
	    A bur oak, 20 in. dia., bears S. 21 E., 37 links dist.
	Thence between sections 4 and 33.

80.06	The quarter-section corner on said line. The difference in measurement, being very small, will be rejected.
	North, between sections 32 and 33, Variation 17° 40' east,
19.85	A beech, 25 in. dia.
32.37	An elm, 30 in. dia.
40.00	Set a post for quarter-section corner, from which A beech, 24 in. dia., bears N. 11 E., 30 links dist.;

Township 25 N., range 2 W., Willamette meridian—Continued.

Chains.	
	A sugar tree, 20 in. dia., bears S. 40 W., 9 links dist.
48.75	A stream, 20 links wide, rapid current, runs east; general course N. E.
58.20	A sugar tree, 30 in. dia.
75.96	A sugar tree, 25 in. dia.
80.00	Set a post with trench for corner to sections 28, 29, 32, and 33, from which
	An elm, 20 in. dia., bears N. 66 W., 29 links dist.;
	A beech, 10 in. dia., bears S. 16 E., 13 links dist.
	No other trees convenient to mark.
	Planted N. E. 4 hickory nuts, and S. W. 4 cherry stones.
	Land gently rolling; good, rich soil.
	Timber, oak, elm, beech, and sugar tree.

	East, on a *random* line between sections 28 and 33,
	Variation 17° 40′ east,
19.50	A stream 25 links wide, runs north; rapid current. The line crosses about two chains below the mouth of a beautiful spring branch, 10 links wide; comes from the hills on the S. E.
40.00	Set a post for temporary quarter-section corner,
60.00	To foot of hills bearing N. and S.
80.12	Intersected the N. and S. line 7 links north of the corner to 27, 28, 33, and 34, from which corner I run
	West, on a *true* line, between sections 28 and 33,
	Variation 17° 37′ east,
40.06	Set a post for quarter-section corner, from which
	A hickory, 10 in. dia., bears N. 25 W., 22 links dist.;
	An elm, 24 in. dia., bears S. 9 W., 14 links dist.
80.12	The corner to sections 28, 29, 32, 33.
	Land, 20 chains, east part very broken; the balance gently rolling; good rich soil.
	Timber, oak, elm, ash, and sugar tree.

	North, between sections 28 and 29,
	Variation 17° 40′ east,
17.13	A sugar tree, 30 in. dia.
29.65	A beech, 24 in. dia.
40.00	Set a post for quarter-section corner, from which
	An elm, 14 in. dia., bears N. 6 W., 200 links dist.;
	A white oak, 12 in. dia., bears S. 41 E., 122 links dist.
52.73	A beech, 36 in. dia.
71.15	Top of limestone bluff, 20 feet high, on south bank of Elk Creek, 200 links wide; rapid current, gravelly bottom, runs west; soon turns S. W.
	Enter low wet bottom, on the right bank of creek.
80.00	Set a post for corner to sections 20, 21, 28, 29, from which
	A hickory, 13 in. dia., bears N. 30 E., 16 links dist.;
	A hickory, 18 in. dia., bears N. 32 W., 22 links dist.;
	A walnut, 17 in dia., bears S. 48 W., 40 links dist.;
	A walnut, 26 in. dia., bears S. 56 E., 34 links dist.
	Land, south of creek, rolling; good, rich soil.
	Timber, oak, elm, beech, and sugar tree; open woods; no undergrowth.

	East, on a *random* line between sections 21 and 28,
	Variation 17° 40′ east,
23.00	A stream, 10 links wide, runs S. W.
40.00	Set a post for temporary quarter-section corner.
43.20	A stream 20 links wide, low, muddy banks and bottoms, runs south.
80.18	Intersected north and south line, 20 links north of the corner to sections 21, 22, 27, 28, from which corner I run

General Instructions of 1855

Township 25 N., range 2 W., Willamette meridian—Continued.

Chains.	
	West, on a *true* line between sections 21 and 28,
	Variation 17° 31' east.
40.09	Set a post about 200 links north of the right bank of the creek for quarter-section corner, from which
	A sugar tree, 14 in dia., bears N. 57 E., 45 links dist.;
	A buckeye, 15 in dia., bears S. 61 W., 61 links dist.
80.18	The corner to sections 20, 21, 28, 29.
	Land, level; wet bottom; subject to inundation from 4 to 6 feet deep.
	Timber, oak, hickory, and ash; no undergrowth.
	North, between sections 20 and 21,
	Variation 17° 40' east,
8.24	A bur oak, 24 in. dia.
28.94	An ash, 15 in. dia., on the S. E. margin of a large lake, across which no sight can be had, because of the water bushes around lake lying principally in section 20, with low, muddy banks; mark said tree for corner to fractional sections 20 and 21, from which
	A red oak, 15 in. dia., bears S. 35 W., 32 links dist.;
	A water willow, 10 in. dia., bears S. 21 E., 12 links dist.
	NOTE.—The point for quarter-section corner being in the lake, it cannot be established.
	I now run as follows around the east end of the lake in section 21.
	N. 35 E., 8.00 chains, thence
	N. 10 E., 6.50 chains, thence
	N. 15 W., 5.50 chains, thence
	N. 40 W., 6.70 chains, to a point in the line between sections 20 and 21.
	The northing on the 4 courses of meanders is 23.39 chains, to which add 28.94 chains, makes
52.33	To the point in the line between sections 20 and 21, on the N. E. bank of the lake. Here set a post for corner to fractional sections 20 and 21, from which
	An elm, 20 in. dia., bears N. 22 E., 24 links dist.;
	A red oak, 24 in. dia., bears N. 17 W., 21 links dist.
54.20	A stream 25 links wide, gentle current, running S. W. into lake.
57.31	A red oak, 16 in. dia.
72.50	Leave level, rich bottom, and enter upland, bearing E. and W.,
80.00	Set a post for corner to sections 16, 17, 20, 21, from which
	A black oak, 10 in. dia., bears N. 53 E., 50 links dist.;
	A beech, 14 in. dia., bears N. 16 W., 14 links dist.;
	A bur oak, 12 in. dia., bears S. 8 W., 20 links dist.;
	A beech, 16 in. dia., bears S. 19 E., 15 links dist.
	Land mostly low, level, rich bottom; subject to inundation from 4 to 6 feet deep.
	Timber, oak, beech, maple, and ash; open woods.
	February 8, 1854.
	East, on a *random* line between sections 16 and 21,
	Variation 17° 40' east,
18.90	A brook, 10 links wide, runs south.
19.50	Same brook runs north.
21.55	Same brook runs south.
40.00	Set a post for temporary quarter-section corner.
61.50	Enter a small bushy swamp.
70.00	Leave swamp, which contains about 15 acres, and lies mostly in section 21.
80.20	Intersected N. and S. line 16 links north of the corner to sections 15, 16, 21, and 22, from which corner I run

Township 25 *N., range* 2 *W., Willamette meridian—Continued.*

Chains.	
	West, on a *true* line between sections 16 and 21, Variation 17° 33' east,
40.10	Set a post for quarter-section corner, from which A beech, 30 in. dia., bears N. 19 W., 31 links dist.; A buckeye, 24 in. dia., bears S. 11 E., 29 links dist.
80.20	The corner to sections 16, 17, 20, 21. Land rolling, 2d rate; wet around swamp. Timber, oak, beech, buckeye, and hickory; thick undergrowth of same and hazel.
	North, between sections 16 and 17, Variation 17° 40' east,
9.72	A bur oak, 30 in. dia.
26.84	A bur oak, 36 in. dia.
39.00	The road from Astoria to Williamsburg, bearing N. 80 W. and S. 80 E.
40.00	Set a post for quarter-section corner, from which A lynn, 15 in. dia., bears N. 88 W., 17 links dist.; A black oak, 18" dia., bears S. 76 E., 21 links dist.
54.20	A white oak 28 in. dia.
80.00	Set a post for corner to sections 8, 9, 16, 17, from which An elm, 10 in. dia., bears N. 28 E., 5 links dist.; A black oak, 10 in. dia., bears N. 13 W., 48 links dist.; An elm, 12 in. dia., bears S. 41 W., 42 links dist.; A bur oak, 6 in. dia., bears S. 17 E., 105 links dist. Land gently rolling; good, 2d rate. Timber, good quality and open woods, oak, elm, ash, and hickory.
	East, on a *random* line between sections 9 and 16, Variation 17° 40' east,
40.00	Set a post for temporary quarter-section corner.
45.00	Enter prairie, bearing N. and S.
81.20	Intersected the N. and S. line 22 links north of the corner to sections 9, 10, 15, 16; section 16 is, therefore, out of the proper limits, and I am of opinion that the error is in the measure of the line between sections 9 and 16; remeasure the line *east* of the temporary quarter-section corner, and find it to be 40.18 chains. There was, therefore, an error of one chain in this part of the line, which brings section 16 within its proper limits. From the corner to sections 9, 10, 15, 16, I run
	West, on a *true* line between sections 9 and 16, Variation 17° 31' east,
40.10	Set a post for quarter-section corner, from which A white oak, 16 in. dia., bears N. 35 E., 32 links dist.; A bur oak, 12 in. dia., bears S. 25 W., 21 links dist.
80.20	The corner to sections 8, 9, 16, 17. Land gently rolling; good, rich soil. The timbered land is open, without undergrowth; oak, hickory, and elm.
	☞ The line between sections 8 and 17 will strike the river in less than 80.00 chains. I therefore run it West, on a *true* line between sections 8 and 17. Variation 17° 40' east,
8.20	A black oak, 16 in. dia.
27.25	A black walnut, 12 in. dia. Here enter Chickeeles River bottom, bearing north and south.
40.00	Set a post for quarter-section corner, from which A hickory, 12 in. dia., bears N. 22 E., 10 links dist.; An ironwood, 8 in. dia., bears S. 7 E., 2 links dist.
55.10	A hickory, 16 in. dia.
56.50	Set a post on the left bank of Chickeeles River, a navigable stream, for

GENERAL INSTRUCTIONS OF 1855   153

Township 25 N., range 2 W., Willamette meridian—Continued.

Chains.	
	corner to fractional sections 8 and 17, from which
	A hickory, 12 in dia., bears N. 25 E., 8 links dist.;
	A hackberry, 12 in. dia., bears S. 25 E., 25 links dist.
	Land, the bottom level and rich, upland rolling.
	Timber, oak, hickory, buckeye, &c.
	North, between sections 8 and 9,
	Variation 17° 40′ east,
7.42	A walnut, 18 in. dia.
40.00	Set a post for quarter-section corner, from which
	A sugar tree, 9 in. dia., bears N. 35 E., 12 links dist.;
	A walnut, 30 in. dia., bears S. 22 W., 11 links dist.
47.42	A walnut, 18 in. dia.
53.74	A sugar tree, 20 in. dia.
80.00	Set a lime stone, 18 in. long, 12 in. wide, and 4 in. thick, for corner to sections 4, 5, 8, 9, from which
	A sand rock, 4 feet square at the surface of the ground, and 2 feet high, bears N. 47½ E., 341 links dist., marked with a (✕) cross, each mark being 6 in. long and ½ in. deep; bearing and distance taken to the cross.;
	A white oak, 36 in. dia., bears N. 24 W., 112 links dist.;
	A white oak, 30 in. dia., bears S. 13 W., 44 links dist.
	No tree in section 9 convenient to mark.
	Land rolling; good, 2d rate.
	Timber, oak, walnut, hickory, and sugar tree.
	Thick undergrowth, same, briers and vines.
	February 9, 1854.
	East, on a *random* line between sections 4 and 9,
	Variation 17° 40′ east,
35.60	Leave timber and enter prairie, bearing south and N. E.
40.00	Set a post for temporary quarter-section corner.
43.50	Northwest edge of a small deep pond of about 15 acres, lying mostly in section 9, offset north 400 chains to a point; thence east 9.50 chains to a point; thence south 4 chains to a point on the east bank of the pond, and in the random line between sections 4 and 9, and
53.00	*East* of the corner to sections 4, 5, 8, 9.
80.24	Intersected the north and south line 21 links south of the corner to sections 3, 4, 9, 10, from which corner I run
	West, on a *true* line between sections 4 and 9,
	Variation 17° 49′ east,
40.12	Set a white oak post, 6 inches diameter, in the eastern edge of prairie for quarter-section corner, from which
	A white oak, 16 in. dia., bears N. 56 W., 497 links dist.;
	A bur oak, 20 in. dia., bears S. 75 W., 512 links dist.
44.75	A black oak, 16 in. dia., in east edge of timber.
80.24	The corner to sections 4, 5, 8, 9.
	Land level; good soil.
	Timber, oak, hickory, and beech; very thick undergrowth; oak and hazel next the prairie.
	The line between sections 5 and 8 will strike Chickeeles River in less than 80 chains, I therefore run it a *true* line
	West, on a *true* line between sections 5 and 8,
	Variation 17° 40′ east,
13.77	A white oak, 20 in. dia.
40.00	Set a post for quarter-section corner, from which
	A white oak, 8 in. dia., bears N. 32 W., 4 links dist.;
	A white oak, 10 in. dia., bears S. 45 E., 5 links dist.
43.11	A white oak, 40 in. dia.
47.50	Leave broken upland and enter the bottom to Chickeeles River, bearing

Township 25 N., range 2 W., Willamette meridian—Continued.

Chains.	

60.65	south and N. E.
	Set a post on the left bank of Chickeeles River, for corner to fractional sections 5 and 8, from which
	    A blue ash, 24 in. dia., bears N. 66 E., 4 links dist.;
	    An elm, 24 in. dia., bears S. 56 E., 20 links dist.
	Land, upland broken, 3d rate; the bottom level and rich.
	Timber, oak, hickory, &c.; in the bottom, elm and ash; undergrowth, same, pawpaw, spice, and vines.

	The line between sections 4 and 5 will strike Chickeeles River before reaching the *township* line; I therefore run it North, on a *true* line between sections 4 and 5, Variation 17° 40′ east,
13.75	A cherry, 20 in. dia;
33.51	A white oak, 24 in. dia.

40.00	Set a post for quarter-section corner, from which
	    A white oak, 12 in. dia., bears N. 24 E., 12 links dist.;
	    A beech, 28 in. dia., bears S. 44 E., 21 links dist.
	No tree west of the line convenient to mark.

43.15	A white oak, 30 in. dia.
45.50	Leave broken upland and enter Chickeeles River bottom, bearing N. E. and S. W.
56.58	A hackberry, 24 in. dia.

66.50	An elm, 12 in. dia., on the left bank of Chickeeles River; mark it for corner to fractional sections 4 and 5, from which
	    A black oak, 14 in. dia., bears S. 10 W., 18 links dist.;
	    An elm, 18 in. dia., bears S. 45 E., 35 links dist.
	The upland broken, 3d rate; the bottom level, 1st rate.
	Timber on upland, oak; in bottom, elm, oak, ash, and hickory; undergrowth, pawpaw and spice. *February* 10, 1854.

	The point for corner to sections 5, 6, 31, and 32 being in a deep swamp, and not having been established, I begin at the witness corner on the S. E. edge of the swamp, 4.00 chains east of said point, and run thence east 250 links (with the line between sections 5 and 32) to a point; thence *north* 7.50 chains to a point; thence *west* 6.50 chains to a point on the north edge of the swamp and in the line between sections 31 and 32, and 7.50 chains *north* of the point for corner to sections 31 and 32, on the south boundary of the township. I here set a post for witness point, from which
	    A bur oak, 16 in. dia., bears N. 31 E., 25 links dist.;
	    An ash, 12 in. dia., bears N. 25 W., 17 links dist.
	From this witness point I run
	North, between sections 31 and 32, counting the distance from the point for corner to said sections in the swamp,
	    Variation 17° 40′ east,

12.98	A walnut, 22 in. dia.
38.19	An ash, 35 in. dia.

40.00	Set a post for quarter-section corner, from which
	    A beech, 20 in. dia., bears N. 12 W., 45 links dist.;
	    A sugar tree, 20 in. dia., bears S. 12 E., 13 links dist.

57.74	An ash, 24 in. dia.
66.19	A white oak, 36 in. dia.

80.00	Set a post with trench for corner to sections 29, 30, 31, 32, from which
	    A beech, 26 in. dia., bears N. 9 W., 12 links dist.;
	    A sugar tree, 24 in. dia., bears S. 13 E., 56 links dist.
	And planted N. E. a butter nut, and S. W. 4 cherry stones.
	Land south, half level, north, half rolling; good soil.
	Timber, oak, beech, sugar tree, and walnut; undergrowth, same, and hazel on north part.

GENERAL INSTRUCTIONS OF 1855   155

Township 25 N., range 2 W., Willamette meridian—Continued.

Chains.	
	East, on a *random* line between sections 29 and 32, Variation 17° 40' east,
40.00	Set a post for temporary quarter-section corner.
80.16	Intersected the N. and S. line 10 links N. of post corner to sections 28, 29, 32, and 33, from which corner I run West, on a *true* line between sections 29 and 32, Variation 17° 36' east,
40.08	Set a post for quarter-section corner, from which A black oak, 18 in. dia., bears N. 36 E., 42 links dist.; A bur oak, 20 in. dia., bears S. 43 W., 47 links dist.
80.16	The corner to sections 29, 30, 31, 32. Land gently rolling; good soil; fit for cultivation. Timber, oak, beech, hickory, and walnut; open woods.
	West, on a *true* line between sections 30 and 31, knowing that it will strike the Chickeeles River in less than 80.00 chains. Variation 17° 40' east,
3.41	A white oak, 15 in. dia.
5.00	Leave upland and enter creek bottom, bearing N. E. and S. W.
8.00	Elk Creek, 200 links wide, gentle current, muddy bottom and banks, runs S. W. Ascertain the distance across the creek on the line as follows, viz: Cause the flag to be set on the right bank of the creek, in the line between sections 30 and 31. From the station on the left bank of creek, at 8.00 chains, I run *south* 245 links to a point from which the flag on the right bank bears N. 45 W., which gives for the distance across the creek on the line between sections 30 and 31, 2 chains, 45 links.
25.17	A bur oak, 24 in. dia.
40.00	Set a post for quarter-section corner, from which A buckeye, 24 in. dia., bears N. 15 W., 8 links dist.; A white oak, 30 in. dia., bears S. 65 E., 12 links.
41.90	Set a post on the left bank of Chickeeles River, a navigable stream, for corner to fractional sections 30 and 31, from which A buckeye, 16 in dia., bears N. 50 E., 16 links dist.; A hackberry, 15 in. dia., bears S. 79 E., 14 links dist. Land, low bottom; subject to inundation 3 or 4 feet deep. Timber, buckeye, hackberry, oak, and hickory.
	North, between sections 29 and 30, Variation 17° 40' east,
6.50	Enter creek bottom, bearing N. E. and S. W.
13.00	Elk creek, 200 links wide, runs S. W.
15.00	Enter a small prairie, about 40 acres.
31.00	Leave prairie and enter timber, bearing E. and W.
40.00	Set a post for quarter-section corner, from which A hickory, 14 in dia., bears N. 78 E., 16 links dist.; A bur oak, 26 in. dia., bears N. 63 W., 19 links dist.
49.71	A black oak, 30 in dia.
68.19	A walnut, 36 in dia.
80.00	Set a post for corner to sections 19, 20, 29, 30, from which A beech, 15 in. dia., bears N. 24 E., 18 links dist.; A blue ash, 24 in. dia., bears N. 79 W., 10 links dist.; A bur oak, 9 in. dia., bears S. 14 W., 10 links dist.; A black oak, 8 in. dia., bears S. 11 E., 14 links dist. Land, first half-mile, level prairie, and brushy, oak and hazel; second half-mile, some good timber, oak, &c.; thick undergrowth same.
	East, on a *random* line between sections 20 and 29, Variation 70° 25' east,
40.00	Set a post for temporary quarter-section corner.
80.10	Intersected the N. and S. line 20 links north of the corner to sections

Township 25 N., *range* 2 W., *Willamette meridian—Continued.*

Chains.	
	20, 21, 28, 29, from which corner I run West, on a *true* line between sections 20 and 29, Variation 17° 31' east,

40.05	Set a post for quarter-section corner, from which
	    A sugar tree, 24 in. dia., bears N. 17 W., 20 links dist.;
	    A walnut, 14 in. dia., bears S. 10 E., 36 links dist.

80.10	The corner to sections 19, 20, 29, 30. Land level, and rather wet. Timber, oak, sugar tree, beech and walnut; open woods.
	West, on a *random* line between sections 19 and 30, Variation 17° 40' east,
40.00	Set a post for temporary quarter-section corner.
75.53	Intersected the west boundary of the township, 20 links south of the corner to sections 19 and 30, from which corner I run East, on a *true* line between sections 19 and 30, Variation 17° 31' east,

35.52	Set a post for quarter-section corner, from which
	    A sugar tree, 18 in. dia., bears N. 26 W., 23 links dist.;
	    An ash, 10 in. dia., bears S. 86 E., 32 links dist.

75.52	The corner to sections 19, 20, 29, 30. Land level; rich soil; not subject to inundation. Timber, sugar tree, beech, walnut, and ash; undergrowth, spice, prickly ash, and vines. *February* 11, 1854.
	North, between sections 19 and 20, Variation 17° 40' east,
7.70	A bur oak, 20 in. dia.
27.16	A locust, 18 in. dia.
34.00	A pond, 200 links wide, muddy bottom, and low banks; water not so deep as to prevent measuring across on the line with the chain. This pond extends about 15 chains east into section 20, and lies mostly in section 19, extending west.

40.00	Set a post for quarter-section corner, from which
	    A beech, 9 in. dia., bears N. 56 E., 44 links dist.;
	    A lynn, 12 in. dia., bears S. 36 W., 111 links dist.

49.00	The S. W. bank of a lake to be meandered.
	Set a post for corner to fractional sections 19 and 20, from which
	    A red oak, 12 in dia., bears S. 45 W., 21 links dist.;
	    A lynn, 15 in. dia., bears S. 23 E., 24 links dist.
	From this corner offset *west* 7.50 chains to a point; thence *north* on an offset line 24.00 chains to a point; thence *east* 7.50 chains to a point in the line between sections 19 and 20, 50 links in advance of lake; thence *south* to N. W. margin of lake, 50 links, where set a post for corner to fractional sections 19 and 20, from which
	    A red oak, 20 in. dia., bears N. 27 E., 31 links dist.;
	    A bur oak, 15 in. dia., bears N. 36 W., 24 links dist.
	This corner is 72.50 chains *north* of the corner to sections 19, 20, 29, 30, and from which I continue the line between sections 19 and 20 *north*, counting the distance from the corner to sections 19, 20, 29, 30.

80.00	Set a post for corner to sections 17, 18, 19, 20, from which
	    A chestnut, 10 in. dia., bears N. 14 E., 14 links dist.;
	    A buckeye, 12 in. dia., bears N. 86 W., 13 links dist.;
	    A beech, 20 in. dia., bears S. 13 W., 16 links dist.;
	    A buckeye, 20 in. dia., bears S. 27 E., 35 links dist.
	Land level; rich soil, but too wet for cultivation.
	Timber, oak, walnut, buckeye, and beech; undergrowth, prickly ash and vines.

Township 25 N., range 2 W., Willamette meridian—Continued.

Chains.	
	East, on a *random* line between sections 17 and 20, **Variation 17° 40' east,**
40.00	Set a post for temporary quarter-section corner.
79.90	Intersected N. and S. line 7 links north of post corner to sections 16, 17, 20, 21, from which corner I run West, on a *true* line between sections 17 and 20, **Variation 17° 37' east,**

39.95	Set a post near the north bank of the lake for quarter-section corner, from which
	  A white oak, 12 in. dia., bears N. 33 E., 19 links dist.;
	  A white oak, 15 in. dia., bears S. 16 W., 34 links dist.
	From this corner I run south 150 links, to a point on the north bank of the lake, where set a meander corner, from which
	  A red oak, 15 in. dia., bears N. 21 E., 15 links dist.;
	  An ash, 12 in dia., bears N. 16 W., 12 links dist.

79.90	The corner to sections 17, 18, 19, 20. Land level and wet; rich soil. Timber, oak, ash, elm, and beech; undergrowth same, briers and vines.

Meanders of Island Lake.

Begin at the corner to fractional sections 19 and 20, on the N. W. margin of the lake, and run thence along the N. W. margin thereof, in fractional section 20, as follows, viz:

N. 79 E., 20.00 chains, thence
N. 84 E., 20.43 chains to the meander corner 150 links *south* of the quarter-section corner, on the line between sections 17 and 20, thence
S. 73 E., 16.00 chains, thence
S. 61 E., 14.00 chains, thence
S. 40½ E., 19.22 chains, to the corner to fractional sections 20 and 21, on the N. E. bank of lake, at 52.33 chains. At 18.00 chains on this line cross the mouth of a branch, 30 links wide, coming from N. E.

Begin at the corner to fractional sections 20 and 21, on S. E. bank of lake, at 28.94 chains, and run thence along the southern bank of said lake in fractional section 20, as follows:

S. 70 W., 20.00 chains, thence
S. 85 W., 23.00 chains, thence ⎫ *At 14.50 chains cross outlet to lake,
N. 70 W., 12.00 chains, thence ⎬ 30 links wide, running W. about 5
N. 30 W., 18.00 chains, thence* ⎭ chains into pond.
N. 63 W., 20.24 chains, to the corner to fractional sections 19 and 20, at 49.00 chains; thence in section 19 as follows, viz:
N. 75 W., 5.00 chains, thence
N. 60 W., 2.00 chains, thence
N. 10 W., 6.00 chains, thence
N. 10 E., 6.00 chains, thence
N. 25 E., 3.00 chains, thence
N. 38¼ E., 8.48 chains to the corner to fractional sections 19 and 20, on the bank of lake at 72.50 chains.

This lake has low, wet, brushy banks, and has an island of timber in the middle, which ought to be meandered. Timber around lake, ash, maple, and red oak. I cause a flag to be set on the north bank of the island *south* of the meander corner, which is 150 links *south* of the quarter-section corner on the line between sections 17 and 20. From the meander corner run a base 7.50 *east* to a point, from which the flag bears S. 45 W., which gives for the distance across the water to the flag on the island 7.50 chains. Set a meander post in the place of the flag, from which a red oak, 15 in. dia., bears S. 21 W. 24 links, and an ash, 10 in. dia., bears S. 25 E., 17 links dist. From the meander post I run around the island as follows:

S. 62 E., 7.50 chains, thence

Between townships 25 *and* 26 *N.,* R. 2 *W., Willamette meridian*—Continued.

Chains.	
	S. 55 E., 10.00 chains, thence
	S. 20 E., 5.00 chains, thence
	South, 4.00 chains, thence
	S. 25 W., 6.00 chains, thence
	S. 62 W., 5.00 chains, thence
	S. 80 W., 4.00 chains, thence
	West, 3.50 chains, thence
	N. 70 W., 5.00 chains, thence
	N. 62 W., 15.00 chains, thence
	N. 45 W., 10.00 chains, thence
	N. 35 W., 6.00 chains, thence
	N. 40 E., 6.50 chains, thence
	N. 82 E., 8.00 chains, thence
	S. 88½ E., 14.20 chains, to the meander corner and place of beginning. This island is well timbered, and is good, dry land.
	Timber, oak, hickory, beech, and ash; undergrowth, same and vines.
	The line between sections 18 and 19 will strike the river before reaching the range line; I therefore run it
	West, on a *true* line between sections 18 and 19,
	Variation 17° 40′ east,
7.91	A buckeye, 15 in. dia.;
16.54	A locust, 24 in. dia.
28.90	Set a post on the left bank of Chickeeles River for corner to fractional sections 18 and 19, from which
	A buckeye, 24 in. dia., bears N. 76 E., 22 links dist.;
	A hackberry, 16 in. dia., bears S. 24 W., 15 links.
	There is an island in the river opposite this corner. To ascertain the distance on the line between sections 18 and 19 to the island, I send my flagman across the slough, who sets the flag on the S. E. bank of the island, and in the line between sections 18 and 19, from the corner to said sections on the left bank of the river. I run south 260 links to a point from which the flag on the island bears N. 45½ W., which gives for the distance 3.79 chains, to which add 28.90 chains, makes
32.69	To the flag. Set a post in the place of the flag for corner to fractional sections 18 and 19, from which
	A white oak, 16 in dia., bears N. 41 W., 37 links dist.;
	A bur oak, 14 in. dia., bears S. 81 W., 16 links dist.
36.52	A white oak, 20 in. dia.;
39.10	A bur oak, 16 in dia.
40.00	Set a post for quarter-section corner, from which
	A white oak, 15 in. dia., bears N. 15 W., 21 links dist.;
	A walnut, 20 in. dia., bears S. 21 E., 17 links dist.
45.50	Set a post on the N. W. bank of the island for **corner to fractional sections** 18 and 19, from which
	A hackberry, 10 in. dia., bears N. 85 E., 15 links dist.;
	A hickory, 15 in. dia., bears S. 51 E., 17 links dist.
	From this corner I meander around the island as follows: In section 19,
	S. 60 W., 10.00 chains, thence
	S. 43 W., 8.00 chains, thence
	South, 2.00 chains, thence
	East, 2.00 chains, thence
	N. 55 E., 4.00 chains, thence
	N. 60 E., 10.00 chains, thence
	N. 66½ E., 14.15 chains, to the corner to fractional sections 18 and 19, on the S. E. bank of the island, thence in section 18
	N. 70 E., 10.00 chains, thence
	N. 75 E., 10.00 chains, thence
	N. 25 E., 4.00 chains, thence

Township 25, N. range 2 W., Willamette meridian—Continued.

Chains.	
	North, 2.50 chains, thence West, 1.00 chains, thence S. 66 W., 2.00 chains, thence S. 75 W., 4.00 chains, thence S. 80 W., 10.00 chains, thence S. 63½ W., 21.10 chains, to the corner to fractional sections 18 and 19, on the N. W. bank of island, and place of beginning. Land, on island and main shore, level and rich; not subject to inundation. Timber, oak, hickory, ash, and walnut; undergrowth, same and vines.
6.57 10.80	North, between sections 17 and 18, Variation 17° 40' east, A hickory, 20 in. dia. Set a post on the left bank of Chickeeles River for corner to fractional sections 17 and 18, from which A buckeye, 8 in. dia., bears S. 25 W., 15 links dist.; A hackberry, 10 in. dia., bears S. 61 E., 3 links dist. MONDAY, *February* 13, 1854.

Meanders of the left bank of Chickeeles River through the township.

Chains.		Distances.	Remarks
		Chains.	Begin at the corner to fractional sections 4 and 33, in the north boundary of the township and on the left and S. E. bank of the river, and run thence down stream with the meanders of the left bank of said river, in fractional section 4, as follows:
S. 76	W.	18.50	
S. 61	W.	10.00	
S. 59	W.	8.30	To the corner to fractional sections 4 and 5; thence in section 5.
S. 54	W.	10.70	
S. 40	W.	5.60	
S. 50	W.	8.50	
S. 37	W.	17.00	
S. 44	W.	22.00	
S. 38	W.	26.72	To the corner to fractional section 5 and 8; thence in section 8.
S. 21	W.	16.00	
S. 10	W.	13.00	
South		8.50	To the head of rapids.
S. 9	E.	5.00	
S. 17	E.	20.00	
S. 10	E.	12.00	To foot of rapids.
S. 22¼	E.	8.46	To the corner to fractional sections 8 and 17. Land, along fractional section 8, high, rich bottom; not subject to inundation. The rapids are 37.00 chains long; rocky bottom; estimated fall 10 feet. *Meanders in section* 17.
S. 17	E.	15.00	At 5 chains discovered a vein of coal, which appears to be 5 feet thick, and may be readily worked.
S. 8	E.	12.00	
S. 4	W.	22.00	At 3.00 chains the ferry across the river to Williamsburg,

Original Instructions Governing Public Land Surveys 1815-1855

Township 25, N. range 2 W., Willamette meridian—Continued.

Meanders of the left bank of Chickeeles River through the township.

Chains.	Distances.	Remarks
	Chains.	on the opposite side of the river.
S. 25 W.	17.00	
S. 78 W.	12.00	
S. 71 W.	9.55	To the corner to fractional sections 17 and 18; thence in section 18.
S. 65 W.	15.00	
S. 73¾ W.	15.93	To the corner to fractional sections 18 and 19.
S. 65 W.	14.00	In section 19.
S. 60 W.	23.00	
S. 42 W.	10.00	
S. 20 W.	10.00	
S. 16½ W.	13.83	☞ At 2 chains cross outlet to pond and lake, 50 links wide, to the corner to fractional sections 19 and 24, on the range line, 32.50 chains north of the corner to sections 19, 30, 24, and 25.
		Begin at the corner to fractional sections 25 and 30, on the range line 1 chain *south* of the quarter-section corner on said line, and run thence down stream with the meanders of the left bank of Chickeeles River, in fractional section 30, as follows, viz:
S. 41 E.	20.00	At 10 chains discovered a fine mineral spring.
S. 49 E.	15.00	Here appear the remains of an Indian village.
S. 42 E.	12.00	
S. 12¾ E.	5.30	To the corner to fractional sections 30 and 31; thence in section 31.
S. 12 E.	10.00	
S. 12 W.	13.50	To the mouth of Elk River, 200 links wide; comes from the east.
S. 41 W.	9.00	At 200 links across the creek.
S. 58 W.	11.00	
S. 35 W.	11.00	
S. 20 W.	20.00	At 15 chains mouth of stream, 25 links wide; comes from S. E.
S. 23¾ W.	8.80	To the corner to fractional sections 31 and 36, on the range line, and 8.56 chains north of the corner to sections 1, 6, 31, and 36, or S. W. corner to this township.
		Land along the left bank of Chickeeles River is level, rich soil, and only a small part subject to inundation.
		Timber, oak, hickory, beech, and elm; not much undergrowth.
		February 14, 1854.

Chains.	
	From the corner to sections 30 and 31, on the west boundary of the township, I run East, on a *true* line between sections 30 and 31, Variation 18° east,
15.10	A white oak, 16 in. dia.
23.50	Intersected the right bank of Chickeeles River, where set a post for corner to fractional sections 30 and 31, from which A black oak, 16 in. dia., bears N. 60 W., 25 links dist.; A white oak, 20 in. dia., bears S. 35 W., 32 links dist. From this corner I run south 12 links, to a point *west* of the corner to fractional sections 30 and 31, on the left bank of the river; thence

GENERAL INSTRUCTIONS OF 1855   161

Township 25, N. range 2 W., Willamette meridian—Continued.

Chains.	
	continue south 314 links, to a point from which the corner to fractional sections 30 and 31, on the left bank of the river, bears N. 72 east; which gives for the distance across the river, 9.65 chains. The length of the line between sections 30 and 31 as follows, viz.:
	Part east of river_____ 41.90 chains.
	Part across river_____ 9.65
	Part west of river_____ 23.50
	Total _____ 75.05
	Commence the meanders of section 31 at the corner to fractional sections 31 and 36, on the right bank of Chickeeles River, and run thence up stream with the meanders of the right bank of said river, in fractional section 31, as follows:
	N. 25 E. 7.00 chains; thence
	N. 38 E. 11.00 chains thence
	N. 50 E. 12.50 chains; thence
	N. 25 E. 10.00 chains; thence
	North 13.40 chains, to the corner to fractional sections 30 and 31; thence, in section 30,
	N. 45° W. 14.00 chains; thence
	N. 40 W. 12.00 chains; thence
	N. 34½ W. 10.50 chains, to the corner to fractional sections 25 and 30, on the right bank of Chickeeles River, 27.73 chains north of the corner to sections 25, 30, 31, 36.
	Land level; rich bottom; not subject to inundation.
	Timber, oak, hickory, and ash; undergrowth, same, spice and vines.
	From the corner to sections 18, 19, 13, and 24, I run East, on a *true* line between sections 18 and 19, Variation 18° 00' east,
3.52	A bur oak, 20 in. dia.
17.31	A white oak, 15 in. dia.
21.00	Set a post on the right bank of Chickeeles River for corner to fractional sections 18 and 19, from which
	A white oak, 15 in. dia., bears N. 10 E., 31 links dist.;
	A black oak, 20 in. dia., bears S. 80 W., 15 links dist.
	From this corner the corner to fractional sections 18 and 19, on the N. W. bank of the island, bears *east*.
	To obtain the distance across the river between the two corners, I run (from the corner on right bank) *north* 375 links to a point from which the corner on the island bears S. 68 E.; which gives for the distance 9.27 chains.
	The length of the line between sections 18 and 19 is 75.77 chains, the several parts of which being as follows:
	East of river and across the island, including 3.79 chains across the slough_____ 45.50 chains.
	Across the river N. W. of island_____ 9.27
	West of river _____ 21.00
	Aggregate, as above _____ 75.77
	From the corner to fractional sections 19 and 24, on the right bank of Chickeeles River, I run up stream with the right bank of said river, in fractional section 19, as follows, viz:
	N. 30 E. 20.00 chains; thence
	N. 45¼ E. 15.50 chains, to the corner to fractional sections 18 and 19; thence, in section 18,
	N. 58 E. 10.00 chains; thence
	N. 63 E. 17.00 chains; thence

Township 25, N. range 2 W., Willamette meridian—Continued.

Chains.	
	N. 75¾ E. 32.12 chains, to a point on the right bank of Chickeeles River *north* of the corner to fractional sections 17 and 18, on the left bank of the river. I here set a post for corner to fractional sections 17 and 18, on the north side of river, from which
	A black oak, 15 in. dia., bears N. 25 E., 21 links dist.;
	A black oak, 20 in. dia., bears N. 27 W., 17 links dist.
	To obtain the distance across the river, on the line between sections 17 and 18, I run a base line *west* 430 links, to a point from which the post corner to fractional sections 17 and 18, on the left and south bank of the river, bears S. 23 east; which gives for the distance 10.13 chains, to which add 10.80 chains, makes
20.93	To the corner to fractional sections 17 and 18, on the right and north bank of the river.

Survey of a claim of 640 *acres, confirmed by law to Samuel Williams.*

Begin at a black oak, 15 inches diameter, on the right bank of Chickeeles River, opposite the head of a small island in said river. Mark said tree with a blaze, 15 inches long and 6 inches wide, a notch at the top and another at the bottom of the blaze, and on the face of the blaze, with a marking iron, the letters P. S. C., (private survey claim.) From the corner tree
    A black oak, 20 in. dia., bears N. 27 W., 55 links dist.;
    A bur oak, 16 in. dia., bears S. 50 W., 41 lins dist.
Both trees marked with a blaze and notch at the lower end of the blaze, facing the corner tree; and on the blaze, with a marking iron, cut the letters W. P. S., (witness private survey.) This is also the S. E. corner of the town of Williamsburg, and from which I run up stream with the meanders of the right bank of Chickeeles River as follows:
At an assumed
                Variation 18° 00' east,
North 17.00 chains; at 11.00 chains ferry landing;
N. 12 W. 16.00 chains;
N. 18 W. 20.00 chains; at 14 chains foot of rapids;
N. 12 W. 27.45 chains, to a point on the right bank of the river, where set a post for corner to this survey, from which
    A black oak, 20 in. dia., bears N. 75 W., 33 links dist.;
    A white oak, 20 in. dia., bears S. 43 W., 35 links dist.
NOTE.—At 3 chains on the last course of meanders cross the mouth of stream, 40 links wide; comes from the N. W.
From this corner I run

	S. 78 W., with the northern line of this survey,
15.17	A black oak, 20 in. dia.
20.00	A stream, 30 links wide, rapid current, runs S. E.
37.51	A bur oak, 20 in. dia.
52.34	A hickory, 16 in. dia.
62.41	A white oak, 20 in. dia.
79.42	Set a post for corner to this survey, from which
	A black oak, 16 in. dia., bears N. 25 E., 16 links dist.;
	A white oak, 20 in. dia., bears N. 10 W., 21 links dist.;
	A white oak, 24 in. dia., bears S. 21 W., 16 links dist.;
	A black oak, 24 in. dia., bears S. 60 E., 17 links dist.; thence
	S. 12 E., with the western line of this survey,
10.25	A black oak, 16 in. dia.
17.51	A white oak, 15 in. dia.
41.73	A sugar tree, 20 in. dia.
55.00	The road to Williamsburg, bearing E. and W.
61.53	An elm, 14 in dia.
80.00	Set a post for corner of this survey, from which

GENERAL INSTRUCTIONS OF 1855 163

*Township 25, N. range 2 W., Willamette meridian—*Continued.

Chains.	
	A white oak, 16 in. dia., bears N. 73 E., 25 links dist.,
	A white oak, 12 in. dia., bears N. 21 W., 17 links dist.;
	A black oak, 20 in. dia., bears S. 61 W., 22 links dist.;
	A black oak, 24 in. dia., bears S. 31 E., 23 links dist.; thence N. 78 E., with the southern line of this survey,
15.73	A black oak, 16 in. dia.
25.31	A black oak, 20 in. dia.
45.61	A white oak, 12 in. dia.
67.20	A white oak, 18 in. dia.
77.68	To the corner tree and place of beginning.
	The land of this claim rolling; good, 2d rate soil, somewhat broken along the rapids in the N. E. part; well timbered, black oak, white oak, hickory, and bur oak; not much undergrowth; some hazel, briers, and vines. The town of Williamsburg, situated on the S. E. part of the claim, is pleasantly located on the right bank of the river, some 8 or 10 feet above high water, and has at this time sixteen families residing in it. Some three or four tenements are now being constructed within the limits of the town.
	February 15, 1854.

	From the corner to fractional sections 17 and 18, on the right and north bank of Chickeeles River, 20.93 chains north of the corner to sections 17, 18, 19, 20, I run
	North, between sections 17 and 18, counting the distance from the corner to sections 17, 18, 19, 20, Variation 18° east,
22.73	A black oak, 20 in. dia.
36.45	Intersected the southern line of Samuel Williams's claim, where set a post for corner to fractional sections 17 and 18, from which
	A black oak, 16 in. dia., bears S. 50 W., 22 links dist.;
	A white oak, 20 in. dia., bears S. 21 E., 31 links dist.
	From this corner I run N. 78 E., along the southern line of the said claim, 20.15 chains, to the corner tree on the right bank of Chickeeles River and S. E. corner of said claim; thence down stream, on the right bank of said river, in fractional section 17, as follows:
	S. 16 W. 10.00 chains; thence
	S. 45 W. 10.00 chains; thence
	S. 72 W. 10.30 chains, to the corner to fractional sections 17 and 18.

	Field-notes of the survey of a small island in Chickeeles River, lying wholly in section 17.
	Cause the flag to be set on the head of the island, at a point bearing S. 45 E. from the black oak tree, the S. E. corner to Samuel Williams's claim; from said corner tree run S. 45 W. 215 links, to a point *west* of the flag on the head of the island; which gives for the distance from the corner tree to the flag 215 links. Set a meander post in the place of the flag, from which
	A bur oak, 16 in dia., bears S. 10 W., 15 links dist.;
	A white oak, 12 in. dia., bears S. 15 E., 21 links dist.
	From the meander post I run around the island as follows:
	S. 16 W. 9.00 chains; thence
	S. 45 W. 10.00 chains; thence
	S. 10 W. 2.00 chains; thence
	South 1.50 chains, to the lower end of island; thence
	East 1.50 chains; thence
	N. 75 E. 4.00 chains; thence
	N. 50 E. 5.00 chains; thence
	N. 30 E. 6.00 chains; thence

Township 25, N. range 2 W., Willamette meridian—Continued.

Chains.	
	N. 10 E. 6.00 chains; thence N. 10 W. 3.00 chains; thence N. 73 W. 2.96 chains, to the meander post and place of beginning. This island is well timbered; white and black oak and hickory; not subject to inundation; undergrowth, same, spice, and vines.
7.93	From the corner to sections 7, 18, 12, and 13, on the range line, I run East, on a *true* line between sections 7 and 18, Variation 18° 00′ east, Intersected the western line of Samuel Williams's survey of 640 acres, and at said intersection set a post for corner to fractional sections 7 and 18, from which A white oak, 15 in. dia., bears N. 25 W., 15 links dist.; A black oak, 20 in. dia., bears S. 34 W., 19 links dist. From this corner I run N. 12 W., with the western line of said Williams's claim, 23.23 chains, to the N. W. corner thereof. Land gently rolling. Timber, oak and hickory.
	From the corner to fractional sections 17 and 18, in the southern line of Samuel Williams's survey, and 36.45 chains *north* of the corner to Sections 17, 18, 19, 20, I run North, on a blank line passing through Samuel Williams's survey, counting the distance from the corner to said sections 17, 18, 19, 20, Variation 18° 00′ east,
40.00	Point for quarter-section corner in Samuel Williams's survey; corner not established.
52.50	The road leading into Williamsburg.
80.00	Set a temporary corner to sections 7, 8, 17, 18, in said Williams's claim. This line passes through the back part of the town of Williamsburg, but I make no connection with the lines of said town.
	North, on a *blank* line between section 7 and 8, Variation 18° 00′ east,
12.50	To creek, 30 links wide; runs east; comes from N. W.
38.10	Intersected the north boundary of Samuel Williams's survey, where set a post for corner to fractional section 7 and 8, from which A black oak, 10 in. dia., bears N. 10 E., 15 links dist.; A bur oak, 15 in. dia., bears N. 16 W., 17 links dist. From this corner I run N. 78 E., on the north line of said claim, 440 links, to the N. E. corner thereof, on the right bank of Chickeeles River. From the corner of fractional sections 7 and 8, in the north line of Samuel Williams's survey, North, on a *true* line between sections 7 and 8, counting the distance from a temporary corner to sections 7, 8, 17, 18, within said Williams's survey, Set a post for quarter-section corner, from which
40.00	A black oak, 15 in. dia., bears N. 25 E., 16 links dist.; A white oak, 16 in. dia., bears N. 73 W., 12 links dist. A white oak, 18 in dia.
45.17	A bur oak, 15 in. dia.
63.71	
80.00	Set a post for corner to sections 5, 6, 7, 8, from which A red oak, 20 in. dia., bears N. 20 E., 40 links dist.; A white oak, 16 in. dia., bears N. 16 W., 43 links dist.; A red oak, 24 in. dia., bears S. 80 W., 39 links dist.; A white oak, 40 in. dia., bears S. 75 E., 22 links dist. Land gently rolling; good rich soil. Timber, oak, hickory, and ash. *February* 16, 1854.

GENERAL INSTRUCTIONS OF 1855 165

Township 25, N. range 2 W., Willamette meridian—Continued.

Chains.	
	East, on a *true* line between sections 5 and 8, Variation 18° 00′ east,
5.16	A white oak, 15 in. dia.
7.41	A bur oak, 12 in. dia.
10.50	Set a post on the right bank of Chickeeles River for corner to fractional sections 5 and 8, west of river, from which
	A red oak, 30 in. dia., bears N. 58 W., 5 links dist.;
	A hickory, 12 in. dia., bears S. 42 W., 5 links dist.
	From this corner the post corner to fractional sections 5 and 8, on the left bank of the river, bears S. 89 E.
	From a point 16 links *south* of this corner, and *west* of the corner to fractional sections 5 and 8, on the left and east bank of the river, I run north 454 links, to a point from which the corner post on the left bank of the river bears S. 63 E., which gives for the distance across the river 8.91 chains. The length of the line between sections 5 and 8, including the distance across the river is, therefore, 80.06 chains, viz:
	East of river _____ 60.65 chains.
	Across river _____ 8.91
	West of river _____ 10.50
	Total _____ 80.06
	West, on a *random* line between sections 6 and 7, Variation 18° 00′ east,
25.10	A stream, 25 links wide, gentle current, runs south.
40.00	Set a post for temporary quarter-section corner.
56.00	A stream, 15 links wide, runs S. E.
76.26	Intersected the west boundary 21 links north of the corner to sections 6 and 7, from which corner I run East, on a *true* line between sections 6 and 7, Variation 18° 09′ east,
36.26	Set a post for quarter-section corner, from which
	A black oak, 16 in. dia., bears N. 15 W., 21 links dist.;
	A white oak, 40 in. dia., bears S. 21 W., 33 links dist.
76.26	The corner to sections 5, 6, 7, 8.
	Land hilly; 2d rate.
	Timber, oak, sugar tree, and hickory; undergrowth, same and hazel.
	North, on a *random* line between sections 5 and 6, Variation 18° 00′ east,
20.00	Enter windfall, bearing N. 60 W. and S. 60 E.
35.00	Leave windfall, having same bearings.
40.00	Set a post for temporary quarter-section corner.
80.06	Intersected the north boundary of the township 24 links east of the corner to sections 5 and 6, from which corner I run South, on a *true* line between said sections 5 and 6, Variation 18° 10′ east,
40.06	Set a post for quarter-section corner, from which
	A hickory, 20 in. dia., bears N. 18 E., 27 links dist.;
	A white oak, 24 in. dia., bears S. 31 W., 18 links dist.
80.06	The corner to sections 5, 6, 7, 8.
	Land rolling, and 2d rate.
	Timber, oak, hickory, sugar tree, and ash; undergrowth, same and hazel.
	From the corner to sections 4, 5, 32, and 33, on the north boundary of the township, I run South, on a *true* line between sections 4 and 5, Variation 18° 00′ east,
2.10	A white oak, 15 in. dia.
4.00	Set a post on the right bank of Chickeeles River for corner to fractional

Township 25, *N. range* 2 *W., Willamette meridian*—Continued.

Chains.	

	sections 4 and 5, from which
	    A bur oak, 16 in. dia., bears N. 25 E., 34 links dist.;
	    A black oak, 20 in. dia., bears N. 33 W., 21 links dist.
	From this corner the post corner to fractional sections 4 and 5, on the left bank of the river, bears S. ½ W. To obtain the distance across the river I run (from the corner on the right bank) N. 89° 30′ W. 326 links, to a point from which the post corner to fractonal sections 4 and 5, on the left bank, bears S. 18° 30′ E., which gives for the distance 9.46 chains. The length of the line between sections 4 and 5 will, therefore, be as follows, viz:
	Part south of the river _____ 66.50 chains.
	Part across the river _____ 9.46
	Part north of the river_____ 4.00
	                                                             —————
	        Aggregate _____ 79.96

	From the corner to fractional sections 4 and 33, on the right bank of Chickeeles River, I run down stream with the meanders of the right and N. W. bank of said river as follows, viz: In section 4— S. 40° 45′ W. 5.35 chains, to the corner to fractional sections 4 and 5; thence, in section 5, S. 72 W. 11.00 chains; thence S. 55 W. 20.00 chains; thence S. 40 W. 20.00 chains, (at this point the bluff comes to the river;) thence S. 42 W. 18.00 chains; thence S. 40 W. 18.00 chains; thence S. 18¼ W. 19.75 chains; to the corner to fractional sections 5 and 8. Land rolling along the last three courses, which are under a bluff bank from 20 to 30 feet high; the bottom, along the first three courses of meanders, good, rich land Timber, oak, hickory, ash, elm, and buckeye; undergrowth, same and vines in the bottom.
	From the corner to fractional sections 5 and 8, on the right bank of the river, I continue the meanders down stream, along fractional section 8, as follows, under a bluff bank from 20 to 30 feet high: S. 26 W. 9.70 chains; thence S. 10 W. 15.00 chains; thence South 15.00 chains, to the head of rapids; thence S. 12 E. 2.55 chains, to the corner to fractional section 8 and N. E. corner of Samuel Williams's claim. Mark the black oak witness tree to this corner, bearing N. 75 W., 33 links distant, "Section 8." Land rolling, and rather broken along the river. Timber, principally oak. *February* 17, 1854.

	Private claim surveyed after public survey.
	Survey of a claim of 640 acres, confirmed by law to Daniel Reed.
	Begin at the corner to fractional sections 5 and 8, on the left bank of Chickeeles River.
	The corner post standing, and witness trees agree with the description furnished me, viz:
	    A blue ash, 24 in. dia., bears N. 66 E., 4 links dist.;
	    An elm, 24 in. dia., bears S. 56 E., 20 links dist.
	From this corner I run down stream with the meanders of the left and east bank of said river S. 21 W. 16.00 chains, to a point where set a post on the left and east bank of Chickeeles River for the S. W. corner of the said Reed's claim, from which
	    A black oak, 16 in. dia., bears N. 44 E., 37 links dist.

Township 25, N. range 2 W., Willamette meridian—Continued.

Chains.	
	This tree marked with a blaze, 15 inches long, 6 inches wide, facing the corner post, with two notches—one at the upper end and the other at the lower end of the blaze; also marked with a marking iron on the face of the blaze the letters D. R., (Daniel Reed,) W. P. C., (witness private claim.)
	A bur oak, 20 in. dia., bears S. 47 E., 45 links dist.
	Marked with a blaze and notch at the lower end of the blaze facing the corner post, with the letters R. 2 W., T. 25 N. , sec. 8.
	From the corner post I run
	S. 54 E. along the S. W. boundary line of said claim,
	Variation 17° 40′ east,
10.51	A bur oak, 16 in. dia.
20.67	A black oak, 20 in. dia.
31.00	Leave river bottom and enter upland, bearing N. and S.
44.73	A white oak, 24 in. dia.
57.34	A white oak, 20 in. dia.
77.90	Set a post for corner of this claim and fractional section 8, from which
	A white oak, 16 in. dia., bears N. 40 W., 31 links dist.
	This tree marked with a blaze and two notches facing the corner post— one notch above and the other below the blaze. Mark the letters W. P. C. (witness private claim) on the face of the blaze.
	A black oak, 20 in dia., bears S. 10 W., 21 links dist.;
	A bur oak, 15 in. dia., bears S. 45 E., 13 links dist.
	Both trees marked with a blaze and notch facing the post, and S. 8 with a marking iron.
	From this corner I run
	N. 36 E. along the southeastern line of this claim,
	Variation 17° 40′ east,
3.41	A white oak, 15 in. dia.
5.45	Intersected the line between section 8 and 9, where set a post for corner to fractional sections 8 and 9, from which
	A white oak, 16 in. dia., bears S. 25 W., 22 links dist.;
	A bur oak, 20 in dia., bears S. 37 E., 18 links dist.
	From this corner I run *south* with the line between said sections 23.70 chains, to the corner to sections 8, 9, 16, 17.
33.73	A white oak, 15 in. dia.
41.17	A bur oak, 16 in. dia.
57.31	A white oak, 20 in. dia.
60.57	A black oak, 30 in. dia.
64.00	Leave timber and enter prairie, bearing N. and S.
75.17	Intersected the line between sections 4 and 9, where set a post with mound and trench for corner to fractional sections 4 and 9.
	Plant N. E. a hickory nut, S. E. 4 apple seeds.
	To obtain the distance on the line between sections 4 and 9, from the fractional-section corner just established to the corner to sections 3, 4, 9, 10, I run as follows:
	North 4.00 chains (to avoid the pond) to a point; thence *east* on an offset line 12.00 chains to a point; thence *south* 4.00 chains, to the line between said sections 4 and 9; thence *east* with said line, and at 39.33 chains, the corner to sections 3, 4, 9, 10, the distance being counted from the corner to fractional sections 4 and 9, in the S. E. line of Daniel Reed's claim.
80.00	To a point for the east corner of the claim. Set a lime stone, 10 inches square and 6 inches thick, and post with mound and trench, as per instructions, for corner to said claim and to fractional section 4. From the corner a white oak, 16 in. dia., standing in the edge of the timber, bears N. 65 W., 555 links distant. Mark said tree with a blaze and two notches—one above and the other below the blaze—facing the corner. With a marking iron cut the letters W. P. C. (witness private claim)

Township 25, N. range 2 W., Willamette meridian—Continued.

Chains.	
	on the face of the blaze. This corner about 3.00 chains N. W. of a small pond. Thence I run
	N. 54 W. along the N. E. boundary line of this claim, Variation 17° 40′ east,
5.50	Leave prairie and enter timber, bearing N. E. and S. W.
10.53	A bur oak, 15 in. dia.
25.34	A black oak, 16 in. dia.
54.07	Intersected the line between sections 4 and 5.
	Here set a post for corner to fractional sections 4 and 5, from which
	A black oak, 16 in. dia., bears N. 43 E., 22 links dist.;
	A white oak, 20 in. dia., bears N. 37 W., 17 links dist.
	From this corner I run *north* with the line between said sections 4 and 5, and at 30.81 chains, the corner to fractional sections 4 and 5, on the left and south bank of Chickeeles River.
64.00	Leave upland, and enter river bottom, bearing N. E. and S. W.
65.50	A bur oak, 20 in. dia.
71.53	A bur oak, 16 in. dia.
75.36	A walnut, 36 in. dia.
77.90	Set a post on the left and S. E. bank of Chickeeles River, for corner of this claim and fractonal section 5, from which
	A white oak, 16 in. dia., bears N. 60 E., 31 links dist.
	Marked with a blaze and notch facing the post, and section 5 on the face of the blaze.
	A bur oak, 15 in. dia., bears S. 40 E., 37 links dist.
	Marked with a blaze and two notches facing the post. The letters W. P. C. (witness private claim) cut with a marking iron on the face of the blaze.
	From this corner I run up stream with the meanders of the left and S. E. bank of the river in fractional section 5.
	N. 37 E., 1.00 chains, thence
	N. 50 E.,, 8.50 chains, thence
	N. 40 E., 5.60 chains, thence
	N. 54 E., 10.70 chains, to the corner to fractional sections 4 and 5, on the left bank of the river.
	From the corner to fractional section 5, and the upper corner to the claim on the left bank of Chickeeles River, I run down stream with the meanders of the left bank of said river, within the claim, as follows:
	S. 37 W., 16.00 chains, thence
	S. 44 W., 22.00 chains, thence
	S. 38 W., 26.72 chains, to the original corner to fractional sections 5 and 8, on the left and east bank of Chickeeles River, and place of beginning.
	Land, much the largest portion of this claim gently rolling upland; good, 2d rate timber, oak, walnut, hickory, and sugar tree. The bottom land along the river is dry, rich land, not subject to inundation.
	Timber, walnut, oak, hickory, and hackberry; undergrowth same, briers and vines.

February 18, 1854.

GENERAL DESCRIPTION

The quality of the land in this township is considerably above the common average. There is a very fair proportion of rich bottom land, chiefly situated on both sides of Chickeeles River, which is navigable through the township for steamboats of light draught, except over the rapids in section 8. These rapids are 37 chains long; estimated fall, about 10 feet.

The uplands are generally rolling, good 1st and 2d rate land, and well adapted for cultivation. Elk River is a beautiful stream of clear water, running through the southern part of the township, and emptying into Chickeeles River, in section 31. There is a fine mill-seat on this stream in section 22.

Timber, chiefly oak, beech, hickory, hackberry, and sugar tree, and is very equally distributed over the township, except in the prairie embracing parts of sections 3, 4, 9, 10, 15, and 16.

The town of Williamsburg was laid out by Samuel Williams, some two years since, on the right bank of Chickeeles River, a little below the foot of the rapids. It now contains sixteen houses, and others are being built; has a good landing in front, with a ferry, and has the appearance of thrift and prosperity.

There are several good quarries of stone (principally lime) along the Chickeeles and Elk Rivers, which will afford inexhaustible quantities of excellent building materials. On the line between sections 1 and 12 I discovered gold dust and auriferous quartz, and in section 17, on the left bank of Chickeeles River, opposite Williamsburg, a valuable coal bank. There are three settlements—one on the N. W. quarter of section 10, one on the N. W. quarter of section 15 and N. E. quarter of section 16, and the other on the N. E. quarter of section 23 and N. W. quarter of section 24.

A valuable salt spring was discovered crossing the south boundary of section 31, running N. W.; also the remains of an Indian village on the left bank of Chickeeles River, in section 30. Fossil remains on the west bank of a small lake in section 26, and ancient works on the left bank of Elk river, in the N. E. quarter of section 27.

LIST OF NAMES.

A list of the names of the individuals employed to assist in running, measuring, or marking the lines and corners described in the foregoing field notes of township No. 25, north of the base line of range No. 2, west of the Willamette meridian, showing the respective capacities in which they acted: Peter Long, chainman; John Short, chainman; George Sharp, axeman; Adam Dull, axeman; Henry Flagg, compassman.

We hereby certify that we assisted Robert Acres, deputy surveyor, in surveying the exterior boundaries and subdividing township number twenty-five north of the base line of range number two west of the Willamette meridian, and that said township has been, in all respects, to the best of our knowledge and belief, well and faithfully surveyed, and the boundary monuments planted according to the instructions furnished by the surveyor general.

PETER LONG, *Chainman.*
JOHN SHORT, *Chainman.*
GEORGE SHARP, *Axeman.*
ADAM DULL, *Axeman.*
HENRY FLAGG, *Compassman.*

Subscribed and sworn to by the above-named persons, before me, a justice of the peace for the county of ———, in the State (or Territory) of ———, this ——— day of ———, 185—.

HENRY DOOLITTLE,
Justice of the Peace.

I, Robert Acres, deputy surveyor, do solemnly swear that, in pursuance of a contract with ——— ———, surveyor of the public lands of the United States in the State (or Territory) of ———, bearing date the —— day of ———, 185—, and in strict conformity to the laws of the United States and the instructions furnished by the said surveyor general, I have faithfully surveyed the exterior boundaries (or subdivision and meanders, as the case may be) of township number twenty-five north of the base line of range number two west of the Willamette meridian, in the ——— aforesaid, and do further solemnly swear that the foregoing are the true and original field notes of such survey.

ROBERT ACRES,
Deputy Surveyor.

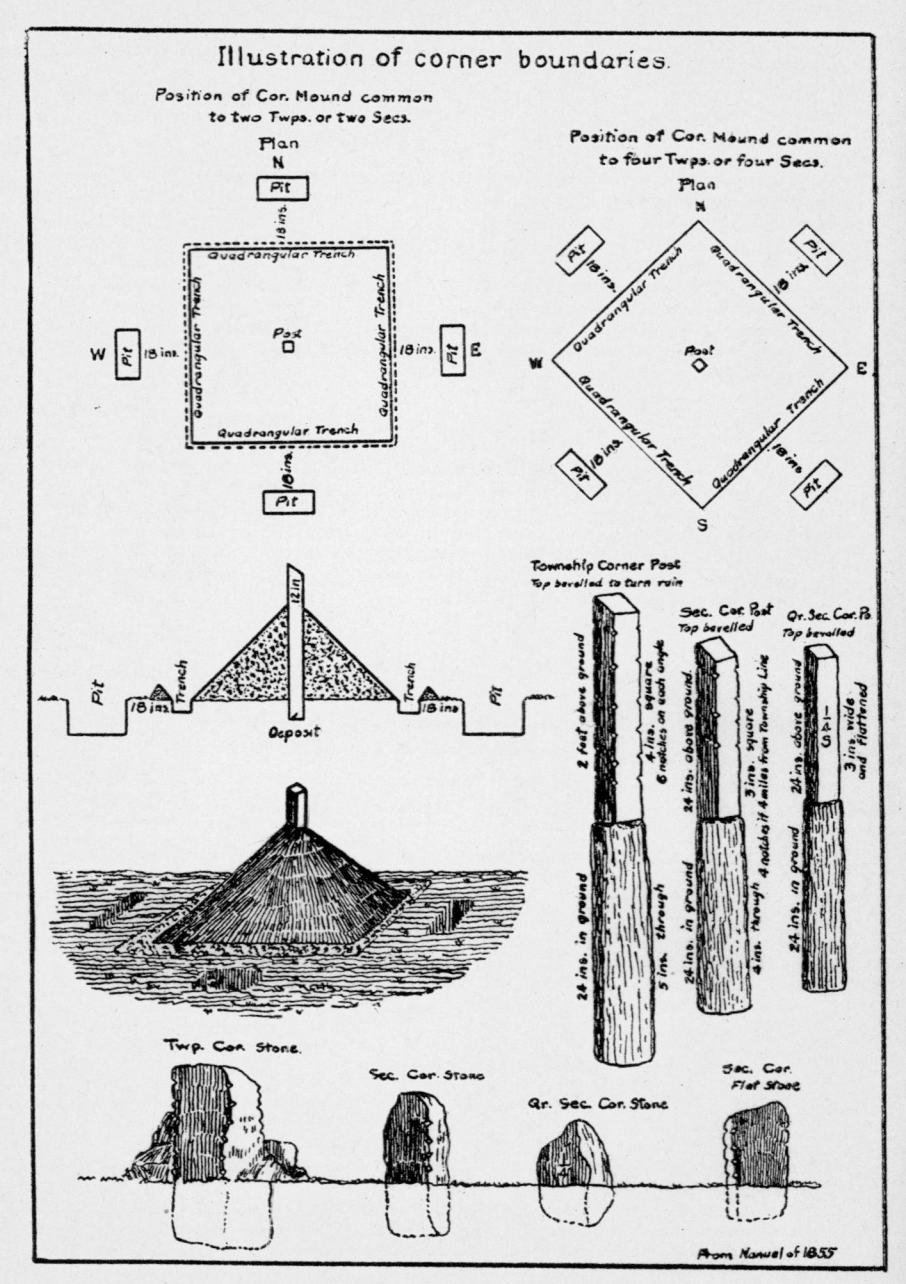

170 ORIGINAL INSTRUCTIONS GOVERNING PUBLIC LAND SURVEYS 1815-1855

DIAGRAM C

Subscribed by said Robert Acres, deputy surveyor, and sworn to before me, a justice of the peace for ———— County, in the State (or Territory) of ————, this ————day of ————, 185—.

HENRY DOOLITTLE,
Justice of the Peace.

To each of the original field books, the surveyor general will append his official approval, according to the following form, or so varied as to suit the facts in the case:

SURVEYOR'S OFFICE AT ———— ————,
———— ————, 185—.

The foregoing field notes of the survey of (here describe the survey) executed by Robert Acres, under his contract of the ———— day of ————, 185—, in the month of ————, 185—, having been critically examined, the necessary corrections and explanations made, the said field notes, and the surveys they describe, are hereby approved.

A. B.,
Surveyor General.

To the copies of the field notes transmitted to the seat of Government, the surveyor general will append to each township the following certificate:

I certify that the foregoing transcript of the field notes of the survey of the (here describe the character of the surveys, whether meridian, base line, standard parallel, exterior township lines, or subdivision lines, and meanders of a particular township) in the State (or Territory) of ————, has been correctly copied from the original notes on file in this office.

A. B.,
Surveyor General.

Table showing the difference of latitude and departure in running 80 chains at any course from 1 to 60 minutes.

Minutes	Links	Minutes	Links	Minutes	Links
1	2⅓	21	49	41	95⅔
2	4⅔	22	51⅓	42	98
3	7	23	53⅔	43	100⅓
4	9⅓	24	56	44	102⅔
5	11⅔	25	58⅓	45	105
6	14	26	60⅔	46	107⅓
7	16⅓	27	63	47	109⅔
8	18⅔	28	65⅓	48	112
9	21	29	67⅔	49	114⅓
10	23⅓	30	70	50	116⅔
11	25⅔	31	72⅓	51	119
12	28	32	74⅔	52	121⅓
13	30⅓	33	77	53	123⅔
14	32⅔	34	79⅓	54	126
15	35	35	81⅔	55	128⅓
16	37⅓	36	84	56	130⅔
17	39⅔	37	86⅓	57	133
18	42	38	88⅔	58	135⅓
19	44⅓	39	91	59	137⅔
20	46⅔	40	93⅓	60	140

COMMENTS OF W. D. JONES

The first instructions given to the deputy surveyors must have been given orally by the Geographer of the United States, who was in the field with the surveyors, and, as later the Surveyors General gave written instructions, said instructions were by letters. The matter that was in those letters of instruction must have developed from the experience of the best surveyors who worked in the field and their reports as to what was needed. And it was only when a letter became especially good that it attracted attention and was published. The instructions of 1871 are a reprint of the 1855 instructions. The more recent the instructions, the more matter they generally contain, but the recent instructions do not tell how the old work was done.

In regard to measurements, the 1815 instructions say, "the level or horizontal length is to be taken, not . . . over the surface of the ground when . . . uneven and hilly; for this purpose . . . let down one end of the chain to the ground and raise the other to a level . . . a plumb should be let fall . . ., and where the land is very steep it will be necessary to shorten the chain by doubling the links together . . . Though the line be measured by a chain of two perches, you are . . . to keep your reckoning in chains of four perches of 100 links."

The same directions, sometimes in a little different words, are contained in the 1834-1846-1850-1851 and 1855 instructions. The 1855 instructions got into more detail by saying, "In measuring with a two-pole chain, every five chains are called a tally because . . . the last of ten tally pins . . . will have been stuck . . . each (chainman) registers the distance by slipping a thimble, (button, or ring of leather,) or something of the kind, on a belt worn for the purpose. The hind chainman then comes up, and having counted in the presence of his fellow the tally pins . . . proceeds (ahead) to set the pins." "Thus the chainmen alternately change places . . . so that one is forward in all odd and the other in all even tallies" . . . "To insure accuracy in measurement, facilitate the recollection of the distance to objects on the line, and render a mistally almost impossible."

Experience has shown that tallies had been forgotten sometimes. It is well for us to remember this two-pole chain. It explains some of the mistakes of five chains we find in the length of section or of half-mile lines. Except that the 1855 instructions say, "on . . . level ground . . . the four-pole chain may be used"; it was not until 1881 that the government allowed the deputy surveyor to use a four-pole chain and then instead of requiring it to be standard length of 66.00 feet they required it to be 66.06 feet long. By that time the old chain "made of good iron wire" (as per 1850 instructions) had gone out of use and the steel tape graduated to the length of a chain had taken its place. It seems that the habit of making a mile measure more than eighty chains, on account of the constant wear of the many joints in the old wire chain, had become so fixed that the officials were afraid to take any chances of making the mile measure less than eighty chains, on account of inaccurate measurement with a correct chain, so they required the chain to be too long by 0.06 of a foot. That practice has now been discontinued. The 1850 instructions provide for a telescope with "two parallel lines . . . in the principal focus" and "a rod, divided into feet, inches and tenths of an inch" with which to measure meander distances, etc. Said instructions say "The principal source of error in surveying is in the measurement by the chain."

In the 1815 and 1834 instructions, the deputy surveyor was allowed to choose the number of tally pins he wished to use; after that eleven tally pins were required. Until 1855 the tally pins could be "seasoned wood pointed with iron or steel," and "weighty enough toward the point to make them drop plumb." By the 1855 instructions said pins were required to be of steel.

Not much is said about Marking Irons except that "There shall be cut with a marking iron," (as per 1815 instructions) until the 1851 instructions which say, "you are to provide yourself with marking irons of the most approved description, which are to be used only by experienced and skillful markers." "In marking of your corners, whether in prairie or timber, particular care is to be taken . . . The importance of this caution will be manifest, when you reflect that it is upon this evidence alone that the settler depends in locating or entering his land." Evidently, the man who wrote these 1851 instructions knew that the true location of a lost quarter corner cannot be ascertained by simply measuring forty chains from a section corner monument.

The 1815 and 1834 instructions say, "all those trees which your line cuts must have two notches made on each side of the trees where the line cuts; but *no spot* or *blaze* . . . and all or most of the trees on each side of the line and near it, must be marked with two spots or blazes diagonally or quartering toward the line." The 1846-1850-1851 and 1855 instructions add to this for the blazes on "two sides" of the tree on each side of the line that "the blazes (are) to approach nearer each other the farther the line passes from the blazed trees, and to be as nearly opposite—coinciding with the line—as possible, in cases where they are barely passed." *Niles Weekly Register* of 1817 and the instructions of 1834 use the term "Station or Line Trees" and the instructions of 1850 and 1855 call them "Sight Trees," "Line Trees" or "Station Trees." In the early instructions, the estimated diameter of line and bearing trees was allowed but by 1846 the measured diameter was required. By the 1815 and 1850 instructions *not all trees* on the true lines were marked as station or line trees but "the names and estimated diameter of at least one or two of these trees . . . with their exact distance on the line, between every two corners."

BEARING TREES AND WITNESS TREES

In 1815 instructions and *Niles Weekly Register* of 1817 say, "The numbers of each section . . . township and range, are marked with a marking iron . . . on a bearing tree or some *other tree* within and near each corner of a section." The 1846 and 1851 instructions say "Bearing trees are those of which you take the course and distance from a corner. Witness trees are . . . marked as above but the course and distance to them, as well as the small chop, are omitted." Of course the letters B. T. do not appear on witness trees. The 1846 instructions say "at interior section corners four trees, one to stand within each of the four sections, are to be marked with the section, township and range, but no record is made of where they stand with reference to the corner. If we find the blaze and iron marks on these "Witness Trees" we know the blaze is on the side of the nearest corner but we do not know within almost 90 degrees what the direction is and we do not know how far the corner is from the tree. Evidently the man who wrote those instructions was not thinking of the land surveyor who should look for that section corner 100 years after it was set, when one witness tree might be the only tree of those four marked trees, left standing.

The letters B.T., meaning bearing tree, were not required until the 1846 instructions, which say, "The letters B.T. are also to be marked upon a smaller chop, directly under the large one and as near the ground as is practicable." And the 1850 instructions say "in case of resurveys, the letters N.B.T. to denote . . . a new bearing tree, must be cut into the wood, in the blaze, a little above the notch."

Having the above mentioned exceptions in mind, a pretty clear understanding of what is said about bearing trees in all of the instructions here mentioned may be had by quoting from the 1834 instructions which say, "You will ascertain and state . . . the course and distance from several section and township corner posts, trees and stones, to a tree in each section for which they stand as a corner; each of said trees you will mark with a notch and blaze facing the post; the notch to be at the lower end of the blaze; and on the blaze . . . you will mark, with a marking iron, . . . the letter S., with the number of the section, and over it the letter T., with the number of the township, and above this the letter R., with the number of the range. And if no tree so state.''

Quarter corners have but two bearing trees because for only two sections, and section corners on the township and range lines the same, (except at township corners), for the same reason. Bearing tree from quarter corners are marked only ¼ S. Two bearing trees are required from posts set at swamps, creeks, etc., to be blazed and notched only. But at navigable rivers or lakes said two trees will also be marked ''with the proper number of the fractional section township and range.'' Therefore it seems the land surveyor was to make that important decision as to what bodies of water are navigable.

Monuments at the section and quarter section corners were stakes, trees, stones, mounds, and after 1834, and perhaps after 1828, ''not less than two quarts of charcoal.'' No charcoal was ever required by any of these instructions at quarter corners. None is mentioned for any corner in the 1815 instructions, nor do the 1815 instructions mention mounds, but *Niles Weekly Register* of April 12, 1817, says, ''But in the prairie . . . where there are no trees . . . a mound of earth is raised at each corner, not less than two and one-half feet high nor less than that in diameter at the base, in which posts are placed.'' Of course such a mound would not stand long against the weather. Probably they were larger at the base. We may say that up to and including 1855 the posts were set in the mounds and the charcoal was under the post when it was provided. Surveyors often say ''I never found charcoal'' and sometimes they say that, when they are working in a part of the country where the sections were created before charcoal was required by the instructions. Of course we cannot say that *no charcoal* was ever set before the instructions required it; it probably was, but if it was, the notes would most likely say so. Since most of the original survey notes in Iowa do not mention charcoal, it is not likely that it was used extensively. It is well to remember that if a tree stands at any section corner, it is notched, as a post would be notched, with six notches on four sides if at a township corner, and, if on a township line, with the number of notches on two sides that it is miles from the township corners; and, if at an interior section corner, with the number of notches it is miles from the township line and range line.

The Running of Line

Section lines, meander lines, township lines, range lines, Indian boundary lines, base lines, principal meridian lines, guide meridians, and correction lines, at least until after 1836 (when Burt's Solar Compass was invented), were all run with the magnetic compass or with the sights of the compass by some "other means" which "must be adopted, so as to ensure the correct execution of the work," as is specified in the 1834 instructions for when "lines cannot be accurately surveyed with . . . the needle," leaving to the deputy surveyor to determine what "other means must be adopted." He was, however, to tell in his notes what he did. The 1846 instructions, and all after them require "Base, meridian, correction and township lines . . . to be run with an instrument that operates independently of the magnetic needle." But up to and including those of 1855, the instructions say, "Where the needle can be relied on . . . the ordinary compass may be used in subdividing and meandering." We sometimes think that the surveyors had too much faith in the needle.

The telescope is not mentioned until the 1850 instructions, which say, "To enable you to have all your random lines correctly run by the sun, . . . independently of the . . . magnetic needle, you are allowed to employ, by the month, an assistant surveyor, who is well skilled in the use of the solar compass." Something must have happened. There must have been a law providing for the payment of that assistant by the United States, not by the contracting deputy surveyor. The truth was beginning to dawn, that you cannot get, by obligation and contract, careful and correct surveys out of men who have not the ability to do that kind of work, and who are paid less than one-tenth of what the kind of work is worth. But none of the other instructions herein discussed make such a provision.

All instructions require "the compass to be adjusted to the true meridian" or in some cases for subdividing work, to the east line of the township. The 1855 instructions tell how to find the true meridian with the compass:

"Drive two posts firmly into the ground" so that they are left about three feet high and four feet apart, about east and west. Upon the posts nail a smooth plank three or four inches wide. Then fasten a compass sight at right angles to a smooth piece of board four or five inches square. Drive a nail just through the small piece of board. At about 12 feet northerly from this "let a plumb be suspended from the top of an inclined . . . pole . . . at such a height that the pole will **appear** about six inches below it; the plumb should be swung in water . . . About twenty minutes before . . . elongation, place the board . . . (with) . . . compass-sight . . . on the horizontal plank and slide it east or west, until "in line with the plumb line and the star. Then if the star depart from the plumb line move the compass-sight east or west along the plank . . . until the star shall attain its greatest elongation, when it will continue behind the plumb-line for several minutes, and will then recede from it in the contrary direction." Now drive the nail which you have in the small piece of board into the plank. You will now have the direction of elongation of the North Star. Turn off the required azimuth angle for the true North. (These instructions are taken almost verbatim from Gummere 1825.)

About all the instructions of 1815 say about the running of township lines is, "All township and section lines which you may survey are to be marked in the "manner hitherto practiced in the surveys of the United States Lands," then telling how to mark trees, posts, etc., and how to measure. Instructions of 1834 say, "Township boundary lines must be run with the compass adjusted to the true meridian" and "range lines . . . will be run north, and corners or sections and quarter sections, will be established thereon at every half-mile and mile, for the sections and quarter sections to the west, and not for those to the east of the line, except at township corners. East and west standard lines will be run east or west, as the case may require, and corners established, thereon for the quarter sections, sections and townships, north of the line, and not for those to the south of it . . . All other east and west township lines will be run west on randoms, and corrected east from township corner to township corner, and the excess or deficiency must be added to or deducted from the south boundary of Section 31, west of the quarter section corner." By these instructions errors are allowed of five chains in closing a township, one chain in closing a section, and one and one-half chains per mile in closing meanders.

The 1846 instructions say also about township lines: "Upon the base or township lines . . . south boundary of your district, township corners are established at . . . six miles. From each of these corners you are to run range lines due north, six miles; . . ., where you will set a temporary township cornerpost. You will then commence at a township corner upon the first range line east of your district and immediately east of the township corner post temporarily set by you, and from thence run due west across your whole district, intersecting your range lines at or within three and one-half chains due north or south of your six-mile posts. At points of intersection, if within three and one-half chains, you will establish a township corner. Upon this township or last mentioned line, quarter section and section corners are to be established observing that the length of each . . . township line . . ., is in no case to exceed or fall short of the length of the corresponding township boundary upon the south, more than three and one-half chains.''

The 1850 and 1851 instructions are about the same as this. So are the 1855, except that the 1855 instructions required the east and west township lines to be run on a random line east and then to run and measure this township line west on true line. The random must not fall more than three and one-half chains north or south of true corner, nor must the measurement vary more than three and one-half chains from its calculated length.

Following the directions for subdividing a township in the 1846 instructions we find the following note: ''Should you find a manifest error in the measurement of any of the township lines of your district, you are to correct the same, by resurveying and reestablishing such line or lines, from the point where the error was detected, to the north and west thereof, noting your intersection with each one of the erroneous corners as you progress, which you are to demolish and deface with all evidence thereof. Of such remeasurement and corrections you are to take full and complete field notes, in a separate book, . . . *For such corrections,* however the Surveyor General *is not authorized to make any compensation.*''

Before discussing the instructions for running the subdividing lines of the townships it may be well for us all to consider what was meant by, a true line, true north, true east or west, and by a random line. Of course a random line is a trial line but as far as being parallel of latitude, the random lines in the Government Surveys were just as near true east and west as the true lines. And the random north lines were just as near meridian lines as were the so-called true north lines. For even though they did have the true meridian they could not hold true north with a magnetic needle. *Now* the United States Government Surveyors run a curved line, a true parallel of latitude as true east and west; and *now* the Canadian Government Surveyors in creating the south boundary of a township make it a six-mile chord to the true parallel of latitude. In our old government surveys a random line, then, is one that was *not* blazed and marked for a true line. And a true line is one that was blazed and marked for a true line.

Just a word about jogs. In the earliest surveys three corners were placed on township and range lines; then two corners, still making a jog at township and range lines. Jogs were also made at the rivers on east and west, and sometimes on north and south lines. The 1846 instructions discontinued the jogs. It is said that the jogs were revived by the 1856 instructions but for those instructions only.

Generally speaking, the method of subdividing a township into sections is pretty well described by the 1834 instructions.

By the 1846 instructions and all after them, except the 1856, the practice of running on a so-called true line between the north and west ranges of sections and for east and west section lines which cross "Navigable rivers or other water courses," was discontinued and therefore the jogs were discontinued.

The instructions of 1815 say: "In fractional townships on rivers it will be necessary to vary from the foregoing rules, and the lines must be continued from the rectilinear boundaries of the township . . ., perpendicularly to those boundaries till they meet the river. The sections, however, must be made complete on the sides of the township bounded by straight lines, and all excess or defect of measure must be thrown into the fractional sections on the river. The measure of the lines from the last entire section corner should be made very exact, in order to calculate the fractional section with exactness.

This note by McDermott, (who is talking about 1858 instructions which seem to be a reprint of 1856 instructions), is of interest. **Mr. McDermott says:** In many of the old surveys, the field notes show that the surveyor ran from corner to corner on the west and north tiers of sections. This appears to be the case in Township 39 N., Range 14 E., of the third principal meridian, surveyed by Mr. John Wall in 1821. This will also appear from the old instructions p. 54, sec. 21, where it is stated as follows: "Previous to 1828, some of the deputies considered, in making the calculations of the area of the north and west tiers of quarter sections in a township, that the quarter section corners on the township and range lines were common to the sections on both sides of the line, whilst others adopted the method now in use. At one time, some of the deputy surveyors, in subdividing a township through which a navigable stream passed, ran a random line east between the proper sections, and corrected it west, making the corner to the fractional sections on both banks of the river, and on the true line. Others pursued the method as now required."

The 1850 instructions are said to be for Michigan and no jogs were made by those instructions at the north line or west line of the townships. That is, the section corners are common with those of the townships adjoining. In such a case of course the quarter corners would be shown to be half way in all but section six and be shown there as common with the corners in the townships adjoining.

The method of subdividing in the 1850 instructions differs from all others mentioned. In those instructions, a random line is run through the center of the township, west from the east line to the west line and then corrected east as if it were a township boundary line. The subdivision is then made by average distances to the south boundary of the township and to the north by throwing any error in measurement into the north half mile next to the north line of the township.

Chapter III

RESTORATION OF LOST AND OBLITERATED CORNERS

The problems which arise in this Middle West area in land surveying are those which naturally follow attempts to retrace surveys made a century or so ago under a remarkable system inadequately executed.

The laws and rules under which surveys were made must govern the acts of the surveyor of today who is trying to restore the old survey. It is therefore important to know the instructions under which the surveys were made. It is also necessary for the competent surveyor to know the laws in force at the time of the surveys and the purchase of lands surveyed thereunder. Furthermore, it is a part of the fundamental education of the practical land surveyor to be familiar with the judicial decisions relating to surveys.

There have been gradual changes in the instructions. There have been changes in the laws and there have been variations in the legal decisions handed down during the development of the law and practice relating to land surveying.

The Land Office circular, No. 1452, *Restoration of Lost and Obliterated Corners*, if read with care and discrimination will prepare the earnest student for most of the pitfalls which lurk in unsuspected parts of the land surveyor's practice.

The Michigan committee report of 1885 which appeared in 1891 as Hodgman's surveying manual contains the result of five years' work by a committee of active civil engineers and surveyors. Mr. Hodgman was the committee chairman. In his preface he states:

The perplexing questions which meet the surveyor are not questions of mathematical calculation or of the use of instruments. On the contrary they are for the most part, questions of how to apply the principles of common law and statutory enactment to the location of boundary lines. These are the controlling considerations in all resurveys; a class which comprises probably nine-tenths of all the land surveys which are made. Scarcely an allusion to these principles was to be found in any of the works on surveying extant. In 1880 the Michigan Association of Surveyors and Civil Engineers appointed a committee on manual, to prepare a work which would give authoritative answers to the many questions of practice which came up before them. The committee spent their spare time for five years in an exhaustive research of the laws and the decisions of the highest courts in the land. The chairman attended the meeting of various surveyors' associations and collected their reports. From the great mass of material thus collected, the leading points in the laws of the United States and the decisions of the courts of last resort were selected, covering, as nearly as possible, all the points relative to surveys and boundary lines which arise in the land surveyor's practice. The legal decisions quoted are a part of the Common law of the whole country and apply wherever the Common law prevails, whether in Canada, England, or the United States. It should be remembered, however, that different courts do not always expound the law alike, and sometimes a court reverses its own decisions. Whenever there appears to be a conflict of authorities, the Surveyor should follow the latest decisions in his own State if there be any. It seemed to the committee to be important that the student in land surveying should be taught these things; that they were as necessary for the beginner to know as for the older practitioner, and hence might properly be incorporated in the text book.

Professor J. B. Johnson's book, *Surveying*, which came out in 1886 contained an appendix on the Judicial Functions of the Surveyor by Justice Cooley which has not been improved upon since. Professor Johnson shows the author's scorn for land surveying in these words, "In treating of the trite subject of Land Surveying . . . ," and "The subject of surveying, both in the books and in the schools has been too largely confined to Land Surveying."

The practicing surveyor would do well to secure Patton on *Land Titles* and read the cases referred to there on nearly every point of surveying practice. The case, *Moreland vs. Page*, 2 Iowa 139, is a classic. It is extensively quoted by Clark.

Many erroneous ideas have been held by surveyors at various times in spite of ample authority covering the correct procedures. In 1856, Thomas A. Hendricks, then Commissioner of the General Land Office, gave the following incorrect rule for locating the center of a section: "Run a true line from the quarter-section corner on the east boundary, to that in the west boundary, and at the equidistance between them establish the corner for the center of the section." This was in harmony with an opinion previously given by the Surveyor General of Missouri and Illinois, and was very generally followed by the surveyors in those states. This rule has not been sustained by the courts, nor by any other ruling of the Land Office, so far as we can learn. It was expressly overruled by the Secretary of the Interior in 1868. Many county surveyors followed the erroneous instruction quoted above.

Professor Raymond, in his book, gave another incorrect rule for establishment of the center of a section. He directed that the north and south quarter line be divided in the middle.

Every land surveyor has access to some good law library, where the state code, the Federal statutes, and the court decisions are available. A few hours a month spent reading the fascinating material contained in a good law library will soon convert a confirmed golfer into a surveying bookworm. The court decisions which are puzzling because they upset sound previous practice are usually traceable to some clever lawyer's brief in which a part of a rule is quoted which seems to fit the case when the whole rule which should apply would give a reverse meaning. Such bad decisions get into the records when a poor lawyer and a poorly equipped surveyor are found on the losing side. The clever lawyer rarely relies upon a surveyor for his material but searches the cases for precedent which can be twisted his way without disclosure to the legal and technical counsel on the opposition. In *Hootman vs. Hootman,* 133 Iowa 632, the court states that while the excess or deficiency is placed in the north and west tier of sections in a township this does not apply to the quarter quarters in such tiers and then he quotes a rule for the placing of corners of half and quarter sections midway between existing corners when not originally set by the government. Of course, he was wrong but a lawyer and a surveyor of the opposing side permitted the error to go unchallenged.

Text book writers have improved their books from one edition to another until a land surveyor can hardly get the type of information he needs, to learn what to expect in the field when retracing a survey in the Middle West. I quote a set of specimen field notes from a recent book:

Chains I commence the subdivisional survey at the cor. of secs. 1, 2, 35, and 36, on the S. bdy. of the Tp., which is a sandstone, 8x6x5 ins. above ground, firmly set, marked and witnessed as described in the official record.

N. 0°01' W., bet. secs. 35 and 36.

Over level bottom land.

20.00 Enter scattering ash and cottonwood.
29.30 SE. cor. of field; leave scattering timber.
31.50 A settler's cabin bears West, 6.00 chs. dist.
39.50 Set an iron post, 3 ft. long, 1 in. diam., 27 ins. in the ground, for witness ¼ sec. cor., with brass cap mkd.

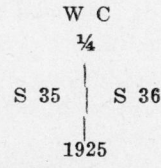

```
            W C
             ¼
             |
    S 35     |    S 36
             |
           1925
```

dig pits,

18x18x12 ins., N. and S. of post, 3 ft. dist.

Enter an ungraded road, bears N. along section line, and E. to Mound City.

40.00 True point for ¼ sec. cor. falls in road.

Deposit a sandstone, 14x8x5 ins., mkd. X, 24 ins. in the ground.

50.50 NE. cor. of field.
51.50 Road to Bozeman bears N. 70° W.
57.50 Enter heavy ash and cottonwood, and dense undergrowth, bears N. 54° E. and S. 54° W.
72.00 Leave undergrowth.

80.00 Set an iron post, 3 ft. long, 2 ins. diam. 27 ins. in the ground, for cor. secs. 25, 26, 35, and 36, with brass cap mkd.

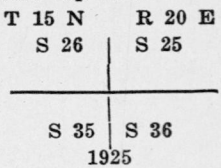

```
        T 15 N   | R 20 E
        S 26     | S 25
        ─────────┼─────────
        S 35     | S 36
               1925
```

from which

A green ash, 13 ins. diam., bears N. 22° E., 26 lks. dist. mkd. T 15 N R 20 E S 25 B T.

A green ash, 23 ins. diam., bears S. 71¼° E., 37 lks. dist. mkd. T 15 N R 20 E S 36 B T.

A green ash, 17 ins. diam., bears S. 65° W., 41 lks. dist. mkd. T 15 N R 20 E S 35 B T.

A cottonwood, 13 ins. diam., bears N. 21¼° W., 36 lks. dist. mkd. T 15 N R 20 E S 26 B T.

Land, level bottom; northern 20 chs. subject to overflow. Soil, alluvial, silt and loam; 1st rate.

Timber, green ash and cottonwood; undergrowth, willow.

The above set of notes is probably quoted from a recent survey such as one made since 1910. Compare this with the actual notes quoted below for three surveys in 1840:

List of hands employed in the execution of the following Surveys:

Andrew Leonard—Hind Chainman
Albert W. Brush—For Chainman
Peter B. Beer—Flagman
Thomas Tayne—Axeman.

At a compensation of $22.50 per month and preparatory to the operations in the field—I administered the oaths appropriate to the several employees.

The oaths follow which were sworn to and subscribed before Geo. W. Harrison, Deputy Surveyor.

July 9, 1840

By an observation taken on the South side of Section 34 T 44 N R 11 E, 3d principal Meridian I ascertained the Variation of the Needle to be 3° 40′ E. but to enable one more correctly to make the subdivision of this Township (T 44 N R 11 E) I retrace the South half mile on the East boundary of Section 36 T 44 N. R 11 E. and find the East boundary of this Township to have been run at a variation of 5° 35′ E. I therefore adjust my compass to that variation and having adjusted my chain to a correct length I then run . . .

North	Between Sections 35 & 36, Township 44 N. R 11 E. 9d. P. M.
13 93	White Oak 12 inches in diameter.
32 20	Burr Oak 20 inches diameter.
40 00	Set a post for quarter Section corner from which a Black Oak 15 inches diameter bears N. 72° W. 108 links and a White Oak 18 in. diam. bears N. 48° E. 130 links distant.
60 08	Black Oak 10 inches diameter.

80 00   Set a post for corner to Sections 25, 26, 35 and 36, from which a White Oak 16 inches diameter bears N. 16° W. 14 links distant—an Ironwood 10 inches diameter bears S. 54° W. 33 links—a Red Oak 18 inches diameter N. 81° E. 33 links and a White Oak 14 inches diameter bears S. 61° E. 63 links distant. Land level and wet. Soil thin—Timber White, Burr, and Black Oak, Hickory, & c.

East   On a Random line between Sections 25 & 36 Township 44 N R 11 E. 3d P.M.
40 00   Set a post for Temporary quarter Sec. cor.
79 87   Intersected East boundary of the Township 13 links North of corner to section 25 and 36 on the Range line and from which corner I run . . .

West   On a true line between Sections 25 & 36 Township 44 North Range 11 East of the 3d P.M.
39 93½   Set a post for quarter Section corner from which a White Oak 18 inches diameter bears S. 25° . . . links and a white oak 12 inches diameter N. 2° E. 20 links distant.
79 87   Corner to Sections 25, 26, 35 & 36.
         Land level, Soil thin—Timber White, Burr and Black Oak and Hickory.

Or the following:

                T 78 N   R 3 E   5th Mer.
North Between Sections 5 & 6
40–00   Set qr section post and made mound.
80–73   Intersect N. boundary 8.42 W. of cor. of Sects. 31 & 32 T. 79 N. R 3 E.
         Set post and Made Mound.
         Land Rolling, 2d Rate
         Prairie.

Or this description:

"*North* Between Sections 17 & 18 T 44 N. R 11 E 3d.
30 00   left Timber and Enter Prairie.
40 00   Set a Post and raised a mound for quarter section corner.
80 00   Deposited 2 quarts of charcoal 3 inches below the natural surface of the Earth over which raised a mound in which set a post for corner to Sections 7, 8, 17 & 18. Land level—Soil good—with Red, Burr & White Oak Timber on 1st ½ mile."

The field notes are quoted at length above to show how difficult it really is to learn from a textbook what to expect when going into the field to retrace a land survey made perhaps 100 years ago.

What is more to the point, copies of the original field notes are frequently not available to the practicing surveyor. In many counties the notes have been carried away. In many, an abstract only is on file which gives only distances and bearing trees. The abstract did not give line trees or stations of natural objects.

This book is intended as an inspiration to better legal and practical preparation on the part of those who make land surveys in the Middle West and those who teach surveying. The material contained herein is not available in the principal current text books.

The quotations from Judge Cooley and the Hodgman report are so well written that no revision is deemed proper. They outline procedures which, if used by the surveyor on retracements, will help him arrive at proper solutions of his problems and will aid in preserving valuable land title evidence which ordinary ignorance and carelessness will destroy.

The surveyor who has access to these original instructions will, in preparation for resurveys, note the date of the original survey, following the procedure suggested in the preface determine what general instructions, what special instructions and what special examinations and resurveys, if any, are applicable to the area.

Then working from this information and that in the original notes, as well as that to be found upon the official plats, he will outline his plan of operation.

With the aerial survey photographs as an extra aid today, and keeping in mind the long line of resurveys probably intervening, the surveyor will try to piece together a lot of conflicting material which will make the resurvey true and reliable.

The sort of aids to be developed from a preliminary study of this kind is varied. The actual post recorded in the original notes is the best possible evidence of location. But a study may show that there is no probability that the original post remains after the lapse of so many years.

The time of year of the original survey is important. For example, if the survey were run in winter, in northern latitudes, probably no original stake remains. The stake was probably driven through snow to refusal in frozen ground. In the spring the snow would melt and the stake would fall over and be destroyed in the first grass or brush fire. Under the same conditions the blazes on the bearing and other marked trees will be high on the trunks indicating depth of snow at the time of the survey.

In prairie regions the surveys were generally conducted in the summer time to facilitate and simplify the camping problems and the digging of pits and building of mounds. Stakes were actually set in summer but usually undersized. Careful search will uncover many of them.

In areas containing meanderable lakes and streams, the section and township lines were frequently run in the summer and the meandering left until winter when ice made meandering simple. Winter surveys were responsible for many erroneous reports as to soil conditions. A township in Northern Minnesota surveyed between Christmas and New Years in 1883 showed sandy soil for example in the timber, when in fact the trees stood upon solid igneous rock ledges and there was barely enough soil for the tree roots. Fancy setting corner posts under such conditions. Of course, any posts set were driven through snow to solid rock. No such posts remain today but the bearing trees are nearly all available although many are dead as the result of fire and scanty soil support.

In the quotations from the Hodgman report, many suggestions appear to assist the surveyors in the interpretation of original surveys. These suggestions should be read again and again in preparation for corner searches.

The General Land Office Circular No. 1452 is so necessary to the proper understanding of the surveyor's problems that extensive extracts applicable to work in the Middle West are included in this chapter by permission of the Commissioner. Many helpful suggestions are given under the head of "Retracements" in articles 1054 to 1080.

Extracts from an address, *The Judicial Functions of Surveyors*, by Justice Cooley of the Michigan Supreme Court:

When a man has had a training in one of the exact sciences, where every problem within its purview is supposed to be susceptible to accurate solution, he is likely to be not a little impatient when he is told that under some circumstances he must recognize inaccuracies, and govern his action by facts which lead him away from the results which theoretically he ought to reach. Observation warrants us in saying that this remark may frequently be made of surveyors.

In the State of Michigan all our lands are supposed to have been surveyed once or more, and permanent monuments fixed to determine the boundaries of those who should become proprietors. The United States, as original owner, caused them all to be surveyed once by sworn officers, and as the plan of subdivision was simple, and was uniform over a large extent of territory, there should have been, with due care, few or no mistakes; and long rows of monuments should have been perfect guides to the place of anyone that chanced to be missing. The truth unfortunately is that the lines were very carelessly run, the monuments inaccurately placed; and, as the recorded witnesses to these were many times wanting in permanency, it is often the case that when the monument was not correctly placed it is impossible to determine by the record, with the aid of anything on the ground, where it was located. The incorrect record of course becomes worse than useless when the witnesses it refers to have disappeared.

It is, perhaps, generally supposed that our town plats were more accurately surveyed, as indeed they should have been, for in general there can have been no difficulty in making them sufficiently perfect for all practical purposes. Many of them, however, were laid out in the woods; some of them by proprietors themselves, without either chain or compass, and some by imperfectly trained surveyors, who, when land was cheap, did not appreciate the importance of having correct lines to determine boundaries when land should become dear. The fact probably is that town surveys are quite as inaccurate as those made under the authority of the general government.

It is now upwards of fifty years since a major part of the public surveys in what is now the State of Michigan were made under authority of the United States. Of the lands south of Lansing, it is now forty years since the major part were sold and the work of improvement begun. A generation has passed away since they were converted into cultivated farms, and few if any of the original corner and quarter stakes now remain.

The corner and quarter stakes were often nothing but green sticks driven into the ground. Stones might be put around or over these if they were handy, but often they were not, and the witness trees must be relied upon after the stake was gone. Too often the first settlers were careless in fixing their lines with accuracy while monuments remained, and an irregular brush fence, or something equally untrustworthy, may have been relied upon to keep in mind where the blazed line once was. A fire running through this might sweep it away, and if nothing were substituted in its place, the adjoining proprietors might in a few years be found disputing over their lines and perhaps rushing into litigation, as soon as they had occasion to cultivate the land along the boundary.

If now the disputing parties call in a surveyor, it is not likely that anyone summoned would doubt or question that his duty was to find, if possible, the place of the original stakes which determined the boundary line between the proprietors. However erroneous may have been the original survey, the monuments that were set must nevertheless govern, even though the effect be to make one half-quarter section ninety acres and the one adjoining but seventy; for parties buy or are supposed to buy in reference to those monuments, and are entitled to what is within their lines, and no more, be it more or less. *McIver v. Walker*, 4 Wheaton Reports 444; *Land Co. v. Saunders*, 103 U. S. Reports 316; *Cottingham v. Parr*, 93 Ill. Reports 233; *Bunton v. Cardwell*, 53 Texas Reports 408; *Watson v. Jones*, 85 Penn. Reports 117.

While the witness trees remain there can generally be no difficulty in determining the locality of the stakes. When the witness trees are gone, so that there is no longer record evidence of the monuments, it is remarkable how many there are who mistake altogether the duty that now devolves upon the surveyor. It is by no means uncommon that we find men whose theoretical education is supposed to make them experts who think that when the monuments are gone, the only thing to be done is to place new monuments where the old ones should have been, and where they would have been if placed correctly. This is a serious mistake. The problem is now the same that it was before; to ascertain, by the best lights of which the case admits, where the original lines were. The mistake above alluded to is supposed to have found expression in our legislation; though it is possible that the real intent of the case to which we shall refer is not what is commonly supposed.

An act passed in 1869, Compiled Laws, p. 593, amending the laws respecting the duties and powers of county surveyors, after providing for the case of corners which can be identified by the original field notes or other unquestionable testimony, direct as follows:

Second. Extinct interior-section corners must be re-established at the intersection of two right lines joining the nearest known points on the original section lines east and west and north and south of it.

Third. Any extinct quarter-section corner, except on fractional lines, must be re-established equidistant and in a right line between the section corners; in all other cases at its proportionate distance between the nearest original corners on the same line.

The corners thus determined, the surveyors are required to perpetuate by noting bearing trees when timber is near.

To estimate properly this legislation, we must start with the admitted and unquestionable fact that each purchaser from the government bought such land as was within the original boundaries, and unquestionably owned it up to the time when the monuments became extinct. If the monument was set for an interior-section corner, but did not happen to be "at the intersection of the two right lines joining the nearest known points on the original section lines east and west and north and south of it," it nevertheless determined the extent of his possessions, and he gained or lost according as the mistake did or did not favor him.

It will probably be admitted that no man loses title to his land or any part thereof merely because the evidences become lost or uncertain. It may become more difficult for him to establish it as against an adverse claimant, but theoretically the right remains; and it remains as a potential fact so long as he can present better evidence than any other person. And it may often happen that, notwithstanding the loss of all trace of a section corner or quarter stake, there will still be evidence from which any surveyor will be able to determine with almost absolute certainty where the original boundary was between the government subdivisions.

There are two senses in which the word extinct may be used in this connection; one of the sense of physical disappearance; the other the sense of loss of all reliable evidence. If the statute speaks of extinct corners in the former sense, it it plain that a serious mistake was made in supposing that surveyors could be clothed with authority to establish new corners by an arbitrary rule in such cases. As well might the statute declare that if a man lost his deed he shall lose his land altogether.

But if by extinct corner is meant one in respect to the actual location of which all reliable evidence is lost, then the following remarks are pertinent:

1. There would undoubtedly be a presumption in such a case that the corner was correctly fixed by the government surveyor where the field notes indicated it to be.

2. But this is only a presumption, and may be overcome by any satisfactory evidence showing that in fact it was placed elsewhere.

3. No statute can confer upon a county surveyor the power to "establish" corners, and thereby bind the parties concerned. Nor is this a question merely of conflict between state and federal law; it is a question of property right. The original surveys must govern, and the laws under which they were made must govern, because the land was bought in reference to them; and any legislation, whether state or federal, that should have the effect to change these, would be inoperative, because disturbing vested rights.

4. In any case of disputed lines, unless the parties concerned settle the controversy by agreement, the determination of it is necessarily a judicial act, and it must proceed upon evidence, and give full opportunity for a hearing. No arbitrary rules of survey or of evidence can be laid down whereby it can be adjudged.

The general duty of a surveyor in such a case is plain enough. He is not to assume that a monument is lost until after he has thoroughly sifted the evidence and found himself unable to trace it. Even then he should hesitate long before doing anything to the disturbance of settled possessions. Occupation, especially if long continued, often affords very satisfactory evidence of the original boundary when no other is attainable; and the surveyor should inquire when it originated, how, and why the lines were then located as they were, and whether a claim of title has always accompanied the possession, and give all the facts due force as evidence. Unfortunately, it is known that surveyors sometimes, in supposed obedience to the state statute, disregard all evidences of occupation and claim of title, and plunge whole neighborhoods into quarrels and litigation by assuming to "establish" corners at points with which the previous occupation cannot harmonize. It is often the case that where one or more corners are found to be extinct, all parties concerned have acquiesced in lines which were traced by the guidance of some other corner or landmark, which may or may not have been trustworthy; but to bring these lines into discredit when the people concerned do not question them not only breeds trouble in the neighborhood, but it must often subject the surveyor himself to annoyance and perhaps discredit, since in a legal controversy the law as well as common sense must declare that a supposed boundary line long acquiesced in is better evidence of where the real line should be than any survey made after the original monuments have disappeared. *Stewart v. Carleton*, 31 Mich. Reports 270; *Diehl v. Zanger*, 39 Mich. Reports 601; *Dupont v. Starring*, 42 Mich. Reports 492. And county surveyors, no more than any others, can conclude parties by their surveys.

The mischiefs of overlooking the facts of possession most often appear in cities and villages. In towns the block and lot stakes soon disappear; there are no witness trees and no monuments to govern except such as have been put in their places, or where their places were supposed to be. The streets are likely to be soon marked off by fences, and the lots in a block will be measured off from these, without looking farther. Now it may perhaps be known in a particular case that a certain monument still remaining was the starting point in the original survey of the town plat; or a surveyor settling in a town may take some central point as the point of departure in his surveys, and assuming the original plat to be accurate, he will then undertake to find all streets and all lots by course and distance according to the plat, measuring and estimating from his point of departure. This procedure might unsettle every line and every monument existing by acquiescence in the town; it would be very likely to change the lines of streets, and raise controversies everywhere. Yet this is what is sometimes done; the surveyor himself being the first person to raise the disturbing questions.

Suppose, for example, a particular village street has been located by acquiescence and use for many years, and the proprietors in a certain block have laid off their lots in reference to this practical location. Two lot owners quarrel, and one of them calls in a surveyor that he may be sure that his neighbor shall not get an inch of land from him. This surveyor undertakes to make his survey accurate, whether the original was, or not, and the first result is, he notifies the lot owners that there is an error in the street line, and that all fences should be moved, say, one foot to the east. Perhaps he goes on to drive stakes through the block according to this conclusion. Of course, if he is right in doing this all lines in the village will be unsettled; but we will limit our attention to the single block. It is not likely that the lot owners will allow the new survey to unsettle their possessions, but there is always a probability of finding someone disposed to do so. We shall then have a lawsuit; and with what result?

It is a common error that lines do not become fixed by acquiescence in a less time than twenty years. In fact, by statute, road lines may become conclusively fixed in ten years; and there is no particular time that shall be required to conclude private owners, where is appears that they have accepted a particular line as their boundary, and all concerned have cultivated and claimed up to it. *McNamara v. Seaton*, 82 Ill. Reports 498; *Bunce v. Bidwell*, 43 Mich. Reports 542. Public policy requires that such lines be not lightly disturbed, or disturbed at all after the lapse of any considerable time. The litigant, therefore, who in such a case pins his faith on the surveyor, is likely to suffer for his reliance, and the surveyor himself to be mortified by a result that seems to impeach his judgment.

Of course nothing in what has been said can require a surveyor to conceal his own judgment, or to report the facts one way when he believes them to be another. He has no right to mislead, and he may rightfully express his opinion that an original monument was at one place, when at the same time he is satisfied that acquiescence has fixed the right of parties as if it were at another. But he would do mischief if he were to attempt to "establish" monuments which he knew would tend to disturb settled rights; the farthest he has a right to go, as an officer of the law, is to express his opinion where the monument should be, at the same time that he imparts the information to those who employ him, and who might otherwise be misled, that the same authority that makes him an officer and entrusts him to make surveys, also allows parties to settle their own boundary lines and considers acquiescence in a particular line or monument, for any considerable period, as strong, if not conclusive, evidence of such settlement. The peace of the community absolutely requires this rule. *Joyce v. Williams*, 26 Mich. Reports 332. It is not long since that, in one of the leading cities of the state, an attempt was made to move houses two or three rods into a street, on the ground that a survey under which the street had been located for many years had been found on more recent survey to be erroneous.

From the foregoing it will appear that the duty of the surveyor where boundaries are in dispute must be varied by the circumstances. 1. He is to search for original monuments, or for the places where they were originally located, and allow these to control if he finds them, unless he has reason to believe that agreements of the parties, express or implied, have rendered them unimportant. By monuments in the case of government surveys we mean of course the corner and quarter stakes: blazed lines or marked trees on the lines are not monuments; they are merely guides or finger-posts, if we may use the expression, to inform us with more or less accuracy where the monuments may be found. 2. If the original monuments are no longer discoverable, the question of location becomes one of evidence merely. It is merely idle for any state statute to direct a surveyor to locate or "establish" a corner, as the place of the original monument, according to some inflexible rule. The surveyor, on the other hand, must inquire into all the facts; giving due prominence to the acts of parties concerned, and always keeping in mind, first, that neither his opinion nor his survey can be conclusive upon parties concerned; second, that courts and juries may be required to follow after the surveyor over the same ground, and that it is exceedingly desirable that he govern his action by the same lights and rules that will govern theirs. On town plats if a surplus or deficiency appears in a block, when the actual boundaries are compared with the original figures, and there is no evidence to fix the exact location of the stakes which marked the division into lots, the rule of common sense and of law is that the surplus or deficiency is to be apportioned between the lots, on an assumption that the error extended alike to all parts of the block. *O'Brien v. McGrane*, 29 Wis. Reports 446; *Quinnin v. Reixers*, 46 Mich. Reports 605.

It is always possible when corners are extinct that the surveyor may usefully act as a mediator between parties, and assist in preventing legal controversies by settling doubtful lines. Unless he is made for this purpose an arbitrator by legal submission, the parties, of course, even if they consent to follow his judgment, cannot, on the basis of mere consent, be compelled to do so; but if he brings about an agreement, and they carry it into effect by actually conforming their occupation to his lines, the action will conclude them. Of course it is desirable that all such agreements be reduced to writing; but this is not absolutely indispensable if they are carried into effect without.

I have thus indicated a few of the questions with which surveyors may now and then have occasion to deal, and to which they should bring good sense and sound judgment. Surveyors are not and cannot be judicial officers, but in a great many cases they act in a quasi-judicial capacity with the acquiescence of parties concerned; and it is important for them to know by what rules they are to be guided in the discharge of their judicial functions. What I have said cannot contribute much to their enlightenment, but I trust will not be wholly without value.

Extracts from a paper by F. Hodgman:

It often happens that one surveyor will fail utterly in finding the marks of an original corner, while another, more apt in discovering the evidences, will strike upon it readily. These evidences are of various kinds, some of which it is the principal aim of this paper to discuss.

I take it that the best possible evidence of the location of an original corner is the monument fixed at that corner when the survey was made (*vide McClintock v. Rogers*, 11 Illinois 279; also *Gratz v. Hoover*, 16 Penn. State Rep. 232; 16 Ga. 141). After this come witness trees, fences, distant corners of the same survey and the testimony of persons.

All these latter kinds of evidence only go to corroborate the first, and may take the place of the first only so far as they may any of them seem to have weight in any particular case.

Many of the corners of the United States survey were marked by planting a post or stake in the ground. These stakes had notches cut in them, were squared at the top, and set in certain regular positions in the ground. These marks tended to distinguish them from other stakes that might chance to be driven in the ground for any purpose. When trees stood conveniently near, two of them were marked, and their directions and distances from the corner were given in the field notes. When no trees were near, a mound was sometimes raised about the post.

Some of the posts have been entirely destroyed, but the bottoms of a great many of them still remain, much decayed, but plainly visible when the surface earth is removed from about them.

To find them, careful manipulation is required. The surveyor first determines as nearly as he can, from extrinsic evidence, the point where the corner post should be looked for. He then, with a shovel, spade or hoe, carefully removes the surface earth, a little at a time, being particular not to strike deep at first into the earth at the level as it was when the stake was set. The best and sometimes the sole evidence of a corner has often been destroyed by an ignorant person striking deep into the ground, expecting to find a sound stake, and casting away the decayed wood and filling up the hole of a rotten one without observing it. If the surveyor is looking in the right place, and the earth has not been previously removed, he will soon come upon the object of his search; but he must be careful lest he mistake it. If the soil is a stiff clay, packed hard, as in a road, or covered with a sward, he will presently find a hole of the size and shape of the stake which made it. This hole will contain the decayed wood of the stake, and a marking pin may be readily thrust to the bottom. By carefully scraping or cutting away the earth from the top, or cutting down at one side of the hole, its size, shape and direction may be readily discovered. Thus it often happens that the position of a corner is as well and satisfactorily marked by the decayed stake as it was by the sound one. It sometimes happens that new stakes have been driven beside the original stake, so that several different ones will be found by the surveyor. He will seldom have any difficulty in deciding which is the true corner by its appearance, for the first stake will be more completely decayed and of a darker color. As a rule, it will be driven deeper and straighter down than the newer stakes. Then, too, the original stakes were generally round, being cut from whole timber, while the later ones were often cut from rails or other split timber, the sharp corners of which can be readily seen in the holes made by them.

There is thus in the appearance of the stakes of the United States survey such peculiarities and such likeness to each other, even when far gone in decay, that the experienced surveyor will be impressed with the appearance of truthfulness pervading them, and will seldom be deceived. This appearance of truthfulness about a stake, which to a surveyor is one of the most valuable parts of the testimony of these silent witnesses, is something that courts and juries can seldom take cognizance of, because, first, they speak in a language that courts and juries do not understand, and secondly, the evidence is itself destroyed by the surveyor in the taking, and does not come before the court or jury in all its freshness, truth and purity. These decayed stakes may be best observed in the light-colored subsoil after the black surface mould has been removed. In sandy soil, the cavity made by the stake is gradually filled by the falling sand as the wood decays, but rotten wood discolors the sand so that where it has been disturbed the position, size and shape of the stake may be readily traced. In the black muck of our marshes and river bottoms it is more difficult to distinguish the stake near the surface, but as the ground is soft and wet, the stakes were driven deep, and we may sometimes find in the wet, peaty subsoil the bottom of the stake so perfectly preserved that even the scratches made in the wood by nicks in axe are plainly to be seen. When the stakes are constantly wet, they do not decay.

Next we consider the bearing or witness trees. These are marked and their direction and distances noted, in order to assist in finding the corner posts set on the survey. These bearing trees are marked with a blaze and a notch near the ground on the side facing the corner. The measures were taken from this notch. At this time most of the living trees have grown to such an extent that only a scar remains in sight, to indicate the point where the notch was cut. In order to get at the notch, the superincumbent wood, which is in some cases a foot in thickness, will have to be cut away. It will not often be necessary to do this, as we can come sufficiently near the correct point to find the stake without it. But if the stake has been destroyed, or there are several stakes near, we shall need to be exact, and measure from the notch. If the tree has been cut down, and a sound stump remains, the marks will be easily exposed. Sometimes the mark is gone, but a part of the stump is left. At others the stump is gone, but a dish-like cavity remains in the earth to show where the tree once stood. We can almost always find under and around these cavities places where the large roots have penetrated the subsoil, and thus be able to locate within a foot or so the position of the bole of the tree when standing. In looking for a corner post, we may frequently assume for the time being that a certain stump or a cavity where a tree has stood was the stump of or the place occupied by a bearing tree. If we then measure the required direction and distance, and find a stake, we may reasonably conclude that our assumption was correct. Such assumptions are frequently of great assistance in finding corners. There may be, and I know there are cases, where the original corner stakes have been destroyed, and can be more nearly restored to their original position by measurements from old stump bottoms or holes in the ground than in any other way. But bearing trees, however good their condition, are by no means infallible witnesses as to the location of a corner. Mistakes in laying down their direction or distance, or both, are not rare. (See *McClintock v. Rogers*, 11 Illinois 279). A direction may be given as north instead of south, east instead of west, or vice versa. The limb may have been wrongly read 64° or 56°. The figures denoting the bearing may have been transposed in setting down, as 53 for 35. So, too, the chain may have been wrongly read, as 48 for 52, the links having been counted from the wrong end. Or they have counted from the wrong tag, as 48 for 38. Mistakes of the nature of these mentioned are common, so that in working from a bearing tree to find a corner, and not finding the stake at the place indicated in the notes, it will be well to test all these sources of error before giving up the search, for as I have said before, the post planted at the time of the original survey is the best evidence of the corner it was intended to indicate.

I next consider fences in their relation to corners. (*Potts v. Everhart*, 26 Penn. St. Rep., 493.) Whether any particular fence may be depended on to indicate the true line will depend on the particular circumstances attending that case. In a general and rough way, a fence will indicate to the surveyor where to begin looking for his corner. But the practice has been, and still is common, for the first settlers on a section to clear and fence beyond the line in order to have a clear place on which to set their permanent fence when they get ready to build it. Afterward they forget where the line is and set the new fence where the old one stood. Many fences, too, were set without any survey or any accurate knowledge where the line was and left there to await a convenient time to have the line established. So, too, where the land has been long settled and occupied, it is a common custom for adjoining land owners by consent to set the fence on one side of the true line, there to remain until they are ready to rebuild, the one party to have the use of the land for that time in consideration of clearing out and subduing the old fence row. The original parties frequently sell out or die, and the new owners have no knowledge of the agreement and suppose the fence to be on the true line. For these reasons, fences should be looked on with suspicion, unless corroborated by other evidence, and the surveyor should enquire pretty closely into the history of a fence before placing any great reliance on it to determine the position of a corner. It may be the best of evidence, or it may be utterly worthless.

It not unfrequently happens that there are no trustworthy marks near a corner to direct the surveyor in his search for the post or from which to replace it if it be destroyed. In these cases, he must visit the nearest corners he can find in each direction (varying with the circumstances whether it be section corner or quarter post he wishes to find or restore), go through the process of identification with each of them, and then make his point so that it will bear the same relation to these corners as did the original corner post. Many very intelligent gentlemen suppose that if the surveyor can but find one of the corners of the original United States survey he can readily determine the position of all the rest from it. They were never more mistaken in their lives. The continual change in the direction of the magnetic needle, the uncertainly as to what its direction was when any particular line was run, the difference in the lengths of chains, and the difference in the men who use them, introduce so many elements of uncertainty into the operation as to render it one of little value, and not to be resorted to except in the absence of trustworthy evidence nearer at hand.

If it be a section corner you desire to find or replace, and have adjacent quarter posts in each direction to work from, you will not be likely on the one hand to fall more than a rod or two out of the way, and on the other hand will not be likely to come within a foot or two of the right place. This method will assist you in searching for the original stake, and if that be destroyed, and no better evidence presents itself, may be used to determine the point where the corner stake shall be placed. The chief difficulty in applying this method to determine corners arises from the fact that the measurements made on the original surveys were not uniform in length on different sections, and frequently not on different parts of the same section. I have measured sections 22 and 23 on a level prairie, along the line of highways, where no obstacles of any kind interfered to prevent accurate work. I took the greatest possible care in the chaining to have it as accurate as chain work can be done. On the north line of section 22 my chaining tallied exactly with that of the United States Survey, viz., 79.60. On the north line of section 23, my measure was 80.96, that of the United States survey, 80.40—a difference of 56 links. Fortunately, all the corners of the original survey on this two miles of line were well preserved, and the distance between quarter post and section corner was uniform on the same section in both sections. But suppose that a part of them had been lost, and it was required to restore the middle section corner (n. e. of 22) from the remaining ones. Omit all consideration of corners, north or south, and there remain four different solutions of the problem, depending on which corners were lost and which preserved. Of these different solutions, one would place the corner 9⅓ links, one 14 links, one 18⅔ links and one 28 links, all east of the true corner. This is not by any means an extreme instance, as I have observed discrepancies twice as great. It is given simply to show how unreliable is the evidence drawn from distant corners of the United States survey.

Lastly, I shall consider the evidence of living persons. (*Weaver v. Robinett*, 17 Missouri 459; *Chapman v. Twitchell*, 37 Maine 39; *Dagget v. Wiley*, 6 Florida 482; *Lewen v. Smith*, 7 Port. (Ala.) 428; *McCoy v. Galloway*, 3 Han. (Ohio) 283; and *Stover v. Freeman*, 6 Mass. 441.) Conceding all men to be equally honest in their evidence, there is a vast deal of difference among them with regard to their habits of observation and their ability to determine localities. Some have an exceedingly acute sense of locality, if we may so call it, and can determine very accurately the position of any object which they have been accustomed to see; while others seem to have little or no capacity of that sort. I have found many men who would describe accurately the sort of monument used to perpetuate a corner and who would tell you that they could put their foot on the very spot to look for it; but when the trial came I have found but few of them who could locate the point within several feet, unless they had some object near at hand to assist the memory, and even then they would frequently fail.

It may happen where a corner post has been destroyed, that its location can be more nearly determined by the testimony of persons who were familiar with it when standing and can testify to its relations to other objects in its vicinity, than in any other way. But the surveyor in receiving this testimony should ascertain as far as possible what are the habits of accurate observation and the memory of localities possessed by the person testifying, in order to know how much weight to give his testimony.

EXTRACTS FROM CIRCULAR 1452
of the General Land Office on the
RESTORATION OF LOST OR OBLITERATED CORNERS

1006. The act of Congress approved September 21, 1918, entitled "An act authorizing the resurvey or retracement of lands heretofore returned as surveyed public lands of the United States under certain conditions" provides authority for the resurvey by the Government of townships theretofore held to be ineligible for resurvey by reason of the disposals being in excess of fifty per centum of the total area thereof. And it provides—"that the Secretary of the Interior is authorized to make all necessary rules and regulations to carry this act into full force and effect." (40 Stat. 965.)

Resurvey of privately-owned lands.

The act of 1918 may be invoked where the major portion of the area is in private ownership, where it is shown that the need for retracement and remonumentation is extensive, and especially if the work that is proposed may be beyond the scope of ordinary local practice. The act requires that the proportionate costs be borne by the landowners.

1007. Under the above mentioned laws, and in principle as well, it is required that no resurvey or retracement shall be so executed as to impair the bona fide rights or claims of any claimant, entryman, or owner of lands so affected.

Likewise in general practice, the surveyor should take precaution not to exercise unwarranted jurisdiction, nor to apply an arbitrary rule, and he should be careful to note the distinction between the rules for original surveys and those that relate to the retracement. The unfortunate disregard of these principles, and in some cases for acquired property rights, prompts the suggestions herein that are intended to help avoid possible oversights.

In unusual cases where the evidence of the survey can not be identified with ample certainty to enable the application of the regular rules the surveyor may submit questions to the Commissioner of the General Land Office, or to the proper public survey office.

ORIGINAL RECORDS

1008. The township plats furnish the basic representation of the surveys and the description of all areas therein. All title records within the area of the former public domain are initiated from a Government grant or patent, with description referred to an official plat; the lands so entered are identified on the ground through the retracement, restoration, and maintenance of the official subdivisions.

The plats are developed from the field notes; both are permanently filed for reference purposes; all are accessible for examination, and copies may be secured.

1009. An opinion by the Department of the Interior relating to the importance or legal significance, of the plats and field notes (45 L. D. 330, 336) is set out as follows:

It has been repeatedly held by both State and Federal courts that plats and field notes referred to in patents may be resorted to for the purpose of determining the limits of the area that passed under such patents. In the case of *Cragin v. Powell* (128 U. S. 691, 696) the Supreme Court said:

"It is a well settled principle that when lands are granted according to an official plat of the survey of such lands, the plat, itself, with all its notes, lines, descriptions and landmarks, becomes as much a part of the grant or deed by which they were conveyed, and controls so far as limits are concerned, as if such descriptive features were written out upon the face of the deed or the grant itself."

1014. The basic Federal laws from which there have been derived the rules for the establishment of the original surveys and for necessary resurveys or retracements include the acts of Congress approved February 11, 1805 (2 Stat. 313); April 24, 1820 (3 Stat. 566); and April 5, 1832 (4 Stat. 503); the provisions are set out at length in the Manual.

1015. The rules for the restoration of lost corners have remained substantially the same since 1883, when first published as such,[1] all of them having been brought into harmony with the leading judicial opinions, and what has been regarded as the most approved surveying practice.

1017. The general rules, which are controlling upon the location of all lands that have been granted or patented, are summarized in the following paragraphs:

First. That the boundaries of the public lands, when approved and accepted, are unchangeable.

Second. That the original township, section, and quarter-section corners must stand as the true corners which they were intended to represent, whether in the place shown by the field notes or not.

Third. That quarter-quarter-section corners not established in the original survey shall be placed on the line connecting the section and quarter-section corners, and midway between them, except on the last half mile of section lines closing on the north and west boundaries of the

---
[1] Restoration of Lost or Obliterated Corners, and Subdivision of Sections, March 13, 1883, 1 L. D. 339; 2d edition 1 L. D. 671; revised October 16, 1896, 23 L. D. 361 revised June 1, 1909, 38 L. D. 1; reprinted in 1916: superseded herewith

township, or on the lines between fractional or irregular sections. (Secs. 1042, 1043, 1049, 1052.)

Fourth. That the center lines of a section are to be straight, running from the quarter-section corner on one boundary to the corresponding corner on the opposite boundary.

Fifth. That in a fractional section where no opposite corresponding quarter-section corner has been or can be established, the center line must be run from the proper quarter-section corner as nearly in a cardinal direction to the meander line, reservation, or other boundary of such fractional section, as due parallelism with the section boundaries will permit. (Secs. 1050, 1051, 1060.)

Sixth. That lost or obliterated corners are to be restored to their original locations whenever it is possible to do so.

Restoration of Lost or Obliterated Corners

1018. The rules for the restoration of lost corners are not to be applied until after the development of all evidence, both original and collateral, that may be found acceptable, though the methods of proportionate measurement will aid materially in the recovery of the evidence, and will indicate what the resulting locations may be as based upon the known control.

An existent corner is one whose position can be identified by verifying the evidence of the monument, or its accessories, by reference to the description that is contained in the field notes, or where the point can be located by an acceptable supplemental survey record, some physical evidence, or testimony.

Even though its physical evidence may have entirely disappeared, a corner will not be regarded as lost if its position can be recovered through the testimony of one or more witnesses who have a dependable knowledge of the original location.

1019. An obliterated corner is one at whose point there are no remaining traces of the monument, or its accessories, but whose location has been perpetuated, or the point for which may be recovered beyond reasonable doubt, by the acts and testimony of the interested landowners, competent surveyors, or other qualified local authorities, or witnesses, or by some acceptable record evidence.

A position that depends upon the use of collateral evidence can be accepted only as duly supported, generally through proper relation to known corners, and agreement with the field notes regarding distances to natural objects, stream crossings, line trees, and off-line tree blazes, etc., or unquestionable testimony.

1020. A lost corner is a point of a survey whose position can not be determined, beyond reasonable doubt, either from traces of the original marks or from acceptable evidence or testimony that bears upon the original position, and whose location can be restored only by reference to one or more interdependent corners.

If there is some acceptable evidence of the original location that position will be employed in preference to the rule that would be applied to a lost corner.

No decision should be made in regard to the restoration of a corner until every means has been exercised that might aid in identifying its true original position. The retracements, which are usually begun at known corners, and run in accord with the plan of the original survey, will ascertain the probable position, and will show what discrepancies are to be expected; any supplemental survey record or testimony should then be considered in the light of the facts thus developed. A line will not be regarded as doubtful if the retracement affords the recovery of acceptable evidence.

1021. In cases where the probable position can not be made to harmonize with some of the calls of the field notes due to errors in description or to discrepancies in measurement, made apparent by the retracement, it must be ascertained which of the calls for distances along the line are entitled to the greater weight. Aside from the technique of recovering the traces of the marks, the main problem is one that treats with the discrepancies in measurement. (Sec. 1068.)

Existing original corners can not be disturbed; conseqently, discrepancies between the new and those of the record measurements will not in any manner affect the measurements beyond the identified corners, but the differences will be distributed proportionately within the several intervals along the line between the corners.

1022. The ordinary field problem consists in distributing the excess or deficiency between two existent corners in such a manner that the amount given to each interval shall bear the same proportion to the whole difference as the record length of the interval bears to the whole record distance. After having applied the proportionate difference to the record length of each interval the sum of the several parts will equal the new measurement of the whole distance.

A proportionate measurement is one that gives concordant relation between all parts of the line, i. e.—the new values given to the several parts, as determined by the remeasurement, shall bear the same relation to the record lengths as the new measurement of the whole line bears to that record.

1023. The term "single proportionate measurement" is applied to a new measurement made on a line to determine one or more positions on that line.

By single proportionate measurement the position of two identified corners controls the direction of that line; the method is sometimes referred to as a "two-way" proportion, such as a meridional or north and south proportion, or a latitudinal or east and west proportion. Examples, a quarter-section corner on the line between two section corners; all corners on standard parallels; and all intermediate positions on any township boundary line.

1024. The term "double proportionate measurement" is applied to a new measurement made between four known corners, two each on intersecting meridional and latitudinal lines, for the purpose of relating the intersection to both.

In effect, by double proportionate measurement the record directions are disregarded, excepting only where there is some acceptable supplemental survey record, some physical evidence, or testimony, that may be brought into the control. The method may be referred to as a "four-way" proportion. Examples, a corner common to four townships, or one common to four sections within a township.

The double proportionate measurement is the best example of the principle that existent or known corners to the north and to the south should control any intermediate latitudinal position, and that corners east and west should control the position in longitude. Lengths of proportioned lines are comparable only when reduced to their cardinal equivalents.

1025. The principle of the precedence of one line over another of less original importance is recognized, relative to single or double proportionate measurement, in order to harmonize the restorative process with the method followed in the original survey, thus limiting the control.

Standard parallels will be given precedence over other township exteriors, and ordinarily the latter will be given precedence over subdivisional lines; section corners will be relocated before the position of lost quarter-section corners can be determined.

1026. In order to restore a lost corner of four townships, a retracement will first be made between the nearest known corners on the meridional line, north and south of the missing corner, and upon that line a temporary stake will be placed at the proper proportionate distance; this will determine the latitude of the lost corner.

Next, the nearest corners on the latitudinal line will be connected, and a second point will be marked for the proportionate measurement east and west; this point will determine the position of the lost corner in departure (or longitude).

Then, through the first temporary stake run a line east or west, and through the second temporary stake a line north and south, as relative situations may determine; the intersection of these two lines will fix the position for the restored corner.

A lost township corner can not safely be restored, nor the boundaries ascertained, without first considering the field notes of the four intersecting lines; it is desirable also to examine the four township plats. In most cases there is a fractional distance in the half-mile to the east of the township corner, and frequently in the half-mile to the south. The lines to the north and to the west are usually regular, i. e.—quarter-section and section corners at normal intervals of 40.00 and 80.00 chains, but there may be closing-section corners on any or all of the boundaries so that it is important to verify all of the distances by reference to the field notes.

1027. A lost interior corner of four sections will be restored by double proportionate measurement.

When a number of interior corners of four sections, and the intermediate quarter-section corners, are missing on all sides of the one sought to be reestablished, the entire distance must, of course, be measured between the nearest identified corners both north and south, and east and west, in accordance with the rule laid down, after first relocating the required lost section corners on the township exteriors.

1028. Where the line has not been established in one direction from the missing township or section corner, the record distance will be used to the nearest identified corner in the opposite direction.

1029. Where the intersecting lines have been established in only two of the directions, the record distances to the nearest identified corners on these two lines will control the position of the temporary points; then from the latter the cardinal offsets will be made to fix the desired point of intersection.

1030. In many of the surveys the field notes and plats indicate two sets of corners along township boundaries, and frequently along section lines where parts of the township were subdivided at different dates. In these cases there are usually corners of two sections at regular intervals, and closing section corners that are placed upon the same line, but which were established later at the points of intersection in accordance with a developed offset. The quarter-section corners on such lines are usually controlling for one side only in the older practice.

In the more recent surveys, where the record calls for two sets of corners, those that are regarded as the corners of the two sections first established, and the quarter-section corners relating to the same sections, will be employed for the retracement, and will govern both the alinement and the proportional measurement along that line. The closing section corners, set at the intersections, will be employed in the usual way, i. e.—to govern the direction of the closing lines.

1031. In order to restore a lost corner by single proportionate measurement, a retracement will be made connecting the nearest identified regular corners on the line in question; a temporary stake (or stakes) will be set on the trial line at the original record distance (or distances); the total distance will be measured, also the falling at the objective corner.

On meridional township lines an adjustment will be made at each temporary stake for the proportional distance along the line, and then it will be set over to the east or to the west for falling, counting its proportional part from the point of beginning.

On east-and-west township lines and on standard parallels the proper adjustment should be made at each temporary stake for the proportional distance along the line, for the falling, and to secure the latitudinal curve, i. e.—the temporary stake will be either advanced or set back for the proportional part of the difference between the record distance and the new measurement, then set over for the curvature of the line, and last corrected for the proportional part of the true falling.

The adjusted position is thus placed on the true line that connects the nearest identified corners, and at the same proportional interval from either as existed in the original survey. Any number of intermediate lost corners may be located on the same plan, by setting a temporary stake for each when making the retracement.

1032. The term "original standard corners" will be understood to mean standard township, section, and quarter-section corners, meander corners terminating the survey of a standard parallel, and closing corners in those cases where they were originally established by measurement along the standard line as points from which to start a survey. No other meander or closing corners along a standard parallel will control the restoration of lost standard corners.

Lost standard corners will be restored to their original posisitions on a base line, standard parallel or correction line, by single proportionate measurement on the true line connecting the nearest identified standard corners on opposite sides of the missing corner or corners, as the case may be.

Corners on base lines are to be regarded the same as those on standard parallels. In the older practice the term "correction line" was used for what has later been called the standard parallel. The corners first set in the running of a correction line will be treated as original standard corners; those that were set afterwards at the intersection of a meridional line will be regarded as closing corners.

1033. All lost section and quarter-section corners on the township boundary lines will be restored by single proportionate measurement between the nearest identified corners on opposite sides of the missing corner, north and south on a meridional line, or east and west on a latitudinal line, after the township corners have been identified or relocated.

An exception to this rule will be noted in the case of any exterior the record of which shows deflections in alinement between the township corners. (Sec. 1039.)

1034. A second exception to the above rule is occasionally important, to be found in those cases where there may be persuasive proof of a deflection in the alinement of the exterior, though the record shows the line to be straight. For example, measurements east and west across a range line, or north and south across a latitudinal township line, counting from a straight-line exterior adjustment, may show distances to the nearest identified subdivisional corners to be materially long in one direction and correspondingly short in the opposite direction. This condition, when supported by corroborative collateral evidence as might generally be expected, would warrant an exception to the straight-line or two-way adjustment under the rules for the acceptance of evidence, i. e.—the evidence outweighs the record. See Retracements. The rules for a four-way or double proportionate measurement would then apply here, provided there is conclusive proof.

1035. All lost quarter-section corners on the section boundaries within the township will be restored by single proportionate measurement between the adjoining section corners, after the section corners have been identified or relocated.

1036. Lost meander corners, originally established on a line projected across the meanderable body of water and marked upon both sides will be relocated by single proportionate measurement, after the section or quarter-section corners upon the opposite sides of the missing meander corner have been duly identified or relocated.

1037. A lost closing corner will be reestablished on the true line that was closed upon, and at the proper proportional interval between the nearest regular corners to the right and left.

In order to reestablish a lost closing corner on a standard parallel or other controlling boundary, the line that was closed upon will be retraced, beginning at the corner from which the connecting measurement was originally made, itself properly identified or relocated; a temporary stake will be set at the record connecting distance, and the total distance and falling will be noted at the next regular corner on that line on the opposite side of the missing closing corner; the temporary stake will then be adjusted as in single proportionate measurement. (Sec. 1068.)

1038. A closing corner not actually located on the line that was closed upon will determine the direction of the closing line, but not its legal terminus; the correct position is at the true point of intersection of the two lines.

1039. Some township boundaries were not established as straight lines, termed an "irregular" exterior, e. g., where parts were surveyed from opposite directions and the intermediate portion was completed later by random and true line, leaving a fractional distance; such irregularity follows some material departure from the basic rules for the establishment of original surveys.

In order to restore one or more lost corners or angle points on such irregular exteriors, a retracement between the nearest known corners will be made on the record courses and distances, to ascertain the direction and length of the closing distance; a temporary stake will be set for each missing corner or angle point; the closing distance will be reduced to its equivalent *latitude and departure*.

On a meridional line the *latitude* of the closing distance will be distributed along the measurement of each course in proportion to its own difference in latitude, and then each temporary stake will be set over to the east or to the west for the *departure* of the closing distance in proportion to the total distance from the starting point.

Angle points and intermediate corners will be treated alike.

On a latitudinal line the temporary stakes should be placed to suit the usual adjustments for the curvature. The *departure* of the closing distance will be distributed along the measurement of each course in proportion to its own difference in departure, and then each temporary stake will be set over to the north or to the south for the *latitude* of the closing distance in proportion to the total distance from the starting point.

1040. Where a line has been terminated with measurement in one direction only, a lost corner will be restored by record bearing and distance, counting from the nearest regular corner, the latter having been duly identified or restored.

Examples will be found where lines have been discontinued at the intersection with large meanderable bodies of water, or at the border of what was classed as impassable ground.

In cases where a retracement has been made of many miles of the original lines, between identified original corners, and there has been developed a definite surplus or deficiency in measurement, or a definite angle from cardinal that characterizes the original survey, it will be proper to make allowance for the average differences. An adjustment will be taken care of automatically in all cases where there exists a suitable basis for proportional measurement, but where such control in one direction is lacking, an average difference, if conclusive, will be made use of by applying the same to the record courses and distances.

Subdivision of Sections

1041. The sections are not usually subdivided in the field by the United States surveyors, but certain of the subdivision-of-section lines are protracted upon the township plats to indicate the lottings in the manner prescribed by law, and the boundaries of the quarter sections are generally shown.

1042. The sections bordering the north and west boundaries of a normal township, excepting section 6, are subdivided by protraction into parts that contain two regular quarter sections, two regular half-quarter sections, and four lots, the latter being the fractional quarter-quarter units that result from the plan of subdivision. In these sections the lines of the half-quarter sections are protracted from three points 20 chains distant from the line that connects the opposite quarter-section corners, i. e.—two on the opposite section lines, and one counting on the center line between the fractional quarter sections. The lines subdividing the fractional half-quarter sections into the fractional lots are protracted from mid-points on the opposite boundaries of the fractional quarter section.

1043. The two interior sixteenth-section corners on the boundaries of the fractional northwest quarter of section 6 are similarly fixed at points 20 chains distant north and west from the center of the section, from which points the lines are protracted to the corresponding points on the west and north boundaries of the section, which results in one regular quarter-quarter section and three fractional lots.

1044. Entrymen are allowed, under the law, to acquire title to any regular quarter-quarter section; such subdivisions are aliquot parts of quarter sections based upon mid-point protraction; it has not been regarded as necessary to indicate the lines upon the plat.

1045. Sections that are invaded by meanderable bodies of water, or by approved claims at variance with the regular legal subdivisions, are subdivided by protraction into regular and fractional parts as may be necessary to form a suitable basis for the entry of the public lands.

1046. The meander line of a body of water and the boundary lines of private claims are platted in accordance with lines run and connections made in the field; the sections so invaded are subdivided as nearly as possible in conformity with the uniform plan already outlined. The subdivision-of-section lines are terminated at the meander line or claim boundary, as the case may be, but their position is controlled precisely as though the section had been completed regularly. In the case of a section whose boundary lines are partly within the limits of a meanderable body of water, or within the boundaries of a private claim, the said fractional section lines are, for the purpose of uniformity, completed in theory; the protracted position of the subdivision-of-section lines is controlled by the theoretical points so determined.

1047. Preliminary to subdivision it is essential to identify the boundaries of the section, as it can not be subdivided until the section corners and quarter-section corners have been found, or restored by proper methods, and the resulting courses and distances determined by survey.

The order of procedure is: First, identify or reestablish the section boundary corners; next, fix the lines of quarter sections; then, form the smaller tracts by equitable and proportionate division, according to the rules that follow.

SUBDIVISION OF SECTIONS INTO QUARTER SECTIONS

1048. The method to be followed in the subdivision of a section into quarter sections is to run straight lines from the established quarter-section corners to the opposite quarter-section corners; the point of intersection of the lines thus run will be the corner common to the several quarter sections, or the legal center of the section.

1049. Upon the lines closing on the north and west boundaries of a regular township the quarter-section corners were established originally at 40 chains to the north or west of the last interior section corners, and the excess or deficiency in the measurement was thrown into the half mile next to the township or range line, as the case may be. If such quarter-section corners are lost they should be reestablished by proportionate measurement based upon the original record.

1050. Where there are double sets of section corners on township and range lines, the quarter-section corners for the sections south of the township line and east of the range line have not usually been established in the original surveys; in subdividing such sections new quarter-section corners are required, to be so placed as to suit the calculation of the areas that adjoin the township boundary, as expressed upon the official plat, adopting proportional measurements where the new measurements of the north or west boundaries of the section differ from the record distances. (Secs. 1030, 1057.)

SUBDIVISION OF FRACTIONAL SECTIONS

1051. The law provides that where opposite corresponding quarter-section corners have not been or can not be fixed, the subdivision-of-section lines shall be ascertained by running from the established corners north, south, east, or west lines, as the case may be, to the water course, reservation line, or other boundary of such fractional section, as represented upon the official plat.

In this the law presumes that the section lines are due north and south, or east and west lines, but this is not usually the case. Hence, in order to carry out the spirit of the law, it will be necessary in running the center lines through fractional sections to adopt mean courses, where the section lines are not on due cardinal, or to run parallel to the east, south, west, or north boundary of the section, as conditions may require, where there is no opposite section line.

SUBDIVISION OF QUARTER SECTIONS

1052. Preliminary to the subdivision of quarter sections, the quarter-quarter- or sixteenth-section corners will be established at points midway between the section and quarter-section corners, and between the quarter-section corners and the center of the section, except on the last half mile of the lines closing on township boundaries, where they should be placed at 20 chains, proportionate measurement, counting from the regular quarter-section corner.

The quarter-quarter- or sixteenth-section corners having been established as directed above, the center lines of the quarter section will be run straight between opposite corresponding quarter-quarter- or sixteenth-section corners on the quarter-section boundaries. The intersection of the lines thus run will determine the legal center of a quarter section.

SUBDIVISION OF FRACTIONAL QUARTER SECTIONS

1053. The subdivisional lines of fractional quarter sections will be run from properly established quarter-quarter- or sixteenth-section corners, with courses governed by the conditions represented upon the official plat, to the lake, water-course, reservation, or other irregular boundary which renders such sections fractional.

Retracements

1054. Where the surveyor is called upon to retrace the township or section boundary lines of the rectangular subdivisions, the problem requires a careful study of the record data; the first step is to assemble copies of the field notes and plats; the second step is to prepare an ownership map showing the limits of the properties, and the names of the owners who will be concerned in the retracement and survey; the third step is to make a thorough search and inquiry with regard to the additional survey records that have intervened subsequent to the approval of the original survey, for this purpose consulting the county surveyor, county clerk, register of deeds, practicing engineers and surveyors, landowners, and others who may furnish useful information.

Court records of boundary disputes should be carefully reviewed, particularly as to whether claimants have based their locations upon evidence of the original survey and a proper application of surveying rules. If there has been a boundary suit, the record testimony and the court's opinion and decree should be carefully examined in so far as these may have a bearing upon the problem in hand.

1055. The law requires that the position of original corners shall not be changed, and there is a penalty for the defacing of the marks, and for changing or removing a corner. The monuments afford the principal means for the identification of the survey, and accordingly the courts attach the greatest weight to the evidence of their location. Discrepancies that may be developed in the directions and lengths of lines, as compared with the original record, do not warrant any alteration of the corner position. (Sec. 1021.)

Obviously, on account of roadways or other improvements, it is frequently necessary to reconstruct a monument in some manner. Alterations of that kind are not regarded as changes in willful violation of the law, but rather that this is in complete accord with the intent, which is to safeguard the evidence. (Sec. 1080.)

1056. Therefore, whatever the purpose of the retracement may be— if it calls for the ascertainment of the true lines of the original survey, or for the running of the subdivisional lines of a section, the rules as outlined require some or all of certain definite steps, as follows:

  a. Secure a copy of the original plat and field notes;
  b. Secure all available data regarding subsequent surveys;
  c. Secure the names and contact the owners of the property adjacent to the lines that are involved in the retracement;
  d. Find the corners that may be required—
  First: By the remaining physical evidence;
  Second: By collateral evidence, supplemental survey records, or testimony, if the original monument is to be regarded as obliterated, but not lost; or,
  Third: By the application of the rules for proportionate measurement, *if lost*;
  e. Reconstruct the monuments as required, including the placing of reference markers where improvements of any kind might interfere, or if the site is such as to suggest the need for supplemental monumentation;
  f. Note the rules for the subdivision of sections where these lines are to be run; and
  g. Prepare and file[2] a suitable record of what was found, the supplemental

---
[2] In many of the States there is a well-established practice for the filing of field notes and plats of surveys, usually in one of the county offices; otherwise the records are the property of whoever pays the cost of the survey, and ordinarily the record would be filed as an exhibit with a deed, or agreement, or court decree, etc.

data that was employed, a description of the methods, the direction and length of lines, the new markers, and any other facts regarded as important.

1057. A study of the early practices, and of the instructions that were in effect at the time of the original survey, will be exceedingly helpful to an understanding of the problem as it was then presented, indicating what was required and how it was intended that the survey should be made.

The plats should be carefully studied with regard to the placing of all fractional parts of sections, and where to expect two sets of corners along township or section lines. It should be noted that certain quarter-section corners relate to one section only, and that corresponding points needed for the subdivision of the adjoining section, usually those located between closing corners on the lines closed upon, were not established in the original survey. The plats will indicate whether these should be at mid-point between the closing corners, or if they should be placed with regard to a fractional distance. (Secs. 1030, 1050.)

It is essential to have the plats for both sides of a township or range line, and for the adjoining parts of a township wherever the whole was not subdivided at one time.

1058. The data for the township boundaries should be examined to ascertain whether there may be certain closing-section corners in addition to the regular quarter-section and section corners. The latter are regarded as having maximum control if the subdivisional lines on both sides of the boundary are based upon the one set of corners. Frequently, in the older surveys, there is a second set of corners, i. e.—the first being the quarter-section and section corners of minimum control that govern the subdivisions on one side only, which are corners that should be employed for the retracement and that will control the proportional measurement; the second set are the closing-section corners for the subdivisional surveys upon the opposite side of the boundary.

1059. The closing-section corners should be carefully considered for their value in the solution of the whole problem, and as evidence. The descriptions of the closing-section corners, and the connecting distances to the regular corners of two sections, will be found in the field notes of the later survey for which these corners are controlling.

1060. Where the section corners on the exteriors are of minimum control, the quarter-section corners have the same status for the same side of the boundary; in the older surveys there are usually no quarter-section corners for the sections on the opposite side of the boundary.

1061. There is nothing especially different or complicated in the matter of one or two sets of corners on the township boundary lines, it is merely a question of assembling the complete data, and of making a proper interpretation of the status of each monument.

The same principles should be applied in the consideration of the data of the subdivisional surveys, where for any of several causes there may be two sets of interior corners.

1066. The needle-compass surveys, before being discontinued, had penetrated into the region of magnetic ore deposits of the Lake Superior watershed in northern Michigan, Wisconsin, and Minnesota; here many township plats were approved, and the lands patented, in which the section boundaries are found to be grossly distorted. There is no way in which to correct these lines, nor to make an estimate, except by retracement, of the extent of the irregularities, which involve excessive discrepancies both in the directions and lengths of lines. Greater experience is required here to make successful retracements, but there are no exceptions to be taken in the application of the rules of procedure either for the restoration of lost corners or for the subdivision of the sections.

1067. One other condition should be considered preparatory to solving the problem of these adjustments—the record will show that in many townships one surveyor ran the south boundary, a second the east boundary, and others the remaining exteriors and subdivisional lines. Accordingly, on needle-compass surveys, all may be reported on cardinal, but no two exactly comparable, i. e.—the east boundary will not be truly normal to the south boundary, etc. Recalling also that under the plan of subdivision the meridional section lines were placed as nearly parallel with the east boundary as could be by actual test of one or more miles of that boundary, these should be found in reasonable agreement. The latitudinal section lines should show an agreement with the south boundary, but the parallelism is frequently disturbed by the discrepancies in measurement. Stated differently, the corrections for bearings may not be the same for the east and west lines as for the north and south lines, and should be considered separately.

1068. The retracements will show various degrees of accuracy in the lengths of lines, where in every case it was intended to secure true horizontal distances. Until after 1900 most of the lines were measured with the Gunter's link chain, so that the surveyor must recall the difficulties of keeping a chain at standard length, and the inaccuracies of measuring steep slopes by this method.

All discrepancies in measurement should be carefully verified, if possible, with the object of placing each difference where it properly belongs. This is exceedingly important at times, because, if disregarded, the effect will be to give weight to a position where it is obviously not justified.

Accordingly, wherever it is possible to do so, the manifest errors in measurement will be removed from the general average difference, and will be placed where the blunder was made. The accumulated surplus or deficiency that then remains is the quantity that is to be uniformly distributed by the methods of proportional measurement.

1069. It is evident that if the trial lines are to be placed in close proximity to the most probable location of the original survey some corrections are thus frequently required in order to orient the record directions to the true meridian, and to adjust the record lengths of lines to a closer agreement with the actual distances that are to be found on the ground.

Where the surveys were faithfully made, there will generally be considerable uniformity in the directions and lengths of lines, so that the methods as explained will indicate what may be expected, excepting where there is local attraction; it will be appreciated that this will give a greatly improved placing of the trial lines.

1071. Having developed certain known corners whose locations can be identified, that constitute the main control upon which the survey pattern may be tested, and before proceeding with restorations by proportionate measurement, consideration will be given to the calls of the field notes, such as distances to stream crossings and to other natural objects, and to the questions of acceptance or non-acceptance of the submitted testimony, later survey marks and records, and the location of roads and property fences.

1072. It is a matter of considerable importance to determine where a tie shall control for both latitude and departure, or for only one position, and finally as to the necessity for applying the rules for proportionate measurement where the distance between identified points is considerable.

A line tree, or a connection to some natural object, or to an improvement, any of which can be identified, may fix a point of the original survey. The mean position of a blazed line, when identified as the original line, will place a meridional line for departure, or a latitudinal line for latitude; and the calls of the field notes for the various items of topography may assist materially in the recovery of the lines.

1073. A retracement between known corners will indicate whether the record courses may be improved by a correction to the right or to the left, and whether the record lengths may be uniformly long or short; these determined values, or corrections, will aid materially in the search for evidence, and in a better placing of the trial lines.

The object sought is to place the temporary lines of the retracement as closely as possible to the probable position of the original survey; this is necessary for the search that is to be made for the marks of the old bearing trees, line blazes, line trees, and to verify the topographic calls of the field notes. Let it be emphasized that in the retracement of the very old surveys there often is no hope whatever of finding the obscure marks except by experienced, intelligent search in the immediate vicinity of the lines.

1074. Original line-tree marks, off-line tree blazes, and scribe marks on bearing trees and tree corner-monuments, whose age exceeds one hundred years, are found occasionally, and are recovered in much greater number for the later surveys. There will be many distinctive marks— some surveyors used hacks instead of blazes, and some used hacks over and under the blazes; some employed distinctive forms of letters and figures. All these will be recognized while retracing the lines of the same survey.

The field notes will give the species and the diameter of the bearing trees and line trees. Some of the smooth-barked trees were marked on the surface, but with that exception most of the marks were made on a flat smoothed-surface of the live wood tissue; the marks will remain as long as the tree is sound. The blaze and marks, and the hacks, will be covered by a gradual overgrowth, showing a scar for many years. The overgrowth will have a lamination similar to the annual rings of the tree, which may be counted in order to verify the date of marking, and to distinguish the original marks from later marks and blazes.

It is advisable, of course, not to cut into a marked tree excepting as necessary to secure proof; the evidence is frequently so abundant, especially in the later surveys, that the proof is conclusive without inflicting an additional injury that would hasten the destruction of the tree.

The finding of original scribe marks, line-tree hacks, and off-line tree blazes, furnishes the most convincing identification that can be desired, and every further proof then adds to the certainty of the location. On the more recent surveys the complete quota of marks should be found, clear cut and plainly legible, but this cannot be expected in the older surveys.

1075. It is not intended to disturb satisfactory local conditions with respect to roads and fences; manifestly the surveyor has no authority to change a property right that has been acquired legally, nor can he accept the location of roads and fences as evidence prima facie of the original survey, i. e.—something is needed in support of these locations. This will come from whatever intervening record there may be; the testimony of individuals who may be acquainted with the facts; and the coupling of these things to the original survey.

1076. There is another important factor that requires careful consideration, i. e.—the rules of the State law and the State court decisions, as distinguished from the rules laid down by the General Land Office (the latter applicable to the public land surveys in all cases). Under State law in matters of agreement between owners, or acquiescence, or adverse possession, property boundaries may be defined by roads, fences, or survey marks, disregarding exact conformation with the original section lines, and will limit the rights as between adjoining owners.

In many cases due care has been exercised to place the property fences on the lines of legal subdivision, and it has been the general practice in the prairie States to locate the public roads on the section lines. These are matters of particular interest to the adjoining owners, and it is a reasonable presumption that care and good faith would be exercised with regard to the evidence of the original survey in existence at the time. Obviously, the burden of proof to the contrary must be borne by the party claiming differently. In a great many cases there are subsurface marks in roadways, such as deposits of a marked stone or other durable material, that are exceptionally important evidence of the exact position of a corner when duly recovered, if the proof can be verified.

1077. A property corner, when placed with due regard to the location of the original survey, should exercise a regular control upon the retracement, but not otherwise excepting in those cases where the agreement is so close as to constitute what is obviously the best available evidence.

1078. The data for the replacement of those corners that may be regarded as obliterated, but not lost, are derived from such collateral evidence as has been found acceptable; the recovery of these corners completes the retracement. All other corners are to be regarded as lost, i. e.—nonexistent; these can be restored only by reference to one or more interdependent corners.

1079. The surveyor will appreciate the great extent to which a successful retracement has depended upon an available record of the previous surveys, and upon the markers that were established by those who preceded him. The same will manifestly follow on subsequent retracements, so that it may well be regarded as exceedingly important, both in the protection of the integrity and accuracy of the work in hand, of the reputation of the surveyor, and of the security of the interested property owners, that durable new markers be constructed in all places where required, and that a good record be filed of the survey as executed.

1080. The preferred markers are of stone, concrete block, glazed sewer-tile filled with concrete, cast-iron or galvanized-iron pipe, and similar durable material. Many engineers and surveyors, counties, and landowners employ specially designed markers with distinctive lettering, including various cast-iron plates or bronze tablets.

Frequently on account of roadways or other improvements, it is advisable to set a subsurface marker and in addition to place a reference monument where it may be found readily, selecting a site that is not likely to be disturbed.

Meander Lines and Riparian Rights

1081. The traverse that is run by a surveyor along the bank of a stream or lake is termed a *meander line*. (Secs. 1017, 1045, 1046.) The meander line is not generally a boundary in the usual sense, as ordinarily the bank itself marks the limit of the survey. All navigable bodies of water are meandered in the public-land surveying practice; also, many other important streams and lakes that have not been regarded as navigable in the broader sense.

1082. All navigable rivers, within the territory occupied by the public lands, remain, and are deemed to be public highways; and, in all cases where the opposite banks of any stream not navigable belong to different persons, the stream and the bed thereof become common to both. (R. S. 2476.)

The public has no proprietorship in the soil under small streams, which are navigable only in a modified sense for floatage of logs, as it has under navigable waters at the common law, where the tide ebbs and flows, or under the larger streams and lakes.

1083. Grants by the United States of its public lands bounded on streams or other waters, made without reservation or restriction, are to be construed as to their effect according to the law of the State in which the lands lie. If there should be changes in the position of the bank line, as by accretion, or by recession of the water, the ownership may, in many States, include the new land.

1084. The Government conveyance of title to a fractional subdivision fronting upon a nonnavigable stream, unless specific reservations are indicated, either in the patent from the Federal Government or in the laws of the State in which the land is located, carries ownership to the middle of the stream.

1085. The above principles are set out in the syllabus in 50 L. D. 678, as follows:

Whenever the question arises in any court, State or Federal, as to whether the title to land, which had once been the property of the United States, has passed, that question must be resolved by the laws of the United States; but when, according to those laws, the title shall have passed, then that property, like other property in the State, is subject to the laws of the State, so far as those laws are consistent with the admission that the title passed and vested according to the laws of the United States.

Upon the admission of a State into the Union the title to all lands under the navigable waters within the State inures to the State as an incident of sovereignty, and the laws of the State govern with respect to the extent of the riparian rights of the shore owners.

With respect to public lands bordering on nonnavigable bodies of water, the Government assumes the position of a private owner, and when it parts with its title to those lands, without reservation or restriction, the extent of the title of the patentee to the lands under water is governed by the laws of the State within which the lands are situated.

Where a survey was fraudulent or grossly inaccurate in that it purported to bound tracts of public lands upon a body of water, when in fact no such body of water existed at or near the meander line, the false meander line and not an imaginary line to fill out the fraction of the normal subdivision marks the limits of the grant of a lot abutting thereon, and, upon discovery of the mistake, the Government may survey and dispose of the omitted area as a part of the public domain.

1086. Where partition lines are to be run *across accretions,* the Federal rule is to apportion the new frontage along the water boundary in the same ratio as that along the line of the record meander courses, on the principle derived from the opinion of the Supreme Court of the United States in the case of *Johnston* v. *Jones* (1 Black 209, 222, 223). The application of this rule should, of course, be brought into harmony with the State law.

1087. Where there is occasion to define the partition lines *within the beds* of nonnavigable streams, the usual rule, under Federal surveying practice, is to begin at the property line at its intersection with the bank, and from that point run a normal to a medial line that is located at midpoint between the banks. Where the normals to the medial line are deflecting rapidly, owing to abrupt changes in the course of the stream, suitable locations are selected above and below the doubtful positions, where acceptable normals may be placed, then the several intervals along the medial line are apportioned in the same ratio as the frontage along the bank. Precaution should be exercised to modify this rule to conform with the State law.